ENVIRONMENTAL REGULATORY GLOSSARY

Fifth Edition

Edited by

G. William Frick

and

Thomas F. P. Sullivan

 Government Institutes, Inc.

PUBLISHER'S NOTE

This publication is designed to provide accurate and authoritative information with regard to the subject matter covered. It is sold with the understanding that the publisher is not engaged in rendering legal, accounting or other professional service. If legal advice or other expert assistance is required, the services of a competent professional person should be sought. From a Declaration of Principles jointly adopted by a Committee of the American Bar Association and a Committee of Publishers.

March 1990

Published by
Government Institutes, Inc.
966 Hungerford Drive, #24
Rockville, MD 20850
U.S.A.

Printed and bound in the United States of America

PREFACE

The 1970s and 1980s produced many new Federal statutes controlling pollution in the United States. Those statutes, in turn, have given rise to an even greater growth in regulations promulgated by the Environmental Protection Agency (EPA), the Occupational Safety and Health Administration (OSHA), and other Federal agencies implementing those statutes. As of July 1988, the number of pages in the Code of Federal Regulations containing EPA's regulations totaled 8,706; OSHA's regulations cover 4,928 pages.

Because violations of regulations expose companies to fines and other penalties, clear and precise guidance on the scope of these requirements is crucial and places great emphasis on the numerous definitions used in the regulations and statutes.

While many regulations created new terminology to implement the statutory and regulatory provisions, many common terms and previously-used definitions assumed new meanings. The Glossary collects these definitions and abbreviations in one convenient book. Definitions have been gathered from Federal agency regulations, from Federal statutes, and from other public sources.

Users of this Glossary should be aware of what it is not. It is not a collection of absolute definitions but a resource to identify basic regulatory concepts. There may be other meanings for many of the terms but the definitions included in the Glossary often reflect use of the term in a specific regulatory or statutory context. Finally, the definitions are not static; use may vary and even the governmental interpretation may change.

Because the definitions are primarily drafted by the government, there may be disagreement about the validity of a particular interpretation of a term included in the Glossary. Moreover, some definitions may only make sense within a particular framework. Explanatory statements have been added in brackets in an attempt to clarify the particular scope of the definition. Each definition also has a code letter indicating the source from which it came.

A glossary is a document that must be updated continuously. This is our fifth attempt at a compilation of the basic terms used in environmental regulations with which persons active in the field must be familiar. We hope that it will provide a useful tool to begin a person's search through the regulatory framework as it now exists.

The Editors:
G. William Frick
Thomas F. P. Sullivan

HOW TO USE THIS GLOSSARY

We have used key official sources for the definitions contained in this Glossary, namely the statutes and the Code of Federal Regulations. The definitions have been compiled with editorial notes where needed.

Generally, at the end of each definition is a capital letter. This capital letter is a code (as shown) to designate the source.

Code	Source Material
A	Code of Federal Regulations, Title 40, Protection of Environment
B	Clean Air Act
C	Federal Insecticide, Fungicide, and Rodenticide Act
D	Federal Water Pollution Control Act (Clean Water Act)
E	Marine Protection, Research and Sanctuaries Act
F	National Environmental Policy Act
G	Noise Control Act
H	Occupational Health and Safety Act
I	Resource Conservation and Recovery Act
J	Safe Drinking Water Act
K	Toxic Substances Control Act
L	Comprehensive Environmental Response, Compensation, and Liability Act (Superfund or CERCLA)

Code	Source Material
M	Superfund Amendments and Reauthorization Act (SARA)
N	Official U.S. Environmental Protection Agency Documents
O	Code of Federal Regulations, Title 29, OSHA-Labor

The Code of Federal Regulations (CFR) is actually published approximately six months after the edition date. For this Fifth Edition, we have used the most current CFR available as of 1989, and that is the revision dated July 1, 1988, for changes and additions to the prior CFRs.

Uncoded terms are those developed from unpublished EPA documents and the work of the GI research staff. Acronyms and abbreviations also are included; an acronym being the first letter of a series of words, while an abbreviation is a shortened version of a word or phrase by leaving out or substituting letters.

ABOUT THE EDITORS

G. William Frick is a specialist in the areas of environment, natural resources and energy law. He is a graduate of the University of Kansas where he received B.A. and J.D. degrees. After practicing with a Kansas City law firm, he joined the Office of General Counsel of EPA as an attorney in the Air Quality Division. During the period 1973-1976, he served as Associate General Counsel and then as Deputy General Counsel. He attained the prestigious position of General Counsel for all of EPA which he held from 1976 until August of 1977 when he resigned to enter private practice. He represented corporate clients on a wide range of environmental issues at the Federal and State levels while practicing in Washington, D.C. and Kansas City for nine years. He is now the Vice President and General Counsel of the American Petroleum Institute in Washington, D.C.

Thomas F. P. Sullivan is an attorney and serves as President of Government Institutes, Inc. He has undergraduate degrees from Kenrick Seminary (B.A. in Philosophy, English & Education) and St. Louis University (B.S. in Physics and Mathematics), and his law degree (J.D.) from Catholic University. He has been in the forefront of the environmental field since the 1960's. Mr. Sullivan has served as editor and author of many books and is a columnist for "Pollution Engineering" magazine. His lecture credits include numerous environmental engineering conferences and seminars.

ABOUT THE PUBLISHER

Government Institutes, Inc., was founded in 1973 to provide practical information and continuing education focusing primarily on environmental compliance and energy topics. GI produces numerous books, seminars, courses and conferences helping professionals interpret and implement the maze of government regulations.

For additional information on Government Institutes' current books, conferences and seminars, and in-plant training programs, please contact us at 966 Hungerford Drive, #24, Rockville, MD 20850 (301/251-9250).

A

a.
Abbreviation for ampere. A

A-scale sound level
A measurement of sound approximating the sensitivity of the human ear, used to note the intensity or annoyance of sounds. N

AAAS
American Association for the Advancement of Science. N

AAEE
American Academy of Environmental Engineers. N

AAQS
Ambient Air Quality Standard.

abandoned mine
A mine where mining operations have occurred in the past and (1) The applicable reclamation bond or financial assurance has been released or forfeited or (2) If no reclamation bond or other financial assurance has been posted, no mining operations have occurred for five years or more. A

abandoned well
A well whose use has been permanently discontinued or which is in a state of disrepair such that it cannot be used for its intended purpose or for observation purposes. A

abatement
Reducing the degree or intensity of, or eliminating, pollution. N

ABEL
EPA's computer model for analyzing a violator's ability to pay a civil penalty. N

above ground storage facility
A tank or other container, the bottom of which is on a plane not more than 6 inches below the surrounding surface. A

above ground tank
A device meeting the definition of "tank" in 40 CFR 260.10 and that is situated in such a way that the entire surface area of the tank is completely above the plane of the adjacent surrounding surface and the entire surface area of the tank (in-

cluding the tank bottom) is able to be visually inspected. A

abrasion
The wearing away of surface material, such as refractories in an incinerator or parts of solid waste handling equipment, by the scouring action of moving solids, liquids, or gases.

abrasive wheel
A cutting tool consisting of abrasive grains held together by organic or inorganic bonds. Diamond and reinforced wheels are included. O

abs.
Abbreviation for absolute. A

ABS/SAN
Acrylonitrile - Butadiene - Styrene and Styrene-Acrylonitrile resin copolymers. A

absolute pressure (p.s.i.a.)
The sum of the atmospheric pressure and gauge pressure (p.s.i.g.) O

absorbed dose
The energy imparted to a unit mass of matter by ionizing radiation. The unit of absorbed dose is the rad. One rad equals 100 ergs per gram.

absorption
The passage of one substance into or through another; e.g., an operation in which one or more soluble components of a gas mixture are dissolved in a liquid. N

academic year
An academic year or its equivalent,

as determined by the Administrator. A

ACBM
Asbestos-Containing Building Material. A

accel.
Abbreviation for acceleration. A

accelerated erosion
The erosion of soil at a faster than natural rate. This occurs when vegetal cover is destroyed or is affected by some human activity.

accelerator
(1) A device for increasing the kinetic energy of charged elementary particles, for example, electrons or protons, through the application of electrical and/or magnetic forces. (2) In radiation science, a device that speeds up charged particles such as electrons or protons. N

Acceptable Quality Level
AQL. The maximum percentage of failings [regulated product] that, for purposes of sampling inspection, can be considered satisfactory as a process average. A

acceptance of a batch
The number of noncomplying vehicles in the batch sample is less than or equal to the acceptance number as determined by the appropriate sampling plan. A [ed. Part of certification procedures used to determine compliance with Federal emission limitations on new motor vehicles].

acceptance of a batch sequence
The number of rejected batches in

the sequence is less than or equal to the sequence acceptance number as determined by the appropriate sampling plan. A [ed. Part of vehicle test certification procedures].

acceptance of a compressor
The measured noise emissions of the compressor, when measured in accordance with the applicable procedure, conforms to the applicable standard. A [ed. Part of noise standard certification procedures under Noise Control Act].

acceptance of a vehicle
The measured emissions of a vehicle when measured in accordance with the applicable procedure, conforms to the applicable standard. A [ed. Part of vehicle test verification procedures].

accepted
An installation that has been inspected and found by a nationally recognized testing laboratory to conform to specified plans or to procedures of applicable codes. O

accessible
[As applied to wiring methods.] Capable of being removed or exposed without damaging the building structure or finish, or not permanently closed in by the structure or finish of the building. (See "concealed.") O

accident
An unexpected, undesirable event, caused by the use or presence of a pesticide, that adversely affects man or the environment. A [ed. As used in connection with FIFRA.]

accidental occurrence
An accident, including continuous or repeated exposure to conditions, which results in bodily injury or property damage neither expected nor intended from the standpoint of the insured. A

accident site
The location of an unexpected occurrence, failure or loss, either at a plant or along a transportation route, resulting in a release of hazardous materials. N

acclimation
Physiological or behavioral adaptation of organisms to one or more environmental conditions associated with a test method (e.g., temperature, hardness, pH). A

acclimatization
(1) The physiological and behavioral adjustments of an organism to changes in its environment. (2) The adaption over several generations of a species to a marked change in the environment. N

accumulated speculatively
A material is accumulated speculatively if it is accumulated before being recycled. A material is not accumulated speculatively, however, if the person accumulating it can show that the material is potentially recyclable and has a feasible means of being recycled; and that--during the calendar year (commencing on January 1)--the amount of material that is recycled, or transferred to a different site for recycling, equals at least 75

percent by weight or volume of the amount of that material accumulated at the beginning of the period. In calculating the percentage of turnover, the 75 percent requirement is to be applied to each material of the same type (e.g., slags from a single smelting process) that is recycled in the same way.(i.e., from which the same material is recovered or that is used in the same way). Materials accumulating in units that would be exempt from regulation are not to be included in making the calculation. (Materials that are already defined as solid wastes also are not to be included in making the calculation). Materials are no longer in this category once they are removed from accumulation for recycling, however. A

accuracy (relative)
The degree of correctness with which the measurement system yields the value of gas concentration of a sample relative to the value given by a defined reference method. This accuracy is expressed in terms of error which is the difference between paired concentration measurements expressed as a percentage of the mean reference value. A

acetaldehyde (CH₃CHO).
A liquid sometimes found as an aerosol formed from gases in the photochemical process; can be further oxidized to acetic acid.

acetylcholine
A substance in the human body having important neurotransmitter effects on various internal systems; often used as a bronchoconstrictor. N

ACFM
Actual Cubic Feet Per Minute. O

ACGIH
See American Conference of Governmental Industrial Hygienists.

acid deposition
A complex chemical and atmospheric phenomenon that occurs when emissions of sulfur and nitrogen compounds and other substances are transformed by chemical processes in the atmosphere, often far from the original sources, and then deposited on earth in either a wet or dry form. The wet forms, popularly called "acid rain," can fall as rain, snow, or fog. The dry forms are acidic gases or particulates. N

acid or ferruginous mine drainage
Mine drainage which before any treatment either has a pH of less than 6.0 or a total iron concentration equal to or more than 10 mg/l. A

acid rain
See acid deposition.

acidity
The quantitative capacity of aqueous solutions to react with hydroxyl ions. It is measured by titration with a standard solution of a base to a specified end point. Usually expressed as milligrams per liter of calcium carbonate.

acidizing
Injection of acid through the borehole or "well" into a "formation" to increase permeability and porosity by dissolving the acid-soluble portion of

the rock constituents. A

ACL
Alternate Concentration Limit, applicable in clean-up standards. N

ACM
Asbestos-Containing Material. A

active ingredient
Any substance (or group of structurally similar substances, if specified by the Agency) that will prevent, destroy, repel or mitigate any pest, or that functions as a plant regulator, desiccant, or defoliant within the meaning of FIFRA sec. 2(a). A

acoustic descriptor
The numeric, symbolic, or narrative information describing a product's acoustic properties as they are determined according to the test methodology that the Agency prescribes. A

AQCR
Air Quality Control Region. N

acquisition cost of purchased nonexpendable personal property
The net invoice unit price of the property including the cost of modifications, attachments, accessories, or auxiliary apparatus necessary to make the property usable for the purpose for which it was acquired. Other charges such as the cost of installation, transportation, taxes, duty, or protective in-transit insurance, shall be included or excluded from the unit acquisition cost in accordance with the grantee's regular accounting practices. A

acrylic fiber
A manufactured synthetic fiber in which the fiber-forming substance is any long-chain synthetic polymer composed of at least 85 percent by weight of acrylonitrile units. A

ACS
American Chemical Society. N

Act
The general term describing the legislative enactment which provides the authority for a particular regulatory action e.g., the Clean Air Act, the Clean Water Act.

act.
Abbreviation for actual. A

act of God
An unanticipated grave natural disaster or other natural phenomenon of an exceptional, inevitable, and irresistible character, the effects of which could not have been prevented or avoided by the exercise of due care or foresight. A, L

actinomycetes
A group of moldlike bacteria that give off an odor characteristic of rich earth and are the significant organisms in the stabilization of organic solid waste by composting.

action level
(1) The exposure level at which OSHA regulations to protect employees take effect, e.g., workplace air analysis, employee training, medical monitoring, and record keeping.

Exposure at or above the action level is termed occupational exposure. (2) Regulatory level recommended by EPA for enforcement by FDA and USDA when pesticide residues occur in food or feed commodities for reasons other than the direct application of the pesticide. As opposed to "tolerances" which are established for residues occurring as a direct result of proper usage, action levels are set for inadvertent residues resulting from previous legal use or accidental contamination. (3) In the Superfund program, the existence of a contaminant concentration in the environment high enough to warrant action or trigger a response under SARA and the National Oil and Hazardous Substances Contingency Plan. The term can be used similarly in other regulatory programs. (See: tolerances). N

activated carbon
A highly adsorbent form of carbon used to remove odors and toxic substances from liquid or gaseous emissions. In waste treatment, it is used to remove dissolved organic matter from waste water. It is also used in motor vehicle evaporative control systems. N

activated sludge
(1) Sludge that has been aerated and subjected to bacterial action; used to speed breakdown of organic matter in raw sewage during secondary waste treatment. N (2) Sludge that results when primary effluent is mixed with bacteria-laden sludge and then agitated and aerated to promote biological treatment. This speeds breakdown of organic matter in raw sewage under-going secondary waste treatment. N

active grant
A project for which grant funds have been awarded, and the project period has not lapsed.

active ingredient
(1) In the case of a pesticide other than a plant regulator, defoliant, or desiccant, an ingredient which will prevent, destroy, repel, or mitigate any pest; (2) In the case of a plant regulator, an ingredient which, through physiological action, will accelerate or retard the rate of growth or rate of maturation or otherwise alter the behavior of ornamental or crop plants or the product thereof; (3) In the case of a defoliant, an ingredient which will cause the leaves or foliage to drop from a plant; and (4) In the case of a desiccant, an ingredient which will artificially accelerate the drying of plant tissue. C

active institutional control
(1) Controlling access to a disposal site by any means other than passive institutional controls; (2) performing maintenance operations or remedial actions at a site; (3) controlling or cleaning up releases from a site; or (4) monitoring parameters related to disposal system performance. A

active mining area
(1) A place where work or other activity related to the extraction, removal, or recovery of metal ore is being conducted, except, with respect to surface mines, any area of land on or in which grading has been completed to return the earth to desired

contour and reclamation work has begun. (2) Areas, on and beneath land, used or disturbed in activity related to the extraction, removal, or recovery of coal from its natural deposits. This term excludes coal preparation plants, coal preparation plant associated areas and post-mining areas. A

active waste disposal site
Any disposal site other than an inactive site. A

ACTS
Asbestos Contractor Tracking System. N

actual emissions
The actual rate of emissions of a pollutant from an emissions unit as determined in accordance with EPA regulations. In general, actual emissions as of a particular date shall equal the average rate, in tons per year, at which the unit actually emitted the pollutant during a two-year period which precedes the particular date and which is representative of normal source operation. The Administrator (reviewing authority) shall allow the use of a different time period upon a determination that it is more representative of normal source operation. Actual emissions shall be calculated using the unit's actual operating hours, production rates, and types of materials processed, stored, or combusted during the selected time period. The Administrator (reviewing authority) may presume that source specific allowable emissions for the unit are equivalent to the actual emissions of the unit. For any emissions unit which has not begun normal operations on the particular

date, actual emissions shall equal the potential to emit of the unit on that date. A

actually be removed
The separation and isolation of discharged hazardous substances from the waters by chemical, physical, or biological means. A [ed. Used to determine application of requirements of 311 of FWPCA which hinge on the actual removability of the substance].

ACUS
Administrative Conference of the United States.

acute
Occurring over a short period of time; used to describe brief exposures and effects which appear promptly after exposure.

acute dermal LD$_{50}$
A single dermal dose of a substance, expressed as milligrams per kilogram of body weight, that is lethal to 50 percent of the test population of animals under specified test conditions. A

acute exposure
A single exposure to a toxic substance which results in severe biological harm or death. Acute exposures are usually characterized as lasting no longer than a day. N

acute health effect
An adverse effect on a human or animal body, with severe symptoms developing rapidly and coming quickly to a crisis. Compare: Chronic Health Effect. N

acute LC$_{50}$

A concentration of a substance, expressed as parts per million parts of medium, that is lethal to 50 percent of the test population of animals under specified test conditions. A [ed. Tests on live animals are used to determine degree of hazard as well as determine compliance with pollution control requirements].

acute oral LD$_{50}$

A single orally administered dose of a substance, expressed as milligrams per kilogram of body weight, that is lethal to 50 percent of the test population of animals under specified test conditions. A

acute respiratory disease

Respiratory infection, characterized by rapid onset and short duration.

acute toxicity

Any poisonous effect produced within a short period of time following exposure, usually up to 24-96 hours, resulting in severe biological harm and often death.

adaptation

A change in structure or habit of an organism that produces a better adjustment to its surroundings. N

add-on control device

An air pollution control device such as carbon adsorber or incinerator which reduces the pollution in an exhaust gas. The control device usually does not affect the process being controlled and thus is "add-on" technology as opposed to a scheme to control pollution through making some alteration to the basic process. N

additions and alterations

The act of undertaking construction of any facility. A [ed. This type of physical change in a pollution source will often constitute a "modification" that will result in application of new source performance standards and certain new source review procedures under CAA and FWPCA].

additive

Any substance, other than one composed solely of carbon and/or hydrogen, that is intentionally added to a fuel named in the designation (including any added to a motor vehicle's fuel system) and that is not intentionally removed prior to sale or use. [ed. Used for § 211 of CAA].

additive manufacturer

Any person who produces or manufactures an additive for use as an additive and/or sells an additive under his own name. [ed. Used for § 211 of CAA]. A

adequate evidence

More than mere accusation but less than substantial evidence. Consideration must be given to the amount of credible information available, reasonableness in view of surrounding circumstances, corroboration, and other inferences which may be drawn from the existence or absence of affirmative facts. A

adequate SO$_2$ emission limitation

An SIP stack emission limitation which was approved or promulgated by EPA as adequate to attain and maintain the NAAQS in the areas affected by the stack emissions without the use of any unauthorized dispersion technique. A

adequately wetted
Sufficiently mixed or coated with water or an aqueous solution to prevent dust emissions. A

adhesion
Molecular attraction which holds the surfaces of two substances in contact, such as water and rock particles. N

ADI
Acceptable Daily Intake. N

adjusted configuration
[New Automobile] test configuration, after adjustment of engine calibrations to retrofit specifications, but excluding retrofit hardware installation. A [ed. Used for vehicle certification on test procedures under CAA].

administering agency
Any department, agency, and establishment in the Executive Branch of the Government, including any wholly owned Government corporation, which administers a program, including Federally assisted construction contracts. A

administrative amendment
An amendment to a [Federal] grant that does not involve additional costs to the government: e.g., rebudgeting of funds, extension of time without additional funds, changes in key personnel.

administrative function
A nontechnical function individual in a Federal contract, sometimes referred to as a "business/fiscal" function. The clear separation of this from the technical area is often impossible.

Administrative Law Judge
Appointed pursuant to 5 U.S.C.3105 (see also 5 CFR Part 930, as amended by 37 FR 16787). Such term is synonymous with the term "Hearing Examiner" as used in the Act or in Title 5 of the United States Code. A [ed. Administrative Law Judges are given responsibility for conducting many adversary proceedings pursuant to environmental statutes. They may be directed to make a final decision on the issue or make a recommendation to the head of the agency or department].

administrative order on consent
AOC. A legal agreement signed by EPA and an individual, business, or other entity through which the violator agrees to pay for correction of violations, take the required corrective or cleanup actions, or refrain from an activity. It describes the actions to be taken, may be subject to a comment period, applies to civil actions, and can be enforced in court. N

administrative order
AO. A legal document signed by EPA directing an individual, a business, or other entity to take corrective action or refrain from an activity. It describes the violations and actions to be taken, and can be enforced in

court. Such orders may be issued, for example, as a result of an administrative complaint whereby the respondent is ordered to pay a penalty for violations of a statute. N

Administrative Procedure Act (APA)
A law that spells out procedures and requirements related to the promulgation of governmental regulations. N

Administrator
The Administrator of the United States Environmental Protection Agency, or any employee of the Agency to whom the Administrator may either herein or by order delegate his authority to carry out his functions, or any person who shall by operation of law be authorized to carry out such functions. A, C, K, I, L

ADR
Alternative Dispute Resolution. N A term applied to mechanisms for resolving disputes other than litigation, e.g. arbitration, mediation, mini-trials.

ADSS
Air Data Screening System. N

adulterants
Chemical impurities or substances that by law do not belong in a food, plant, animal, or pesticide formulation. N

adulterated
The term "adulterated" applies to any pesticide if: (1) its strength or purity falls below the professed standard of quality as expressed on its labeling under which it is sold; (2) any substance has been substituted wholly or

in part for the pesticide; or (3) any valuable constituent of the pesticide has been wholly or in part abstracted. C

advanced air emission control devices
Air pollution control equipment, such as electrostatic precipitators and high energy scrubbers, that are used to treat an air discharge which has been treated initially by equipment including knockout chambers and low energy scrubbers.

advanced waste water treatment
(1) Any treatment of sewage that goes beyond the secondary or biological water treatment stage and includes the removal of nutrients such as phosphorus and nitrogen and a high percentage of suspended solids. (2) The tertiary stage of sewage treatment. (See primary, secondary treatment). N

advanced waste treatment
Any biological, chemical, or physical treatment process used during any stage of treatment that employs unconventional techniques.

adversary adjudication
An adjudication required by statute to be held pursuant to 5 U.S.C. 554 in which the position of the United States is represented by counsel or otherwise, but excludes an adjudication for the purpose of granting or renewing a license. A

advertised engine displacement
The rounded off volumetric engine capacity used for marketing purposes by the motorcycle manufacturer. A

advisory
A non-regulatory document that communicates risk information to persons who may have to make risk management decisions. N

AEA
Atomic Energy Act. N

AEC
(1) Associate Enforcement Counsels. C (2) U.S. Atomic Energy Commission. In 1975, the Atomic Energy Commission was divided into two new agencies. The regulatory portion became the Nuclear Regulatory Commission, and the reactor development portion became part of the Energy Research and Development Administration which in turn was absorbed into the U.S. Department of Energy.

AECD
Auxiliary Emission Control Device. A

AEM
Acoustic Emission Monitoring. N

aerated pond or lagoon
A natural or artificial wastewater treatment pond or basin in which mechanical or diffused air aeration is used to supplement oxygen supply.

aeration
To circulate oxygen through a substance, as in waste water treatment where it aids in purification. N

aeration tank
A chamber used to inject air into water. N

aerobic
Life or processes that require, or are not destroyed by, the presence of oxygen. (Compare: anaerobic). L

aerobic bacteria
Those bacteria that require free oxygen to live and grow. Used in certain types of waste water treatment processes.

aerobic treatment
Process by which microbes decompose complex organic compounds in the presence of oxygen and use the liberated energy for reproduction and growth. Types of aerobic processes include extended aeration, trickling filtration, and rotating biological contactors. N

aerosol
A particle of solid or liquid matter that can remain suspended in the air because of its small size. Particulates under 1 micron in diameter are generally called aerosols.

aerosol propellant
A liquefied or compressed gas in a container where the purpose of the liquefied or compressed gas is to expel liquid or solid material from the container different from the aerosol propellant. A

AES
Augur Electron Spectometry. N

AFCA
Area Fuel Consumption Allocation. N

affected facility
With reference to a stationary source, any apparatus to which a [air pollutant emission] standard is applicable. A

affiliate
Any person whose governing instruments require it to be bound by the decision of another person or whose governing board includes enough voting representatives of the other person to cause or prevent action, whether or not the power is exercised. It may also include persons doing business under a variety of names, or where there is a parent/subsidiary relationship between persons. A

affiliated entity
A person who directly, or indirectly through one or more intermediaries, controls, is controlled by, or is under common control with the owner or operator of a source. A

afterburner
(1) A/B. An exhaust gas incinerator used to control emissions of particulate matter. A (2) In incinerator technology, a burner located so that the combustion gases are made to pass through its flame in order to remove smoke and odors. It may be attached to or be separated from the incinerator proper. N

aftermarket part manufacturer
(1) A manufacturer of an aftermarket part or (2) A party that markets aftermarket parts under its own brand name, or (3) A rebuilder of original equipment or aftermarket parts, or (4) A party that licenses others to sell its parts. A

aftermarket part
Any part offered for sale for installation in or on a motor vehicle after such vehicle has left the vehicle manufacturer's production line. A

AGA
American Gas Association.

Agency
(1) An Executive Department, as defined in 5 U.S.C. 101, or any employing unit or authority of the Executive Branch of the Government. O (2) The Environmental Protection Agency. J

agent orange
A toxic herbicide and defoliant which was used in the Vietnam conflict. It contains 2,4,5-trichlorophenoxyacitic acid (2,4,5-T) and 2-4 dichlorophenoxyacetic acid (2,4-D) with trace amounts of dioxin. N

agglomeration
The process by which precipitation particles grow larger by collision or contact with cloud particles or other precipitation particles. N

agglutination
The process of uniting solid particles coated with a thin layer of adhesive material or of arresting solid particles by impact on a surface coated with an adhesive. N

aggregate
Crushed rock or gravel screened to sizes for use in road surfaces, concrete, or bituminous mixes.

agreement states

Those states which, pursuant to Section 274 of the Atomic Energy Act of 1954, as amended, have entered into an agreement with the NRC for assumption of regulatory control of byproduct, source, and small quantities of special nuclear materials. Before approving an agreement state, NRC must determine that the state's radiation control program is compatible with NRC's regulatory program and is adequate to protect public health and safety.

agricultural commodity

Any plant, or part thereof, or animal, or animal product, produced by a person (including farmers, ranchers, vineyardists, plant propagators, Christmas tree growers, aquaculturists, floriculturists, orchardists, foresters, or other comparable persons) primarily for sale, consumption, propagation, or other use by man or animals. A

agricultural pollution

The liquid and solid wastes from farming, including runoff and leaching from pesticides, fertilizers, and feedlots; erosion and dust from plowing; animal manure and carcasses; crop residues; and debris. N

agricultural solid waste

The solid waste that is generated by the rearing of animals, and the producing and harvesting of crops or trees. A

AHERA

Asbestos Hazard Emergency Response Act. (1986) N

AICE

American Institute of Chemical Engineers. N

AIHC

American Industrial Health Council. N

air

So-called pure air is a mixture of gases containing about 78 percent nitrogen; 21 percent oxygen; less than 1 percent of carbon dioxide, argon, and other inert gases; and varying amounts of water vapor.

Air Act

The Clean Air Act, as amended (42 U.S.C. 7401 et seq.). A

air bleed to intake manifold retrofit

A system or device (such as a modification to the engine's carburetor) that results in engine operation at an increased air-fuel ratio to achieve reduction in exhaust emissions of hydrocarbon and carbon monoxide from 1967 and earlier light-duty vehicles of at least 21 and 58 percent, respectively, and from 1973 and earlier medium-duty vehicles of at least 15 and 30 percent, respectively. A

air bleed control device

A system or device (such as a modification to the engine's carburetor) that results in engine operation at an increased air-fuel ratio to achieve reduction in exhaust emissions of hydrocarbon and carbon monoxide from 1967 and earlier light-duty vehicles of at least 21 and 58 percent, respectively. A

air bleed/exhaust gas recirculation device

A system or device (such as modification of the engine's carburetor or positive crankcase ventilation system) that results in engine operation at an increased air-fuel ratio to achieve reductions of hydrocarbons and carbon monoxide of 25 percent and 40 percent, respectively, from light-duty vehicles of model years 1968 through 1971. A

air classifier

A system that uses a forced-air stream to separate mixed material according to size, density, and aerodynamic drag of the pieces.

air contaminant

(1) Any substance of either man-made or natural origin in the ambient air, such as dust, fly ash, gas, fumes, mist (other than H_2O), smoke, radiation, heat, noise, etc. (2) Any particulate matter, gas, or combination thereof, other than water vapor or natural air. (See: air pollutant). N

air curtain

A method of containing oil spills. Air bubbling through a perforated pipe causes an upward water flow that slows the spread of oil. It can also be used to stop fish from entering polluted water. N

air emissions

The release or discharge of a pollutant (from a stationary source) by an owner or operator into the ambient air either (1) by means of a stack or (2) as a fugitive dust, mist or vapor as a result inherent to the manufac-turing or formulating process. A [ed. Pollutants may also be discharged from mobile sources, from area sources such as roads and fields, and from non-manufacturing stationary sources].

air flow controllers

Devices capable of maintaining constant air flows within $\pm$ 2% of the required flowrate. A

air flowmeters

Calibrated flowmeters capable of measuring and monitoring air flowrates with an accuracy of $\pm$ 2 percent of the measured flowrate. A

air heater

A heat exchanger through which air passes and is heated by a medium of a higher temperature, such as hot combustion gases in metal tubes.

air jets

Streams of high-velocity air that issue from nozzles in an incinerator enclosure to provide turbulence, combustion air, or a cooling effect.

air mass

A widespread body of air that gains certain meteorological or polluted characteristics--e.g., a heat inversion or smogginess-while set in one location. The characteristics can change as it moves away. N

air monitoring

The continuous sampling for, and measuring of, pollutants present in the atmosphere. N

air pollutant

(1) Dust, fumes, mist, smoke and

other particulate matter, vapor, gas, odorous substances, or any combination thereof. **A** (2) Any air pollution agent or combination of such agents, including any physical, chemical, biological, radioactive (including source material, special nuclear material, and byproduct material) substance or matter which is emitted into or otherwise enters the ambient air. **B** (3) Any substance in air which could, if in high enough concentration, harm man, other animals, vegetation, or material. Pollutants may include almost any natural or artificial composition of matter capable of being airborne. They may be in the form of solid particles, liquid droplets, gases, or in combinations of these forms. Generally, they fall into two main groups: (1) those emitted directly from identifiable sources and (2) those produced in the air by interaction between two or more primary pollutants, or by reaction with normal atmospheric constituents, with or without photoactivation. Exclusive of pollen, fog, and dust, which are of natural origin, about 100 contaminants have been identified and fall into the following categories; solids, sulfur compounds, volatile organic chemicals, nitrogen, compounds, oxygen compounds, halogen compounds, radioactive compounds, and odors. **N**

air pollution episode
A period of abnormally high concentration of air pollutants, often due to low winds and temperature inversion, that can cause illness and death. **N**

air pollution requirement
Any emission limitation, schedule or timetable for compliance, or other requirement, which is prescribed under any Federal, State, or local law or regulation, including the Clean Air Act (except for any requirement prescribed under section 119(c) or (d), section 110(a)(2)(F)(v), or section 303 of the [Clean Air] Act), and which limits stationary source emissions resulting from combustion of fuels (including a prohibition on, or specification of, the use of any fuel of any type, grade, or pollution characteristic). **A**

air pollution
The presence in the outdoor atmosphere of any dust, fumes, mist, smoke, other particulate matter, vapor, gas, odorous substances, or a combination thereof, in sufficient quantities and of such characteristics and duration as to be, or likely to be, injurious to health or welfare, animal or plant life, or property, or as to interfere with the enjoyment of life or property. **A** [ed. air pollution can occur in indoor locations, e.g. factories, but the EPA's authority under the Clean Air Act only extends to the outdoor atmosphere].

air pollution control agency
(1) A single State agency designated by the Governor of that State as the official State air pollution control agency for purposes of the Clean Air Act; (2) An agency established by two or more States and having substantial powers or duties pertaining to the prevention and control of air pollution; (3) A city, county, or other local government health authority, or, in the case of any city, county, or other local government in which there is an agency other than the health authority

charged with responsibility for enforcing ordinances or laws relating to the prevention and control of air pollution, such other agency; or (4) An agency of two or more municipalities located in the same State or in different States and having substantial powers or duties pertaining to the prevention and control of air pollution. A, B

air pollution regulations
Legal constraints on pollutant emissions, production processes, or control systems.

air quality criteria
The levels of pollution and lengths of exposure above which adverse effects may occur on health and welfare. Also includes the compendia of data developed under §108 of the Clean Air Act as the basis for ambient air quality standards. L

air quality restricted operation of a spray tower
An operation utilizing formulations (e.g., those with high non-ionic content) which require a very high rate of wet scrubbing to maintain desirable quality of stack gases, and thus generate much greater quantities of waste water than can be recycled to process. A

air quality control region
An area designated by the Federal Government pursuant to § 107 of the Clean Air Act in which communities share a common air pollution problem, sometimes involving several States. N

air quality standards
The level of pollutants prescribed by law or regulation that cannot be exceeded during a specified time in a defined area. N

air-cooled wall
A refractory wall with a lane directly behind it through which cool air flows.

air/fuel control retrofit
A system or device (such as modification to the engine's carburetor or positive crankcase ventilation system) that results in engine operation at an increased air/fuel ratio to achieve reduction in exhaust emissions of hydrocarbon and carbon monoxide. A

airborne particulates
Total suspended particulate matter found in the atmosphere as solid particles or liquid droplets. Chemical composition of particulates varies widely, depending on location and time of year. Airborne particulates include: windblown dust, emissions from industrial processes, smoke from the burning of wood and coal, and the exhaust of motor vehicles. N

airborne pathogen
A disease-causing microorganism which travels in the air or on particles in the air.

airborne release
Release of any chemical into the air. N

aircraft
Any airplane for which a U.S. standard airworthiness certificate or equivalent foreign airworthiness certificate is issued. A

aircraft exhaust emissions
Substances emitted to the atmosphere from the exhaust discharge nozzle of an aircraft or aircraft engine. A

aircraft operation
An aircraft take-off or landing. A [ed. The number of aircraft operations influences air quality around an airport and may lead to regulation of the airport as an indirect source of air pollution].

aircraft power setting
The power or thrust output of an engine in terms of kilonewtons thrust for turbojet and turbofan engines and shaft power in terms of kilowatts for turboprop engines. A

airshed
A term, denoting a geographical area, the whole of which, because of topography, meteorology, and climate, shares the same air mass.

airway resistance
The resistance to the passage of air exhibited by any part of the respiratory tract.

ALAPO
Association of Local Air Pollution Control Officers. N

ALARA
As Low As Reasonably Achievable. N

aldehydes
A class of fast-reacting organic compounds containing oxygen, hydrogen, and carbon.

Aldrin/Dieldrin
"Aldrin" means the compound aldrin as identified by the chemical name, 1, 2, 3, 4, 10, 10 - hexachloro -1, 4, 4a, 5, 8, 8a- hexa-hydro1, 4- endo - 5, 8 - exo - dimethanonaphthalene; "Dieldrin" means the compound dieldrin as identified by the chemical name 1, 2, 3, 4, 10, 10 - hexachloro- 6, 7 - epoxy - 1, 4, 4a, 5, 6, 7, 8, 8a - octahydro - 1, 4-endo - 5, 8 - exo-dimethanonaphthalene. A

Aldrin/Dieldrin formulator
A person who produces, prepares or processes a formulated product comprising a mixture of either aldrin or dieldrin and inert materials or other diluents, into a product intended for application in any use registered under the Federal Insecticide, Fungicide and Rodenticide Act, as amended (7 U.S.C. 135, et seq.) A

Aldrin/Dieldrin manufacturer
A manufacturer, excluding any source which is exclusively an aldrin/ dieldrin formulator, who produces, prepares or processes technical aldrin or dieldrin or who uses aldrin or dieldrin as a material in the production, preparation or processing of another synthetic organic substance. A

alert level
That concentration of pollutants at which first stage control actions is to begin. An alert will be declared when

any one of the following levels is reached at any monitoring site: (1) SO_2--ug/m^3, (0.3 ppm), 24-hour average. (2) Particulate--375 ug/m^3, 24-hour average. (3) SO_2 and particulate combined--product of SO ug/m^3, 24-hour average and particulate ug/m^3, 24-hour average equal to 65 x 10^3. (4) CO--17 mg/m^3 (15 ppm), 8-hour average. (5) Ozone (O_3)--200 ug/m^3 (0.1 ppm)--1-hour average. (6) NO_3--1130 ug/m^3 (0.6 ppm), 1-hour average, 282 ug/m^3 (0.15 ppm), 24-hour average and meteorological conditions are such that pollutant concentrations can be expected to remain at the above levels for twelve or more hours or increase, or in the case of ozone, the situation is likely to reoccur within the next 24 hours unless control actions are taken. (See "termination.") A

algae
Simple rootless plants that grow in bodies of water in relative proportion to the amounts of nutrients available. Algal blooms, or sudden growth spurts can affect water quality adversely. N [ed. Restrictions on discharges and other sources of pollutants are often intended to reduce nutrient loadings in the waters of the U.S.]

algal blooms
Sudden spurts of algal growth, which can affect water quality adversely and indicate potentially hazardous changes in local water chemistry. N

aliquot
A sample of specified volume used to make up a total composite sample. N

alive or live (energized)
Electrically connected to a source of potential difference, or electrically charged so as to have a potential significantly different from that of the earth in the vicinity. The term "live" is sometimes used in place of the term "current-carrying," where the intent is clear, to avoid repetition of the longer term. O

ALJ
Administrative Law Judge. N

alkali
Any chemical substance which forms soluble soaps with fatty acids. Alkalis are also referred to as bases. They may cause severe burns to the skin. Alkalis turn litmus paper blue and have pH values from 8 to 14. N

alkaline cleaning
Using a solution (bath), usually detergent, to remove lard, oil, and other such compounds from a metal surface. Alkaline cleaning is usually followed by a water rinse. The rinse may consist of single or multiple stage rinsing. An alkaline cleaning operation is defined as a bath followed by a rinse, regardless of the number of rinse stages. Each alkaline cleaning bath and rinse combination is entitled to a discharge allowance. A

alkaline mine drainage
Mine drainage which, before any treatment, has a pH equal to or more than 6.0 and a total iron concentration of less than 10 mg/1. A

alkalinity
The measurable ability of solutions

or aqueous suspensions to neutralize an acid.

all-electric melter

A glass melting furnace in which all the heat required for melting is provided by electric current from electrodes submerged in the molten glass, although some fossil fuel may be charged to the furnace as raw material only. A

allergen

Any of various sorts of material that, as a result of coming into contact with appropriate tissues of an animal body, after a latent period, induces a state of sensitivity and/or resistance to infection or toxic substances.

alley collection

The collection of solid waste from containers placed adjacent to or in an alley. A

allocable costs

[In connection with Federal grants or contracts] those costs incurred specifically for the cost objectives of a particular project. For example, salary costs incurred on one project cannot be charged to another project. Note also, that an allowable cost may be unallocable, and an allocable cost may be ineligible or even unallowable. In order for a cost to be allocable to a grant or contract, it must: (1) be incurred specifically for the grant or contract; (2) benefit both the grant or contract and other work, or both Government work and other work, and be distributable to them in reasonable proportion to the benefits received; or (3) be necessary to the overall opera-

tion of the business, although a direct relationship to any particular cost objective cannot be shown. Costs allocable to a specific cost objective, e.g., grant or contract, may not be shifted to other cost objectives in order to meet deficiencies covered by overruns or other fund considerations, to avoid restrictions imposed by law or the terms of the grant agreement, or for other reasons of convenience.

allocable credits

[In connection with Federal grants or contracts] receipts or negative expenditure types of transactions which operate to offset or reduce expense items that are allocable to a grant project as direct or indirect costs are considered allocable credits. Typical examples of such credits are: purchase discounts, rebates, or allowances; recoveries or indemnities on losses; and adjustments of overpayments or erroneous charges.

allotment

An amount representing a state's share of funds requested in the President's budget or appropriated by Congress for an environmental program, as EPA determines after considering any factors indicated by this regulation. The allotment is not an entitlement but rather the objective basis for determining the range for a state's planning target. A

allowable costs

Those eligible, reasonable, necessary, and allocable costs which are permitted under the appropriate Federal cost principles, in accordance with EPA policy, within the scope of the project and authorized for EPA participation. [ed. Applicable to Federal grants and establishing those items for which EPA will pay].

allowable emissions

The emissions rate of a stationary source calculated using the maximum rated capacity of the source (unless the source is subject to Federally enforceable limits which restrict the operating rate, or house of operation, or both) and the most stringent of the following: (a) The applicable standards set forth in 40 CFR Part 60 or 61; (b) Any applicable State Implementation Plan emissions limitation including those with a future compliance date; or (c) The emissions rate specified as a Federally enforceable permit condition, including those with a future compliance date. A [ed. The allowable emissions are the primary enforceable requirement imposed on stationary sources of air pollution].

alpha particle

The least penetrating type of radiation, usually not harmful to life. N

alternative method

Any method of sampling and analyzing for an air pollutant which is not a reference method or an equivalent method but which has been demonstrated to the Administrator's satisfaction to produce, in specific cases, results adequate for his determination of compliance. A [ed. The administrator's prescribed "reference" method of sampling must normally be used by a source unless the administrator approves the source's request for an alternative method].

alternative technology

Proven wastewater treatment processes and techniques which provide for the reclaiming and reuse of water, productivity recycle wastewater constituents or otherwise eliminate the discharge of pollutants, or recover energy. Specifically, alternative technology includes land application of effluent and sludge; aquifer recharge; aquaculture; direct reuse (non-potable); horticulture; revegetation of disturbed land; containment ponds; sludge composting and drying prior to land application; self-sustaining incineration; methane recovery; co-disposal of sludge and solid waste and individual and on-site systems. A

alternative to conventional treatment works for a small community

For purposes of 40 CFR §§ 35.2020 and 35.2032, alternative technology used by treatment works in small communities include alternative technologies defined in paragraph (b)(4), as well as, individual and onsite systems; small diameter gravity, pressure or vacuum sewers conveying treated or partially treated wastewater. These systems can also include small diameter gravity sewers carrying raw wastewater to cluster systems. A

alternative wastewater treatment works

A wastewater conveyance and/or treatment system other than a conventional system. Includes small diameter pressure and vacuum sewers and small diameter gravity sewers carrying partially or fully treated wastewater. A

alternative wastewater treatment processes and techniques

Alternative waste water treatment processes and techniques are proven methods which provide for the reclaiming and reuse of water, productively recycle waste water constituents or otherwise eliminate the discharge of pollutants, or recovery energy. (a) In the case of processes and techniques for the treatment of effluents, these include land treatment, aquifer recharge, aquaculture, silviculture, and direct reuse for industrial and other nonpotable purposes, horticulture and revegetation of disturbed land. Total containment ponds and ponds for the treatment and storage of waste water prior to land application and other processes necessary to provide minimum levels of reapplication treatment are considered to be part of alternative technology systems for the purpose of this section. (b) For sludges, these include land application for horticultural, silvicultural, or agricultural purposes (including supplemental processing by means such as composting or drying), and revegetation of disturbed lands. (c) Energy recovery facilities include codisposal measures for sludge and refuse which produce energy; anaerobic digestion facilities (Provided, That more than 90 percent of the methane gas is recovered and used as fuel); and equipment which provides for the use of digester gas within the treatment works. Self-sustaining incineration may also be included provided that the energy recovered and productively used is greater than the energy consumed to dewater the sludge to an autogenous state. (d) Also included are individual and other onsite treatment systems with subsurface or other means of effluent disposal and facilities constructed for the specific purpose of septage treatment. (e) The term "alternative" as used in this definition includes the terms "unconventional" and "alternative to conventional" as used in the FWPCA but not collector sewers, interceptors, storm or sanitary sewers or the separation thereof; or major sewer rehabilitation, except insofar as they are alternatives to conventional treatment works for small communities under 40 CFR § 35.915-1(e) or part of individual systems under 40 CFR § 35.918. A

altitude performance adjustments

Adjustments or modifications made to vehicle, engine, or emission control functions in order to improve emission control performance at altitudes other than those for which the vehicles were designed. A

alum tan

The process of converting animal skin into leather using a form of aluminum. A

aluminum basis material

Aluminum, aluminum alloys and aluminum coated steels which are processed in coil coating. A

aluminum equivalent

An amount of aluminum which can be produced from a Mg of anodes produced by an anode bake plant as determined by 40 CFR § 60.195(g). A

alveoli

The tiny air spaces at the end of the terminal bronchioles of the lungs, where the exchange with the blood of oxygen and carbon dioxide takes place.

AMA
American Medical Association. N

AMBIENS
Atmospheric Mass Balance of Industrially Emitted and Natural Sulfur (experimental investigation by the MAP3S Community). N

ambient
Environmental or surrounding conditions.

ambient air
(1) That portion of the atmosphere, external to buildings, to which the general public has access. A [ed. This is the area subject to jurisdiction of CAA]. (2) Any unconfined portion of the atmosphere: open air, surrounding air. N

ambient water criterion
That concentration of a toxic pollutant in a navigable water that, based upon available data, will not result in adverse impact on important aquatic life, or on consumers of such aquatic life, after exposure of that aquatic life for periods of time exceeding 96 hours and continuing at least through one reproductive cycle; and will not result in significant risk of adverse health effects in a large human population based on available information such as mammalian laboratory toxicity data, epidemiological studies of human occupational exposures, or human exposure data, or any other relevant data. A

amendment
Any change to a grant in terms of work scope, increase or decrease in funding level, changes in key personnel, site conditions, etc.

amendment review
Review of any application requiring Agency approval to amend the registration of a currently registered product, or for which an application is pending Agency decision, not entailing a major change to the use pattern of an active ingredient. A

American Conference of Governmental Industrial Hygienists
ACGIH. An organization of professionals in governmental agencies or educational institutions engaged in occupational safety and health programs. ACGIH develops and publishes recommended occupational exposure limits for chemical substances and physical agents (see TLV). (6500 Glenway Avenue, Bldg. D-7, Cincinnati, OH 45211; (513) 661-7881). N

ammonia stripping
The process in which ammonia is condensed from alkaline aqueous solutions after contact with steam at atmospheric pressure. It is commonly used in the treatment of hazardous waste.

ammonium sulfate dryer
A unit or vessel into which ammonium sulfate is charged for the purpose of reducing the moisture content of the product using a heated gas stream. The unit includes foundations, super-

structure, material charger systems, exhaust systems, and integral control systems and instrumentation. A

ammonium sulfate feed material streams
(1) The sulfuric acid feed stream to the reactor/crystallizer for synthetic and coke oven byproduct ammonium sulfate manufacturing plants. (2) The total or combined feed streams (the oximation ammonium sulfate stream and the rearrangement reaction ammonium sulfate stream) to the crystallizer stage, prior to any recycle streams. A

amount of pesticide
The weight or volume of the pesticide, expressed as weight for solid or semi-solid products and as weight or volume for liquid products. A

ampacity
Current-carrying capacity of electric conductors expressed in amperes. O

AMPS
Automatic Mapping and Planning System. N

AMS
American Meteorological Society. N

AMSA
Association of Metropolitan Sewer Agencies. N

anadromous
(1) Fish that swim upriver to spawn, as do salmon. (2) Fish that spend their adult life in the sea but swim upriver to fresh-water spawning grounds to reproduce. N

anaerobic
A life or process that occurs in, or is not destroyed by, the absence of oxygen. N

anaerobic bacteria
Those bacteria that live and grow in the absence of free oxygen, to whom oxygen is lethal.

angina pectoris
Severe constricting pain in the chest which may be caused by ischemia of the heart muscle; usually caused by coronary artery disease.

anhydrous product
The theoretical product that would result if all water were removed from the actual product. A

animal
All vertebrate and invertebrate species, including but not limited to man and other mammals, birds, fish, and shellfish. C

animal feed
Any crop grown for consumption by animals, such as pasture crops, forage, and grain. A

animal feeding operation
A lot or facility (other than an aquatic animal production facility) where the following conditions are met: (i) Animals have been, are or will be stabled or confined and fed or maintained for a total of 45 days or more in any 12 month period, and (ii) Crops, vegetation, forage growth or post-harvest residues are not sustained in the normal growing season over any portion of the lot or facility. Two or

more animal feeding operations under common ownership are deemed to be a single animal feeding operation if they are adjacent to each other or if they utilize a common area or system for the disposal of wastes. A

animal studies
Investigations using animals as surrogates for humans, on the expectation that results in animals are pertinent to humans.

animal unit
A unit of measurement for any animal feeding operation calculated by adding the following numbers: The number of slaughter and feeder cattle multiplied by 1.0, plus the number of mature dairy cattle multiplied by 1.4, plus the number of swine weighing over 55 pounds multiplied by 0.4, plus the number of sheep multiplied by 0.1, plus the number of horses multiplied by 2.0. A [ed. The animal units determine whether the operation is a "concentrated" animal feeding operation that must have an NPDES permit if it discharges pollutants to the navigable waters].

animal waste
The high organic waste that is generated by the breeding, maintenance, use and slaughter of animals.

animals
Appropriately sensitive living organisms which carry out respiration by means of a lung structure permitting gaseous exchange between air and the circulatory system. A

annual average
The maximum allowable discharge of BOD5 or TSS as calculated by multiplying the total mass (kkg or 1000 lb) of each raw commodity processed for the entire processing season or calendar year by the applicable annual average limitation. A [ed. This period of measurement is one element of effluent limitations imposed on direct discharges].

annual precipitation and annual evaporation
The mean annual precipitation and mean annual lake evaporation respectively, as established by the U.S. Department of Commerce, Environmental Science Services Administration, Environmental Data Services, or equivalent regional rainfall and evaporation data. A [ed. These measurements are used to determine the minimum size of some water treatment systems that utilize retention ponds].

anode bake plant
A facility which produces carbon anodes for use in a primary aluminum reduction plant. A

ANPR
Advance Notice of Proposed Rulemaking. N

ANPRM
Advance Notice of Proposed Rulemaking. A preliminary notice that an agency is considering a regulatory action. It is issued before the agency develops a detailed proposed rule. It usually describes the general area that will be subject to the regulation, lists the alternatives that are under consid-

eration, and asks for public comment in developing a regulation. [ed. Often used by Federal agencies to stimulate data development and public discussion of a new program before a decision is made on the content of a proposed regulation].

ANSI
American National Standards Institute. A privately funded, voluntary membership organization that identifies industrial and public need for national consensus standards and coordinates the development. N

ANSI S3.19-1974
A revision of the ANSI Z24.22-1957 measurement procedure using one-third octave band stimuli presented under diffuse (reverberant) acoustic field conditions. A

ANSI Z24.22-1957
A measurement procedure published by the American National Standards Institute (ANSI) for obtaining hearing protector attenuation values at nine of the one-third octave band center frequencies by using pure tone stimuli presented to ten different test subjects under anechoic conditions. A

Antarctic "Ozone Hole"
Refers to the seasonal depletion of ozone in a large area over Antarctica. N

anthracite
Coal that is classified as anthracite according to the American Society of Testing and Materials' (ASTM) Standard Specification for Classification of Coals by Rank D388-77. A

anti-degradation
Part of federal air quality and water quality requirements prohibiting deterioration where pollution levels are above the legal limit. N

anti-degradation clause
Regulatory concept that limits deterioration of existing air or water quality by restricting the addition of pollutants.

antibodies
Proteins produced in the body by immune system cells in response to antigens, and capable of combining with antigens. N

anticoagulant
A chemical that interferes with blood clotting. N

antidote
A remedy to relieve, prevent, or counteract the affects of a poison. N

antigen
A substance that causes production of antibodies when introduced into animal or human tissue. N

antimicrobial agents
Includes all substances or mixtures of substances, except those defined as fungicides and slimicides, intended for inhibiting the growth of, or destroying any bacteria, fungi pathogenic to man and other animals or viruses declared to be pests under 40 CFR §162.14 and existing in any environment except those specifically excluded: (i) Antimicrobial agents include, but are not limited to: (A) Disinfectants intended to destroy or irreversibly inactivate

infectious or other undesirable bacteria, pathogenic fungi, or viruses on surfaces or inanimate objects. (B) Sanitizers intended to reduce the number of living bacteria or viable virus particles on inanimate surfaces, in water, or in air; (C) Bacteriostats intended to inhibit the growth of bacteria in the presence of moisture; (D) Sterilizers intended to destroy viruses and all living bacteria, fungi and their spores, on inanimate surfaces; (E) Fungicides and fungistats intended to inhibit the growth of, or destroy fungi (including yeasts), pathogenic to man or other animals on inanimate surfaces; and (F) Commodity preservatives and protectants intended to inhibit the growth of, or destroy bacteria in or on raw materials (such as adhesives and plastics) used in manufacturing, or manufactured products (such as fuel, textiles, lubricants, and paints). (ii) Antimicrobial agents do not include those antimicrobial substances or mixtures of substances subject to the provisions of the Federal Food, Drug and Cosmetic Act, as amended (21 U.S.C. 301 et seq.), such as: (A) Substances or mixtures of substances intended to inhibit the growth of, inactivate or destroy fungi, bacteria, or viruses in or on living man or other animals; and (B) Substances or mixtures of substances intended to inhibit the growth of, inactivate or destroy fungi, bacteria, or viruses in or on processed food, beverages, or pharmaceuticals including cosmetics. A

antimony
The total antimony present in the process wastewater stream exiting the wastewater treatment system. A

ANWR
Alaska Arctic National Wildlife Refuge. N

AO.
Administrative Order.

AOC
Administrative Order on Consent.

APA
Administrative Procedure Act.

APCA
Air Pollution Control Association. N

APCD
Air Pollution Control District. N

APHA
American Public Health Association. N

API
American Petroleum Institute. A

API gravity
An empirical scale for measuring the density of liquid petroleum products, the unit being called the "degree API." A

appearance
A description of a substance at normal room temperature and normal atmospheric conditions. Appearance includes the color, size, and consistency of a material. N

appliances
Utilization equipment, generally other than industrial, normally built in standardized sizes or types, which is installed or connected as a unit to

perform one or more functions such as clothes washing, air conditioning, food mixing, deep frying, etc. O

applicable effluent standards and limitations
All state and Federal effluent standards and limitations to which a discharge is subject under the [Clean Water] Act, including, but not limited to, effluent limitations, standards of performance, toxic effluent standards and prohibitions, and pretreatment standards. A

applicable legal requirements
(1) In the case of any major source, any emission limitation, emission standard, or compliance schedule under a EPA-approved state implementation plan (regardless of whether the source is subject to a Federal or state consent decree). (2) In the case of any source, any emission limitation, emission standard, standard of performance, or other requirement (including, but not limited to, work practice standards) established under Section 111 or 112 of the [Clean Air] Act. (3) In the case of a source that is subject to a Federal or Federally approved state judicial consent decree or EPA approved extension, order, or suspension, any interim emission control requirement or schedule of compliance under that consent decree, extension, order or suspension. (4) In the case of a nonferrous smelter which has received a primary nonferrous smelter order issued or approved by EPA under Section 119 of the [Clean Air] Act, any interim emission control requirement (including a requirement relating to the use of supplemental or intermittent controls) or schedule of

compliance under that order. A

applicable standards and limitations (NPDES)
All state, interstate, and Federal standards and limitations to which a "discharge" or a related activity is subject under the CWA, including "effluent limitations," water quality standards, standards of performance, toxic effluent standards or prohibitions, "best management practices," and pretreatment standards under sections 301, 302, 303, 304, 306, 307, 308, 403, and 405 of CWA. A

applicable water quality standards
State water quality standards adopted by the state and approved by EPA pursuant to section 303 of the [Federal Water Pollution Control] Act or promulgated by EPA pursuant to that section. A

applicant
The person who requests a permit, grant, or other governmental authorization under Federal, state or local pollution laws.

application
The EPA standard national forms for applying for a permit, including any additions, revisions or modifications to the forms; or forms approved by EPA for use in "approved States," including any approved modifications or revisions. A

application of a pesticide
The placement for effect of a pesticide at or on the site where the pest control or other response is desired. A

Application, Part A
That part of the Consolidated Permit Application forms which a RCRA permit applicant must complete to qualify for interim status under Section 3005(e) of RCRA and for consideration for a permit. Part A consists of Form 1 (General Information) and Form 3 (Hazardous Waste Application Form). N

Application, Part B
That part of the application which a RCRA permit applicant must complete to be issued a permit. (Note: EPA is not developing a specific form for Part B of the permit application, but an instruction booklet explaining what information must be supplied is available from the EPA Regional Office). N

applied coating solids
Volume of dried or cured coating solids which is deposited and remains on the surface of the automobile or light-duty truck body. A

approach angle
The smallest angle in a plan side view of an automobile, formed by the level surface on which the automobile is standing and a line tangent to the front tire static loaded radius arc and touching the underside of the automobile forward of the front tire. A

appropriate program official
The official at each decision level to whom the Assistant Administrator has delegated responsibility for carrying out the environmental review process. A

appropriate sensitive benthic marine organisms
At least one species each representing filter-feeding, deposit-feeding, and burrowing species chosen from among the most sensitive species accepted by EPA as being reliable test organisms to determine the anticipated impact on the site; provided, however, that until sufficient species are adequately tested and documented, interim guidance on appropriate organisms available for use will be provided by the Administrator, Regional Administrator, or the District Engineer, as the case may be. A [ed. Used to determine the acceptability of a site for ocean dumping of wastes].

appropriate sensitive marine organisms
At least one species each representative of phytoplankton or zooplankton, crustacean or mollusk, and fish species chosen from among the most sensitive species documented in the scientific literature or accepted by EPA as being reliable test organisms to determine the anticipated impact of the wastes on the ecosystem at the disposal site. Bioassays, except on phytoplankton or zooplankton, shall be run for a minimum of 96 hours under temperature, salinity, and dissolved oxygen conditions representing the extremes of environmental stress at the disposal site. Bioassays on phytoplankton or zooplankton may be run for shorter periods of time as appropriate for the organisms tested at the discretion of EPA, or EPA and the Corps of Engineers, as the case may be. A [ed. Used to determine the acceptability of a site for ocean dumping of wastes].

appropriations

Budget authority provided through the congressional appropriation process that permits Federal agencies to incur obligations and to make payments.

approved for the purpose

Approved for a specific purpose, environment, or application described in a particular standard requirement. Suitability of equipment or materials for a specific purpose, environment or application may be determined by a nationally recognized testing laboratory, inspection agency or other organization concerned with product evaluation as part of its listing and labeling program. (See "labeled" or "listed.") O

approved POTW pretreatment program

A program administered by a POTW that meets the criteria established in [40 CFR] §§ 403.8 and 403.9 and which has been approved by a Regional Administrator or State Director in accordance with [40 CFR] § 403.11. A [ed. Approval of a program allows the POTW to determine applicability of certain aspects of national pretreatment standards].

approved program or approved state

A state or interstate program which has been approved or authorized by EPA under 40 CFR Part 123. A, N

APU

Auxiliary Power Unit. A

AQCCT

Air Quality Criteria and Control Techniques. N

AQCR

Air Quality Control Region. [ed. Every area of every state is included in an AQCR. State implementation plans must provide for achievement of NAAQS in every AQCR]. N

AQDHS

Air Quality Data Handling System (OAR). N

AQDM

Air Quality Display Model. N

AQL

Acceptable Quality Level.

AQMA

Air Quality Maintenance Area. N

AQMP

Air Quality Management Plan. N

AQSM

Air Quality Simulation Model. N

AQTAD

Air Quality Technical Assistance Demonstration. N

aquaculture project

A defined managed water area which uses discharges of pollutants into that designated area for the maintenance or production of harvestable freshwater, estuarine, or marine plants or animals. A [ed. Regulated by § 318 of FWPCA]. "Designated area" means the portions of the waters of the United States within which the applicant plans to confine the cultivated species, using a method of plan or operation (including, but not limited to, physical confinement) which, on the basis of reliable scientific evidence, is expected to ensure that the specific individual organisms comprising an aquaculture crop will enjoy increased growth attributable to the discharge of pollutants and be harvested within a defined geographic area. N

aquatic animal production facility
A hatchery, fish farm, or other facility which contains, grows or holds: (1) Fish or other aquatic animals in ponds, raceways or other similar structures for purposes of production and from which there is a discharge on any 30 days or more per year, but does not include: (i) Closed ponds which discharge only during periods of excess runoff, or (ii) Facilities which produce less than 20,000 pounds of aquatic animals per year; (2) Any species of fish or other aquatic animal [other than carp (Cyprinum carpio), goldfish (Carassius auratus), or brown trout (Salmo trutta)] non-native to the United States (non-native fish are as defined in "Special Publication No. 6" of the American Fisheries Society entitled "A List of Common and Scientific Names of Fishes from the U.S. and Canada") and from which there is a discharge at any time. "Special Publication No. 6" may be ordered through the American Fisheries Society, 1319 18th Street, N.W., Washington, D.C. 20036. A

aquatic animals
Appropriately sensitive wholly aquatic animals which carry out respiration by means of a gill structure permitting gaseous exchange between the water and the circulatory system. A

aquatic flora
Plant life associated with the aquatic eco-system including, but not limited to, algae and higher plants. A

aquepts
Soils with an aquic moisture regime and showing some soil development in the B-horizon; wet Inceptisols. N

aquic moisture regime
A moisture condition associated with a seasonal reducing environment that is virtually free of dissolved oxygen because the soil is saturated by ground water or by water of the capillary fringe, as in soils in Aquic suborders and Aquic subgroups. N

aquiclude
A saturated but poorly permeable underground bed, formation, or group of formations that impedes groundwater movement and does not yield water freely to a well or spring. However, an aquiclude may transmit appreciable water to or from adjacent aquifers, and where sufficiently thick, may constitute an important groundwater storage unit.

aquifer
(1) An underground bed or layer of earth, gravel, or porous stone that contains water. (2) A geological "formation," group of formations, or part of a formation that is capable of yielding a significant amount of water to a well or spring. N

ARAR
Applicable or Relevant and Appropriate Requirements. N

arbitration
A process for the resolution of disputes. Decisions are made by an impartial argitrator selected by the parties. These decisions are usually legally binding. (See: mediation). N

architectural coating
A coating used for buildings and their appurtenances. A

architectural or engineering (A/E) services
Consultation, investigation, reporting and design services offered within the scope of the practice of architecture or professional engineering as defined by the laws of a State or territory. A

area director
The employee or officer regularly or temporarily in charge of an area office of the Occupational Safety and Health Administration, U.S. Department of Labor, or any other person or persons who are authorized to act for such employee or officer. The latter authorizations may include general delegations of the authority of an area director under this part to a Compliance Safety and Health Officer or delegations to such an officer for more limited purposes, such as the exercise of the area director's duties under § 1903.14(a). The term also includes any employee or officer exercising supervisory responsibilities over an Area Director. A supervisory employee or officer is considered to exercise concurrent authority with the area director. O

area method
A sanitary landfilling method in which the waste is spread and compacted on the surface of the ground and cover material is spread and compacted over it. A

area of review
The area surrounding an injection well which is described according to the criteria set forth in 40 CFR Section 146.06. N

area permit
A UIC permit applicable to all or certain wells within a geographic area, rather than to a specified well, under 40 CFR Section 122.37. N

area source
Any small residential, governmental, institutional, commercial, or industrial fuel combustion operations [that contribute air pollutants to the ambient air but canot be modified as a point source]: onsite solid waste disposal facility; motor vehicles, aircraft, vessels, or other transportation facilities; or other miscellaneous sources as identified through inventory techniques similar to those described in: "A Rapid Survey Technique for Estimating Community Air Pollution Emissions," Public Health Service Publication No. 999-AP-29, October 1966. A [ed. Although emissions of pollutants from any one operation may be minimal, in the aggregate these small sources may be significant contributors to air pollution and require regulation on an area-wide basis].

areal cover
A measure of dominance that defines the degree to which above

ground portions of plants cover the ground surface; it is possible for the total areal cover for all strata combined in a community or for single stratum to exceed 100 percent because: (1) most plant communities consist of two or more vegetative strata; (2) areal cover is estimated by vegetative layer; and (3) foliage within a single layer may overlap. N

areawide agency
An areawide management agency designated under section 208(c)(1) of the [Clean Water] Act. A

armored cable
Type AC armored cable is a fabricated assembly of insulated conductors in a flexible metallic enclosure. O

ARO
Alternate Regulatory Option. N

ARRP
Acid Rain Research Program. N

article
A manufactured item (1) which is formed to a specific shape or design during manufacture, (2) which has end use function(s) dependent in whole or in part upon its shape or design during end use, and (3) which has either no change of chemical composition during its end use or only those changes of composition which have no commercial purpose separate from that of the article and that result from a chemical reaction that occurs upon end use of other chemical substances, mixtures, or articles, as described in 40 CFR, 720.3 and 723.175, except that

fluids and particles are not considered articles regardless of shape or design as described in 710.2. A

as expeditiously as practicable
As expeditiously as practicable but in no event later than three years after the date of approval of a plan revision under this section (§ 110) (or the date of promulgation oɪ such a plan revision in the case of action by the Administrator under section 110(c) [of the Clean Air Act]). B [ed. The congressional time limit imposed on states for achievement of NAAQS under the CAA].

ASA
American Standards Association.

asbestos
The asbestiform varieties of: chrysotile (serpentine); crocidolite (riebeckite); amosite (cummingtonite-grunerite); anthophyllite; tremolite; and actinolite. A

asbestos debris
Pieces of ACBM that can be identified by color, texture, composition; or dust, if the dust is determined by an accredited inspector to be ACM. A

asbestos material
Asbestos or any material containing asbestos. A

asbestos mill
Any facility engaged in the conversion of any intermediate step in the conversion of asbestos or into commercial asbestos. Outside storage of asbestos materials is not considered a part of such facility. A

asbestos mixture

A mixture which contains bulk asbestos or another asbestos mixture as an intentional component. An asbestos mixture may be either amorphous or a sheet, cloth fabric, or other structure. This term does not include mixtures which contain asbestos as a contaminant or impurity. A

asbestos sampling area

Any area, whether contiguous or not, within a school building which contains friable material that is homogeneous in texture and appearance. A

asbestos tailings

Any solid waste product of asbestos mining or milling operations which contains asbestos. A

asbestos-containing building material

ACBM. Surface ACM, thermal system insulation ACM, or miscellaneous ACM that is found in or on interior structural members or other parts of a school building. A

asbestos-containing material

Any material which contains more than one percent asbestos by weight. A

asbestos-containing waste materials

(1) Any waste which contains commercial asbestos including asbestos mill tailings, control device asbestos waste, friable asbestos waste material, and bags or containers that previously contained commercial asbestos. A (2) Any waste that contains commercial asbestos and is generated by a source subject to the provisions of this subpart. This term includes asbestos mill tailings, asbestos waste from control devices, friable asbestos waste material, and bags or containers that previously contained commercial asbestos. However, as applied to demolition and renovation operations, this term includes only friable asbestos waste and asbestos waste from control devices. K

asbestosis

A disease associated with chronic exposure to and inhalation of asbestos fibers. The disease makes breathing progressively more difficult and can lead to death. N

ASCII

American Standard Code for Information Interchange. N

ASDWA

Association of State Drinking Water Administrators. N

ash

Inorganic residue remaining after ignition of combustible substances determined by definite prescribed methods. A

ash pit

A pit or hopper located below a furnace in which residue is accumulated and from which it is removed.

ash sluice

A trench or channel in which water transports residue from an ash pit to a disposal or collection point.

ash transport water
Water used in the hydraulic transport of either fly ash or bottom ash. A

ash-free basis
The method whereby the weight of ash in a fuel sample is subtracted from its total weight and the adjusted weight is used to calculate the percentages of certain constituents present. For example, the percentage of fixed carbon (FC) on an ash-free basis is computed as follows:

$$\frac{FC(weight) \times 100}{fuel\ sample(weight) - ash(weight)}$$

$$= percentage\ of\ ash\text{-}free\ FC.$$

ASHAA
Asbestos in Schools Hazard Abatement Act. N

ASIWCPA
Association of State and Interstate Water Pollution Control Administrators. N

askarel
A generic term for a group of nonflammable synthetic chlorinated hydrocarbons used as electrical insulating media. Askarels of various compositional types are used. Under arcing conditions the gases produced, while consisting predominantly of noncombustible hydrogen chloride, can include varying amounts of combustible gases depending upon the askarel type. O

ASMDHS
Airshed Model Data Handling System. N

asphalt catalyst
A substance which, when added to asphalt flux in a blowing still, alters the penetrating softening point relationship or increases the rate of oxidation of the flux. A

asphalt concrete plant
Any facility used to manufacture asphalt concrete by heating and drying aggregate and mixing with asphalt cements. For the purpose of 40 CFR §60.90, an asphalt concrete plant is comprised only of any combination of the following: dryers; systems for screening, handling, storing, and weighing hot aggregate; systems for loading, transferring, and storing mineral filler; systems for mixing asphalt concrete; and the loading, transfer, and storage systems associated with emission control systems. A

asphalt processing plant
A plant which blows asphalt for use in the manufacture of asphalt products. A

asphalt storage tank
Any tank used to store asphalt at asphalt roofing plants, petroleum refineries, and asphalt processing plants. [ed. See also "cutback asphalts" and "emulsified asphalts"]. A

asphalts
Black, solid or semisolid bitumens which occur in nature or are obtained as residues during petroleum refining. A

asphyxiant
A vapor of gas that can cause unconsciousness or death by suffo-

cation (lack of oxygen). Most simple asphyxiants are harmful to the body only when they become so concentrated that they reduce oxygen in the air (normally about 21 percent) to dangerous levels (18 percent or lower). Asphyxiation is one of the principal potential hazards of working in confined and enclosed spaces. N

ASRL
Atmospheric Sciences Research Laboratory. N

assay
A test for a particular chemical or effect.

assets
All existing and all probable future economic benefits obtained or controlled by a particular entity. A

assimilation
The ability of a body of water to purify itself of pollutants. N

assimilative capacity
The capacity of a natural body of water to receive: (a) wastewaters, without deleterious effects; (b) toxic materials, without damage to aquatic life or humans who consume the water; (c) BOD, within prescribed dissolved oxygen limits.

assistance agreement
The legal instrument EPA uses to transfer money, property, services, or anything of value to a recipient to accomplish a public purpose. It is either a grant or a cooperative agree-

ment and will specify: budget and project periods; the Federal share of eligible project costs; a description of the work to be accomplished; and any special conditions. A

Associate Enforcement Counsels
Senior managers in EPA's office of enforcement.

associated parking area
A parking facility or facilities owned and/or operated in conjunction with an indirect source. A

asthma
A term currently used in the context of bronchial asthma in which there is widespread narrowing of the airways of the lung which leads to "wheezing" and shortness of breath. Abnormal responsiveness of the air passages to certain substances including air pollutants is common. An attack consists of a widespread narrowing of the bronchioles by muscle spasm, swelling of the mucous membrane, or thickening and increase of mucous secretions, accompanied by wheezing, gasping, and sometimes coughing.

ASTHO
Association of State and Territorial Health Officers. N

ASTM
American Society for Testing and Materials which is the world's largest source of voluntary consensus standards for materials, products, systems, and services. ASTM is a resource for sampling and testing methods, health and safety aspects of materials, safe

performance guidelines, effects of physical and biological agents and chemicals. N

ASTSWMO
Association of State and Territorial Solid Waste Management Officials. N

asymptomatic
Showing no symptoms. N

ATA
Atmosphere Absolute. O

atmosphere
The body of air surrounding the earth; the troposphere. N

atmosphere an
A standard unit of pressure representing the pressure exerted by a 29.92-inch column of mercury at sea level at 45' latitude and equal to 1000 grams per square centimeter. The whole mass of air surrounding the earth, composed largely of oxygen and nitrogen. N

atmospheric pressure
The pressure of air at sea level, usually 14.7 p.s.i.a. (1 atmosphere), or 0 p.s.i.g. O

atomic pile
A nuclear reactor. N

atomize
To divide a liquid into extremely minute particles, either by impact with a jet of steam or compressed air, or by passage through some mechanical device. N

ATSDR
Agency for Toxic Substances and Disease Registry (HHS). N

attainment area
For any air pollutant, an area which has been designated under Section 107 of the Clean Air Act as having ambient air quality levels better than any national primary or secondary ambient air quality standard for that pollutant. Standards have been set for sulfur oxides, particulate matter, nitrogen dioxide, carbon monoxide, ozone, lead, and hydrocarbons. For purposes of the Glossary, "attainment area" also refers to "unclassifiable area," which means, for any pollutants, an area designated under Section 107 as unclassifiable with respect to that pollutant due to insufficient information. N (2) An area considered to have air quality as good as or better than the national ambient air quality standards as defined in the Clean Air Act. An area may be an attainment area for one pollutant and a non-attainment area for others. N

attenuation
(1) A decrease in the concentration or quantity of a chemical or biological material carried in a fluid, resulting from a physical, chemical, and/or biological reaction occurring in the period considered. (2) The process by which a compound is reduced in concentration over time, through adsorption, degradation, dilution, and/or transformation. N

attractant

All substances or mixtures of substances which, through their property of attracting certain animals, are intended to mitigate a population of, or destroy any vertebrate or invertebrate animals declared to be pests under §162.14. (i) Attractants include, but are not limited to: (A) Sensory stimulants (such as pheromones, synthetic attractants, and certain extracts from naturally-occurring organic materials) when used alone, or when in combination with toxicants that can kill certain vertebrate or invertebrate animals, that are intended to draw certain animals into traps or away from crops or sites; these sensory stimulants are considered to be active ingredients in pesticide products; and (B) Naturally-occurring foods and certain extracts from such foods, when in combination with toxicants that can kill certain vertebrate or invertebrate animals, that are intended to draw certain animals into traps or away from crops or sites; these foods and extracts are considered to be inert ingredients in pesticide products. (ii) Attractants do not include: (a) Substances or mixtures of substances intended to attract vertebrate or invertebrate animals for survey or detection purposes only, and (b) Naturally-occurring foods, when used alone or separately and not marketed in mixtures with toxicants, for the purpose of attracting vertebrate or invertebrates animals. O

attrition

Wearing or grinding down a substance by friction. A contributing factor in air pollution, as with dust. N

audiometer

An instrument that measures hearing sensitivity. N

audit

A fiscal or accounting review, and sometimes a programmatic review, of a grant period or a part thereof, or perhaps of several grants in one grantee institution.

augmentation

A requirement for additional funds for a project previously awarded funds in the same funding/budget period. Project nature and scope are unchanged. (Requires a grant amendment.)

authorization

Basic substantive legislation enacted by Congress that sets up or continues the legal operation of a Federal program or agency. Such legislation is normally a prerequisite for subsequent appropriations, but does not usually provide budget authority.

auto-ignition temperature

The temperature to which a closed, or nearly closed container must be heated in order that the flammable liquid, when introduced into the container, will ignite spontaneously or burn. N

autogenous combustion

See autothermic combustion.

automated method or analyzer

A method for measuring concentrations of an ambient air pollutant in which sample collection, analysis, and measurement are performed automatically. A

automatic
Self-acting, operating by its own mechanism when actuated by some impersonal influence, as, for example, a change in current strength, pressure, temperature, or mechanical configuration. O

automatic temperature compensator
A device that continuously senses the temperature of fluid flowing through a metering device and automatically adjusts the registration of the measured volume to the corrected equivalent volume at a base temperature. A

automobile
Any four-wheel vehicle propelled by a combustion engine using onboard fuel or by an electric motor drawing current from rechargeable storage batteries or other portable energy storage devices (rechargeable using energy from a source off the vehicle such as residential electric service) which is manufactured primarily for use on public streets, roads, or highways (except any vehicle operated on a rail or rails) and which is rated at 8,500 pounds gross vehicle weight or less or is a type of vehicle which the Secretary determines is substantially used for the same purposes. A

autothermic combustion (or autogenous)
The burning of a wet organic material where the moisture content is at such a level that the heat of combustion of the organic material is sufficient to vaporize the water and maintain combustion. No auxiliary fuel is required except for start-up.

autotrophic
An organism that produces food from inorganic substances. N

Auxiliary Emission Control Device
AECD. Any element of design which senses temperature, vehicle speed, engine RPM, transmission gear, manifold vacuum, or any other parameter for the purpose of activating, modulating, delaying, or deactivating the operation of any part of the emission control system. A

auxiliary power unit
Any engine installed in or on an aircraft exclusive of the propulsion engines. A

auxiliary-fuel firing equipment
Equipment used in an incinerator to supply additional heat by burning auxiliary fuel. Resulting higher temperatures (1) dry and ignite the waste material, (2) maintain their ignition, and (3) effect the complete combustion of combustible solids, vapors, and gases.

available purchase power
Means the lesser of the following: (a) The sum of available system capacity in all neighboring companies. (b) The sum of the rated capacities of the power interconnection devices between the principal company and all neighboring companies, minus the sum of the electric power load on these interconnections. (c) The rated capacity of the power transmission lines between the power interconnection devices and the electric generating units (the unit in the principal company that has the malfunctioning

flue gas desulfurization system and the unit(s) in the neighboring company supplying replacement electrical power) less the electric power load on these transmission lines. A

available system capacity
[For a utility system] the capacity determined by subtracting the system load and the system emergency reserves from the net system capacity. A

average fuel economy
The unique fuel economy value as compiled under 40 CFR § 600.510 for a specific class of automobiles produced by a manufacturer that are subject to average fuel economy standards. A

average monthly discharge limitation
NPDES. The highest allowable average of "daily discharges" over a calendar month, calculated as the sum of all daily discharges measured during a calendar month divided by the number of daily discharges measured during that month. A

average weekly discharge limitation
NPDES. The highest allowable average of "daily discharges" over a calendar week, calculated as the sum of all daily discharges measured during a calendar week divided by the number of daily discharges measured during that week. A

avg.
Abbreviation for average. A

award
The obligation of funds by the formal offer of a grant agreement to an applicant.

awarding official
The official who obligates grant funds by signing the award documents; not to be confused with the "decision official."

AWT
Advanced Waste Treatment.

AWWA
American Water Works Association. N

axle clearance
The vertical distance from the level surface on which an automobile is standing to the lowest point on the axle differential of the automobile. A

axle ratio
The number of times the input shaft to the differential (or equivalent) turns for each turn of the drive wheels. A

B

backend loader
A collection vehicle that loads refuse from the rear and compacts it.

backend system
Informal term for any process that recovers valuable resources from organic solid waste. Examples are refuse-derived fuel recovery, fluid bed incineration, fiber reclamation, composting, and conversion to animal feed.

backfill
The material used to refill a ditch or other excavation, or the process of doing so. N

background level
With respect to air pollution, amounts of pollutants present in the ambient air due to natural sources. N

background patent
A foreign or domestic patent (regardless of its date of issue relative to the date of the EPA grant): (i) Which the grantee, but not the Government, has the right to license to others, and (ii) Infringement of which cannot be avoided upon the practice of a Subject Invention or Specified Work Object. A

background soil pH
The pH of the soil prior to the addition of substances that alter the hydrogen ion concentration. A

backhoe tamping
A processing step, often used in direct-dump transfer systems, in which a conventional backhoe is used to compact waste contained in an open-top transfer trailer.

BACT
Best Available Control Technology. A emission limitation based on the maximum degree of emission reduction which (considering energy, environmental, and economic impacts and other costs) is achievable through application of production processes and available methods, systems, and techniques. In no event does BACT permit emissions in excess of those allowed under any applicable Clean Air Act provisions. Use of the BACT concept is allowable on a case by case basis for major new or modified emissions sources in attainment and applies to each regulated pollutant.

bacteria

(1) Single-celled microorganisms that possess cell walls. Some bacteria cause disease, and some are beneficial and promote the stabilization of solid waste. (2) Single-celled microorganisms lack chlorophyll. Some cause diseases, others aid in pollution control by breaking down organic matter in air and water. N (3) Can aid in the pollution control by consuming or breaking down organic matter in sewage, or by similarly acting on oil spills or other water pollutants. Bacteria in soil, water or air can also cause human, animal and plant health problems. N

baffle

A deflector that changes the direction of flow or velocity of water, sewage, or particulate matter. Also used to deaden sound. N

baffle chamber

In incinerator design, a chamber designed to promote the settling of fly ash and coarse particulate matter by changing the direction and/or reducing the velocity of the gases produced by the combustion of the refuse or sludge. N

bagasse

An agricultural waste material consisting of the dry pulp residue that remains after juice is extracted from sugar cane or sugar beets. The residue is used in the manufacture of pulp and paper.

baghouse

An air pollution abatement device used to trap particulates by filtering gas streams through large fabric bags usually made of glass fibers. N

baghouse filter

Large fabric bag, usually made of glass fibers, used to eliminate intermediate and large (greater than 20 microns in diameter) particles. This device operates in a way similar to the bag of an electric vacuum cleaner, passing the air and smaller particulate matter, while entrapping the larger particulates. N

bake oven

A device that uses heat to dry or cure coatings. A

balanced, indigenous population

An ecological community which: (1) Exhibits characteristics similar to those of nearby, healthy communities existing under comparable but unpolluted environmental conditions; or (2) May reasonably be expected to become re-established in the polluted water body segment from adjacent waters if sources of pollution were removed. A

baler

A machine used to compress solid wastes, primary materials, or recoverable materials, with or without binding, to a density or from which will support handling and transportation as a material unit rather than requiring a disposable or re-useable container. This specifically excludes briquetters and stationary compaction equipment which is used to compact materials into disposable or reuseable containers. A

baling
Compacting solid waste into blocks to reduce volume. N

ballast
The flow of waters, from a ship, that is treated along with refinery waste-waters in the main treatment system. A

ballistic separator
A machine that sorts organic from inorganic matter for composting. N

band application
In pesticides, the spreading of chemicals over or next to each row of plants in a field. L

banking
A system for recording qualified air emission reductions for later use in bubble, offset, or netting transactions. (See: emissions trading). N

barometric condensing operations
Those operations or processes directly associated with or related to the concentration and crystallization of sugar solutions. A

barometric damper
A hinged or pivoted plate that automatically regulates the amount of air entering a duct, breeching, flue connection, or stack, thereby maintaining a constant draft in the incinerator.

barrel
Forty-two United States gallons at sixty degrees Fahrenheit. A, D, O

barricade
An obstruction to deter the passage of persons or vehicles. O

barrier
Any material or structure that prevents or substantially delays movement of water or radionuclides toward the accessible environment. For example, a barrier may be a geologic, structure, a canister, a waste form with physical and chemical characteristics that significantly decrease the mobility of radionuclides, or a material placed over and around waste, provided that the material or structure substantially delays movement of water or radionuclides. A

barrier coating(s)
A layer of a material that acts to obstruct or prevent passage of something through a surface that is to be protected, e.g. grout, caulk, or various sealing compounds; sometimes used with polyurethane membranes to prevent corrosion or oxidation of metal surfaces, chemical impacts on various materials, or, for example, to prevent soil-gas-borne radon from moving through walls, cracks, or joints in a house. N

bar screen
In wastewater treatment, a device used to remove large solids. N

BART

Best Available Retrofit Technology.

basal application

In pesticides, the spreading of a chemical on plant stems or trunks just above the soil line. N

base date

The date which is used as a reference for determination of compliance with regulations. A

base date period

The thirty day period immediately preceding the base date. A

base level

A unique combination of basic engine, inertia weight, and transmission class. A

base load

The load level at which a gas turbine is normally operated. A

base temperature

An arbitrary reference temperature for determining liquid densities or adjusting the measured volume of a liquid quantity. A

base vehicle

The lowest priced version of each body style that makes up a car line. A

baseline area

Any intrastate area (and every part thereof) designated as attainment or unclassifiable under section 107(d)(1) (D) or (E) of the CAA in which the major source or major modification establishing the baseline date would construct or would have an air quality impact equal to or greater than 1 ug/m^3 (annual average) of the pollutant for which the baseline date is established. Area redesignations under section 107(d)(1)(D) or (E) of the CAA cannot intersect or be smaller than the area of impact of any major stationary source or major modification which: (a) Establishes a baseline date; or (b) Is subject to 40 CFR 52.21 and would be constructed in the same state as the state proposing the redesignation. A

baseline concentration

With respect to a pollutant, the ambient concentration levels which exist at the time of the first application for a permit in an area subject to [PSD regulations], based on air quality data available in EPA or a State air pollution control agency and on such monitoring data as the permit applicant is required to submit. Such ambient concentration levels shall take into account all projected emissions in, or which may affect, such area from any major emitting facility on which construction commenced prior to January 6, 1975, but which has not begun operation by the date of the baseline air quality concentration determination. Emissions of sulfur oxides and particulate matter from any major emitting facility on which construction commenced after January 6, 1975, shall not be included in the baseline and shall be counted against the maximum allowable increases in pollutant concentrations established under 40 CFR Part 52. A, B

baseline configuration

The unretrofitted test configuration, tuned in accordance with the automobile manufacturer's specifications. [ed. Used in automobile emissions certification procedures]. A

baseline date

(i) The earliest date after August 7, 1977, on which the first complete application under 40 CFR 52.21 is submitted by a major stationary source or major modification subject to the requirements of 40 CFR 52.21. (ii) The baseline date is established for each pollutant for which increments or other equivalent measures have been established if: (a) the area in which the proposed source or modification would construct is designated as attainment or unclassifiable under section 107(d)(i)(D) or (E) of the CAA for the pollutant on the date of its complete application under 40 CFR 52.21; and (b) In the case of a major stationary source, the pollutant would be emitted in significant amounts, or, in the case of a major modification, there would be a significant net emissions increase of the pollutant. [ed. This definition established the date from which new sources will have to demonstrate they do not violate air quality increments designed to prevent significant deterioration of air quality]. A

baseline model year

With respect to any pollutant emitted from any vehicle or engine, or class or category thereof, the model year immediately preceding the model year in which Federal standards applicable to such vehicle or engine, or class or category thereof, first applied with

respect to such pollutant. B

basic engine

A unique combination of manufacturer, engine displacement, number of cylinders, fuel system (as distinguished by number of carburetor barrels or use of fuel injection), catalyst usage, and other engine and emission control system characteristics specified by the Administrator of EPA. A

Basic Oxygen Process Furnace

BOPF. Any furnace producing steel by charging scrap steel, hot metal, and flux materials into a vessel and introducing a high volume of an oxygen-rich gas. A

Basic Oxygen Furnace

BOF. A furnace in which steel is produced from oxidation of a molten mixture of pig iron and steel scrap. Pure oxygen is introduced at supersonic speeds by a lance immersed in the mixture and left for 20 minutes. The process uses 35 percent or less of steel scrap.

basic oxygen furnace steelmaking

The production of steel from molten iron, steel scrap, fluxes, and various combinations thereof, in refractory lined furnaces by adding oxygen. A

basic vehicle frontal area

The area enclosed by the geometric projection of the basic vehicle along the longitudinal axis, which includes tires but excludes mirrors and air deflectors, onto a plane perpendicular to the longitudinal axis of the vehicle. A

basin
Includes, but is not limited to, rivers and their tributaries, streams, coastal waters, sounds, estuaries, bays, lakes, and portions thereof, as well as the lands drained thereby. D

BAT
Best Available Technology. A

batch
The collection of a substance or a product of the same category or configuration, as designated by the Administrator in a test request, from which a batch sample is to be randomly drawn and inspected to determine conformance with acceptability criteria. A

batch sample
The collection of substances or products of the same category, configuration or subgroup thereof which are drawn from a batch and from which test samples are drawn. A

batch-fed incinerator
An incinerator that is periodically charged with solid waste; one charge is allowed to burn down or burn out before another is added.

BATEA
Best Available Technology Economically Achievable. N

battery configuration
The electrochemical type, voltage, capacity (in Watt-hours at the c/3 rate), and physical characteristics of the battery used as the tractive energy storage device. A

battery wall
A double or common wall between two incinerator combustion chambers; both faces are exposed to heat.

bauxite
Ore containing alumina monohydrate or alumina trihydrate which serves as the principal raw material for the production of alumina by the Bayer process or by the combination process. A

BCS
Buildings and Community Systems.

BCT
(1) Best Control Technology. N (2) Best Conventional Pollutant Control Technology under section 304(b)(4) of the Clean Water Act. A

BDAT
Best Demonstrated Achievable (or Available) Technology. N

BDT
Best Demonstrated Technology. N

Be
Abbreviation for beryllium. A

beehive cokemaking
Those operations in which coal is heated with the admission of air in controlled amounts for the purpose of producing coke. There are no by-product recovery operations associated with beehive cokemaking operations. A

begin actual construction
Initiation of physical on-site construction activities on an emissions

unit which are of a permanent nature. Such activities include, but are not limited to, installation of building supports and foundations, laying of underground pipework, and construction of permanent storage structures. With respect to a change in method of operating this term refers to those on-site activities other than preparatory activities which mark the initiation of the change. A

BEJ
Best Expert Judgment. N

belowground storage facility
A tank or other container located other than as defined as "aboveground." A

belt pole
A device used in shifting belts on and off fixed pulleys on line or countershaft where there are no loose pulleys (sometimes called a "belt shipper" or "shipper pole.") O

belt shifter
A device for mechanically shifting belts from tight to loose pulleys or vice versa, or for shifting belts on cones of speed pulleys. O

belts
All power transmission belts, such as flat belts, round belts, V-belts, etc., unless otherwise specified. O

BEN
EPA's computer model for analyzing a violator's economic gain from not complying with the law. N

bench mark
A fixed, more or less permanent reference point or object of known elevation; the U.S. Geological Survey (USGS) installs brass caps in bridge abutments or otherwise permanently sets bench marks at convenient locations nationwide; the elevations on these marks are referenced to the National Geodetic Vertical Datum (NGVD), also commonly known as Mean Sea Level (MSL); locations of these bench marks on USGS topographic maps are shown as small triangles; since the marks are sometimes destroyed by construction or vandalism, the existence of any bench mark should be field verified before planning work which relies on a particular reference point; the USGS or local state surveyors office can provide information on the existence, exact location and exact elevation of bench marks. N

beneficial use
Produced water that is of good enough quality to be used for livestock watering or other agricultural uses and is being put to such use. A

beneficiation process
The dressing or processing of gold bearing ores for the purpose of (i) Regulating the size of, or recovering, the ore or product, (ii) Removing unwanted constituents from the ore, and (iii) Improving the quality, purity, or assay grade of a desired product. A

benign
Not recurrent or not tending to progress. N

Benthic Organism
Benthos. A form of aquatic plant or animal life that is found on or near the bottom of a stream, lake or ocean. N

benthic region
The bottom layer of a body of water. N

benzidine
The compound benzidine and its salts as identified by the chemical name 4,4'-diaminobiphenyl. A

benzidine manufacturer
A manufacturer who produces benzidine or who produces benzidine as an intermediate product in the manufacture of dyes commonly used for textile, leather and paper dyeing. A

benzidine-based dye applicator
An owner or operator who uses benzidine-based dyes in the dyeing of textiles, leather or paper. A

beryllium
An airborne metal that can be hazardous to human health when inhaled. It is discharged by machine shops, ceramic and propellant plants, and foundries. N

beryllium alloy
Any metal to which beryllium has been added in order to increase its beryllium content and which contains more than 0.1 percent beryllium by weight. A

Best Available Control Technology
BACT. An emission limitation based on the maximum degree of reduction of each pollutant subject to regulation under this Act emitted from or which results from any major emitting facility, which the permitting authority, on a case-by-case basis, taking into account energy, environmental, and economic impacts and other costs, determines is achievable for such facility through application of production processes and available methods, systems, and techniques, including fuel cleaning or treatment or innovative fuel combustion techniques for control of each such pollutant. In no event does BACT permit emission in excess of those allowed under any applicable Clean Air Act provisions. Use of the BACT concept is allowable on a case by case basis for major new or modified emissions sources in attainment areas and applies to each regulated pollutant. N

Best Available Retrofit Technology
BART. Emission limitations imposed on existing sources of air pollutants to protect visibility in certain areas where visibility is a particularly valuable resource, e.g. national parks required by § 4169A of CAA.

Best Available Technology Economically Achievable
BATEA. Technology-based effluent limitations on direct dischargers are to meet by July 1, 1984, pursuant to §301 (b)(2)(A) of the FWPCA. The level of control is generally described as the "best of the best" technology in use and is to include controls on toxic pollutants.

Best Available Technology

BAT. The best technology, treatment techniques, or other means which the Administrator finds, after examination for efficacy under field conditions and not solely under laboratory conditions, are available (taking cost into consideration). For the purposes of setting Maximum Contaminant Levels (MCLs) for synthetic organic chemicals, any BAT must be at least as effective as granular activated carbon. A

Best Conventional Pollutant Control Technology

BCT. Technology-based effluent limitations for conventional pollutants that direct dischargers must meet by July 1, 1984, pursuant to §301 (b)(2)(E) of the FWPCA. The level of control is to be no less stringent than BPT.

Best Management Practices

BMP. A practice, or combination of practices, that is determined by a State (or designated areawide planning agency) after problem assessment, examination of alternative practices, and appropriate public participation to be the most effective, practicable (including technological, economic, and institutional considerations) means of preventing or reducing the amount of pollution generated by nonpoint sources to a level compatible with water quality goals. A

Best Practical Control Technology Currently Available

BPT. Technology-based effluent limitations direct dischargers were to meet by July 1, 1977, pursuant to §301(b)(1)(A) of the FWPCA. The level of control is generally described as the "average of the best" technology in use to control wastes from that industry.

beta particle

An elementary particle emitted by radioactive decay that may cause skin burns. It is halted by a thin sheet of metal. N

beverage

Carbonated natural or mineral waters; soda water and similar carbonated soft drinks; and beer or other carbonated malt drinks in liquid form and intended for human consumption. A

beverage containers

Any metal, glass, plastic, or wax-coated paper containers used to hold beverages. Such containers can become institutional, municipal, or residential solid waste.

bhp

Abbreviation for brake horsepower. A

BHT

Butalyated Hydroxytoluene.

bicycle
A non-motorpowered, 2-wheeled vehicle. A

bicycle lane
A route for the exclusive use of bicycles, either constructed specifically for that purpose or converted from an existing lane. A

bicycle parking facility
Any storage facility for bicycles, which allows bicycles to be locked securely. A

BID
Background Information Document. N

BIF
Boilers, Incinerators and Furnaces.

bike path
A route for the exclusive use of bicycles separated by grade or other physical barrier from motor traffic. A

bike route
A route in which bicycles share road space with motorized vehicles. A

bikeways
Bike paths, bike lanes and bike routes. A

bilge oil
Waste oil which accumulates, usually in small quantities, in the lower spaces in a ship, just inside the shell plating. Usually mixed with larger quantities of water. A

bioaccumulative
A characteristic of a chemical species when the rate of intake into a living organism is greater than the rate of excretion or metabolism. This results in an increase in tissue concentration relative to the exposure concentration.

bioassay
Using living organisms to measure the effect of a substance, factor, or condition by comparing before-and-after data. Term is often used to mean cancer bioassays. N

Biochemical Oxygen Demand
BOD. (1) The dissolved oxygen required to decompose organic matter in water. It is a measure of pollution because heavy waste loads have a high demand for oxygen. N (2) A measure of the amount of oxygen consumed in the biological processes that break down organic matter in water. The greater the BOD, the greater the degree of pollution. N

bioconversion
A resource recovery method that uses the biological processes of living organisms to transform organic waste into usable material (e.g., humus, compost).

biodegradable
Any substance that decomposes through the action of microorganisms. N

biodegradation
Decomposition of a substance into more elementary compounds by the action of microorganisms such as bacteria.

biological additives
Microbiological cultures, enzymes, or nutrient additives that are deliberately introduced into an oil discharge for the specific purpose of encouraging biodegradation to mitigate the effects of the discharge. A

biological control
Using means other than chemicals to control pests, such as predatory organisms, sterilization, or inhibiting hormones. N

biological magnification
(1) The concentration of certain substances up a food chain. A very important mechanism in concentrating pesticides and heavy metals in organisms such as fish. N (2) Refers to the process whereby certain substances such as pesticides or heavy metals move up the food chain, work their way into a river of lake and are eaten by large birds, animals or humans. The substances become concentrated in tissues or internal orgrans as they move up the chain (See: bioaccumulative). N

biological monitoring
The determination of the effects on aquatic life, including accumulation of pollutants in tissue, in receiving waters due to the discharge of pollutants (A) by techniques and procedures, including sampling of organisms representative of appropriate levels of the food chain appropriate to the volume and

the physical, chemical, and biological characteristics of the effluent, and (B) at appropriate frequencies and locations. D

biological oxidation
The process by which microorganisms decompose complex organic materials. The process is used in activated sludge wastewater treatment and in self-purification of bodies of water. Also called biochemical oxidation.

biological treatment
A treatment technology that uses bacteria to consume waste. This treatment breaks down organic materials. N

biological waste
Waste derived from living organisms.

biological wastewater treatment
A type of wastewater treatment in which bacterial or biochemical action is intensified to stabilize, oxidize, and nitrify the unstable organic matter present. Intermittent sand filters, contact beds, trickling filters, and activated sludge tanks are examples of the equipment used.

biomass
(1) The amount of living matter in a given unit of the environment. (2) All of the living material in a given area, often refers to vegetation. Also called "biota." N

biomonitoring
(1) The use of living organisms to test the suitability of effluents for discharge into receiving waters and to

test the quality of such waters downstream from the discharge. (2) Analysis of blood, urine, tissues, etc., to measure chemical exposure in humans. N

biopsy
Removal and examination of tissue from the living body. N

biosphere
The portion of earth and its atmosphere that can support life. N

biostabilizer
A machine that grinds and aerates organic waste materials to produce compost.

biota
All living organisms that exist in an area. N

biotechnology
Techniques that use living organisms or parts of organisms to produce a variety of products (from medicines to industrial enzymes) to improve plants or animals or to develop microorganisms for specific uses such as removing toxics from bodies of water, or as pesticides. N

biotic community
A naturally occurring assemblage of plants and animals that live in the same environment and are mutually sustaining and interdependent. N

bird hazard
An increase in the likelihood of bird/aircraft collisions that may cause damage to the aircraft or injury to its occupants. A

bird poisons and repellents
All substances or mixtures of substances intended for preventing, destroying, repelling, or mitigating birds declared to be pests under 40 CFR §162.14. Bird poisons and repellents include, but are not limited to: (i) Toxicants intended to kill or destroy certain birds; (ii) Toxicants intended to cause, by pharmacological action, repelling of birds away from certain sites; (iii) Sensory agents utilizing taste, sight, touch, or other means, intended to repel certain bird species or populations from certain sites, to reduce their predation of certain seed and crops, or to protect other organisms or objects from injury, soiling, or harassment; and (iv) Reproductive inhibitors intended to reduce or otherwise alter the reproductive capacity or potential of certain birds. A

bitterns
The saturated brine solution remaining after precipitation of sodium chloride in the solar evaporation process. A

bituminous coal
Solid fossil fuel classified as bituminous coal by A.S.T.M. Designation D-388-66. A

black liquor
The leftover liquid from wood chips treated by the sulfite process. (See: Multiple-effect evaporater system.)

black lung
A disease of the lungs caused by habitual inhalation of coal dust. N

blackwater
Water that contains animal, human, or food wastes. N

blast furnace
Any furnace used to recover metal from slag. A

blast gate
A sliding metal damper in a duct, usually used to regulate the flow of forced air.

blend fertilizer
A mixture of dry, straight and mixed fertilizer materials. A

BLM
Bureau of Land Management. N

bloom
A proliferation of algae and/or higher aquatic plants in a body of water; often related to pollution, especially when pollutants accelerate growth. N

blowdown
The minimum discharge of recirculating water for the purpose of discharging materials contained in the process, the further buildup of which would cause concentrations or amounts exceeding limits established by best engineering practice. A

blower
A fan used to force air or gas under pressure.

blowing still
The equipment in which air is blown through asphalt flux to change the softening point and penetration rate. A

blowing tap
Any tap in which an evolution of gas forces or projects jets of flame or metal sparks beyond the ladle, runner, or collection hood. A

blowout
A sudden violent escape of gas and oil from an oil well when high pressure gas is encountered and preventive measures have failed. A

BLS
Bureau of Labor Statistics. N

BMP('s)
Best Management Practice(s). N

BMR
Baseline Monitoring Report (CWA). N

BOA
Basic Ordering Agreement.

BOD
Biological Oxygen Demand. N

BOD5 input
The biochemical oxygen demand of the materials entered into process. It can be calculated by multiplying the fats, proteins and carbohydrates by factors of 0.890, 1.031 and 0.691 respectively. Organic acids (e.g., lactic acids) should be included as carbohydrates. Composition of input materials may be based on either direct analyses or generally accepted published values. A (2) The amount of dissolved oxygen consumed in five days by biological processes breaking down organic matter. N

BOD7

The biochemical oxygen demand as determined by incubation at 20° C for a period of 7 days using an acclimated seed. Agitation employing a magnetic stirrer set at 200 to 500 rpm may be used. A

body burden

The total amount of a toxic material that a person has ingested or inhaled from all sources over time. N

body style

A level of commonality in vehicle construction as defined by number of doors and roof treatment (e.g., sedan, convertible, fastback, hatchback) and number of seats (i.e., front seat, second or third seat) requiring seat belts pursuant to National Highway Traffic Safety Administration safety regulations. Station wagons and light trucks are identified as car lines. A

body type

A name denoting a group of vehicles that are either in the same car line or in different car lines provided the only reason the vehicles qualify to be considered in different car lines is that they are produced by separate divisions of a single manufacturer. A

BOF

Basic Oxygen Furnace. N

bog

Wet, spongy land usually poorly drained, highly acid and rich in plant residue; the result of lake eutrophication. N

boiler operating day

A 24-hour period during which fossil fuel is combusted in a steam generating unit for the entire 24 hours. A

boiling point

The temperature at which the vapor pressure of a liquid is equal to the pressure of the atmosphere. A

Boiling Water Reactor

BWR. A reactor in which water, used as both coolant and moderator, is allowed to boil in the core. The resulting steam can be used directly to drive a turbine.

boom

A floating device used to contain oil on a body of water. N

booster cycle

The period during which additional hydraulic pressure is exerted to push the last charge of solid waste into a transfer trailer or a container attached to a stationary compactor.

BOP

Basic Oxygen Process. N

BOPF

Basic Oxygen Process Furnace. N

borosilicate recipe

Raw material formulation of the following approximate weight proportions: 72 percent silica; 7 percent nepheline syenite; 13 percent anhydrous borax; 8 percent boric acid; and 0.1 percent miscellaneous materials. A

borrowing authority
Statutory authority not necessarily provided through the appropriations process, that permits Federal agencies to incur obligations and to make payments from borrowed moneys.

botanical pesticide
A pesticide whose active ingredient is a plant produced chemical such as nicotine or strychnine. N

bottle bill
Proposed or enacted legislation which requires a returnable deposit on beer or soda containers and provides for retail store or other redemption centers. Such legislation is designed to discourage use of throw-away containers. N

bottom ash
The ash that drops out of the furnace gas stream in the furnace and in the economizer sections. Economizer ash is included when it is collected with bottom ash. A

bottom land hardwoods
Forested freshwater wetlands adjacent to rivers in the southeastern United States. They are especially valuable for wildlife breeding and nesting and habitat areas. N

boxboard
Paperboard used to manufacture boxes and cartons.

BOYSNC
Beginning of Year Significant Non-Compliers. N

BP
Boiling Point. N

BPJ
Best Professional Judgment. N

BPT
Best Practicable Control Technology. N

BPTCA
The Best Practicable Control Technology Currently Available under section 304(b)(1) of the Clean Water Act. A

BPWTT
Best Practicable Waste Treatment Technology. The cost-effective technology that can treat wastewater, combined sewer overflows and nonexcessive infiltration and inflow in publicly owned or individual wastewater treatment works, to meet the applicable provisions of: (i) 40 CFR Part 133--secondary treatment of wastewater; (ii) 40 CFR Part 125, Subpart G--marine discharge waivers; (iii) 40 CFR 122.44(d)--more stringent water quality standards and State standards; or (iv) 41 FR 6190 (February 11, 1976) -- Alternative Waste Management Techniques for Best Practicable Waste Treatment (treatment and discharge, land application techniques and utilization practices, and reuse). A

brackish water
A mixture of fresh and salt water. N

brake
The mechanism used on a mechanical power press to stop and/or hold the crankshaft, either directly or through a gear train, when the clutch is disengaged. O

branch circuit
The circuit conductors between the final overcurrent device protecting the circuit and the outlet(s). O

brass or bronze
Any metal alloy containing copper as its predominant constituent, and lesser amounts of zinc, tin, lead, or other metals. A

breakover angle
The supplement of the largest angle, in the plan side view of an automobile, that can be formed by two lines tangent to the front and rear static loaded radii arcs and intersecting at a point on the underside of the automobile. A

breeching
A passage that conducts the products of combustion to a stack or chimney.

breeching bypass
An arrangement in which breechings and dampers permit the intermittent use of two or more passages to direct or divert the flow of the products of combustion.

breeder
A nuclear reactor that produces more fuel than it consumes. N

bridge wall
A partition between chambers over which the products of combustion pass.

briquetter
A machine that compresses a material, such as metal turnings or coal dust, into small pellets.

British thermal unit
BTU. The amount of heat required to raise the temperature of one pound of water one degree Fahrenheit at or near 39.2° F. The term is used in resource recovery to indicate the amount of heat energy available in a given unit of waste or recovered fuel.

broadcast application
In pesticides, the spreading of chemicals over an entire area. N

broke
Paper that is discarded at any time during its manufacture. It is usually returned to a repulping unit for reprocessing.

bronchiole
Small branch of the bronchus.

bronchiolitis
Inflammation of the smallest bronchial tubes.

bronchitis
Inflammation of the mucous membrane of the bronchial tubes. It may aggravate an existing asthmatic condition.

bronchoconstrictor
An agent that causes a reduction in the caliber (diameter) of a bronchial tube.

bronchodilator
An agent which causes an increase in the caliber (diameter) of a bronchus or bronchial tube.

bronchus
A major airway of the respiratory system.

BSCO
Brake Specific Carbon Monoxide. A

BSHC
Brake Specific Hydrocarbons. A

BSNO$_x$
Brake Specific Oxides of Nitrogen. A

Btu
British thermal unit. A

bubble policy
A concept which treats individual sources of pollution in an existing plant collectively rather than individually. As long as it meets an overall emissions reduction goal, a company can reduce emissions from different sources in the same plant by different amounts. N Emissions sources can propose alternate means to comply with a set of emissions limitations; under the bubble concept, sources can control more than required at one emission point where control costs are relatively low in return for a comparable relaxation of controls at a second emission point where costs are higher. (See: emissions trading). N

bucket
An open container affixed to the movable arms of a wheeled or tracked vehicle to spread solid waste and cover material and to excavate soil.

budget
The financial plan for expenditure of all Federal and non-Federal funds for a project, including other Federal assistance, developed by cost components in the grant application.

budget amendment
A formal request submitted to the Congress by the President, after his formal budget transmittal but prior to completion of appropriate action by the Congress, that revises his previous budget request.

Budget Authority
BA. Authority provided by law to enter into obligations that will result in immediate or future outlays. It may be classified by the period of availability (1-year, multiple-year, no-year), by the timing of congressional action (current or permanent), or by the manner of determining the amount available (definite or indefinite). The basic forms of budget authority are: Appropriations--budget authority provided through the congressional appropriation process that permits Federal agencies to incur obligations and to make payments. Borrowing authority -- statutory authority not necessarily provided through the appropriations process, that permits Federal agencies to incur obligations and to make payments from borrowed moneys. Contract authority--statutory authority, not necessarily provided

through the appropriations process, that permits Federal agencies to enter into contracts or incur other obligations in advance of an appropriation.

budget period
The period specified in a grant agreement during which granted Federal funds are authorized to be expended, obligated, or firmly committed by the grantee for the purposes specified in the grant agreement.

budget receipts
Money, net of refunds, collected from the public by the Federal Government through the exercise of its governmental or sovereign powers, as well as gifts, contributions and premiums from voluntary participants in Federal social insurance programs closely associated with compulsory programs. Excluded are amounts received from strictly business-type transactions (such as sales, interest, or loan repayments) and payments between Governmental accounts.

budget surplus or deficit
The difference between budget receipts and outlays.

buffer
Any of certain combinations of chemicals used to stabilize the pH values or alkalinities of solutions.

buffer strips
Strips of grass or other erosion-resisting vegetation between or below cultivated strips or fields. N

building
A structure which stands alone or

which is cut off from adjoining structures by fire walls with all openings therein protected by approved fire doors. A

building manager
The person who manages one or several buildings under the authority of a Federal agency. For example, a building manager may be the GSA person who manages buildings for GSA. O

building-related illness
A discrete, identifiable disease or illness. Can be traced to a specific pollutant or source within a building. (Contrast: sick building syndrome.) N

building, structure, facility, or installation
All of the pollutant-emitting activities which belong to the same industrial grouping, are located on one or more contiguous or adjacent properties, and are under the control of the same person (or persons under common control) except the activities of any vessel. Pollutant-emitting activities shall be considered as part of the same industrial grouping if they belong to the same "Major Group" (i.e., which have the same first two-digit code) as described in the Standard Industrial Classification Manual, 1972, as amended by the 1977 Supplement (U. S. Government Printing Office stock numbers 4101-0066 and 003-005-00176-0, respectively). A

bulk asbestos
Any quantity of asbestos fiber of any type or grade, or combination of

types or grades, that is mined or milled with the purpose of obtaining asbestos. This term does not include asbestos that is produced or processed as a contaminant or an impurity. A

bulk container
A large container that can either be pulled or lifted mechanically onto a service vehicle or emptied mechanically into a service vehicle. A

bulk gasoline plant
A facility for the storage and dispensing of gasoline that employs tank trucks, trailers, railroad cars, or other mobile non-marine vessels for both incoming and outgoing gasoline transfer operations. A

bulk resin
A resin which is produced by a polymerization process in which no water is used. A

bulky waste
Large items of solid waste such as household appliances, furniture, large auto parts, trees, branches, stumps, and other oversize wastes whose large size precludes or complicates their handling by normal solid wastes collection, processing, or disposal methods. A

bull clam
A tracked vehicle that has a hinged, curved bowl on top of the front of the blade.

bulwark
The side of a ship above the upper deck. O

bunker "c" oil
A general term used to indicate a heavy viscous fuel oil. A

bunker fuel
A general term for heavy oils used as fuel on ships and in industry; often refers to No. 5 or 6 fuel oil. A

bunkering
The process of fueling a ship. A

burial ground (graveyard)
A disposal site for unwanted radioactive materials that uses earth or water for a shield. N

burn
The degree of heat treatment to which refractory bricks are subjected during their manufacture.

burning agents
Those materials which, through physical or chemical means, improve the combustibility of the materials to which they are applied. A

burning area
The horizontal projection of a grate, a hearth, or both.

burning hearth
A solid surface to support the solid fuel or solid waste in a furnace during drying, ignition, or combustion, without air openings in it; or, the surface upon which materials are placed for combustion.

burning rate
The volume of solid waste incinerated or the amount of heat released

during incineration. The rate is usually expressed in pounds of solid waste per square foot of burning area per hour or in British thermal units per sq. ft. of burning area per hour.

bursting pressure
The pressure at which a pressure containment device would fail structurally. O

burying
Disposal of waste materials by depositing them in the earth.

bus/carpool lane
A lane on a street or highway open only to buses (or buses and carpools), whether constructed especially for that purpose or converted from existing lanes. A

bushing
An insulating structure including a through conductor, or providing a passageway for such a conductor, with provisions for mounting on a barrier, conducting or otherwise, for the purpose of insulating the conductor from the barrier and conducting current from one side of the barrier to the other. O

business
Any person engaged in a business, trade, employment, calling or profession, whether or not all or any part of the net earnings derived from such engagement by such person inure (or may lawfully inure) to the benefit of any private shareholder or individual. A

business confidentiality claim
A claim or allegation that business information is entitled to confidential treatment for reasons of business confidentiality, or a request for a determination that such information is entitled to such treatment. A

business information
Any information which pertains to the interests of any business, which was developed or acquired by that business, and (except where the context otherwise requires) which is possessed by EPA in recorded form. A

butterfly damper
A plate or blade installed in a duct, breeching, flue connection or stack that rotates on an axis to regulate the flow of gases.

by-pass
The circumventing of a particular portion of a process or pollution control system.

byproduct
A chemical substance produced without a separate commercial intent during the manufacture, processing, use or disposal of another chemical substance(s) or mixture(s). A

byproduct utilization
The manufacture of products from bark and wood waste materials, but does not include the manufacture of insulation board, particleboard, or hardboard. A

C

C.
Celsius.

CAA
Clean Air Act.

CAB
Civil Aeronautics Board.

cabinet
An enclosure designed either for surface or flush mounting, and provided with a frame, mat, or trim in which a swinging door or doors are or may be hung. O

cable
A conductor with insulation, or a stranded conductor with or without insulation and other coverings (single-conductor cable) or a combination of conductors insulated from one another (multiple-conductor cable). O

cable-pullout unloading method
A procedure in which a landfill tractor empties a transfer trailer by pulling a cable network from the front to the rear of the vehicle.

cadmium
A heavy metal element that accumulates in the environment. N

CAER
Community Awareness and Emergency Response Program. N

CAFE
Corporate Average Fuel Economy. N

cage
A guard that may be referred to as a cage or basket guard which is an enclosure that is fastened to the side rails of the fixed ladder or to the structure to encircle the climbing space of the ladder for the safety of the person who must climb the ladder. O

CAIR
Comprehensive Assessment Information Rule.

caisson
A wood, steel, concrete or reinforced concrete, air- and water-tight chamber in which it is possible for men to work under air pressure greater than atmospheric pressure to excavate material below water level. O

cake
The solids discharged from a dewatering apparatus.

cal.
Calorie.

calcination
The process of heating a waste material to a high temperature without fusing in order to effect useful changes (e.g., oxidation, pulverization); commonly used in the treatment of hazardous waste, especially high-level radioactive waste.

calcine
The solid materials produced by a roaster. A

calciner
A unit in which the moisture and organic matter of phosphate rock is reduced within a combustion chamber. A

calcining
The exposure of an inorganic chemical compound or mineral to a uniform high temperature to alter its chemical form and drive off a substance which was originally part of the compound. Most commonly used in processing high-level radioactive wastes. This process involves heating a solid waste material to high temperatures without melting to make useful changes, such as oxidation or pulverization.

calcium carbide
Material containing 70 to 85 percent calcium carbide by weight. A

calibrating gas
A gas of known concentration which is used to establish the response curve of an analyzer. A

calibration
The set of specifications, including tolerances, unique to a particular design, version or application of a component or component assembly capable of functionally describing its operation over its working range. A

calibration drift
The change in measurement system output over a stated period of time of normal continuous operation when the pollutant concentration at the time of the measurement is the same known upscale value. A

calibration error
The difference between the pollutant concentration indicated by the measurement system and the known concentration of the test gas mixture. A

calibration of equipment
Measurement of dispersal or output of application equipment and adjustment of such equipment to control the rate of dispersal, and droplet or particle size of a pesticide dispersed by the equipment. A

CAMU
Correction Action Management Unit.

cancellation
Refers to Section 6 (b) of the Federal Insecticide, Fungicide and Rodenticide Act (FIFRA) which authorizes cancellation of a pesticide registration if unreasonable adverse effects to the environment and public health develop when a product is used

according to widespread and commonly recognized practice, or if its labeling or other material required to be submitted does not comply with FIFRA provisions. N

cancer
An abnormal, potentially unlimited, disorderly new cell growth.

candidate method
A method of sampling and analyzing the ambient air for an air pollutant for which an application for a reference method determination or an equivalent method determination is submitted in accordance with [applicable EPA] procedures. A

CAO
Corrective Action Order. N

cap
A layer of clay, or other highly impermeable material installed over the top of a closed landfill to prevent entry of rainwater and minimize production of leachate. N

capable of transportation of property on a street or highway
A vehicle that: (1) Is self propelled and is capable of transporting any material or fixed apparatus, or is capable of drawing a trailer or semi-trailer. (2) Is capable of maintaining a cruising speed of at least 25 mph over level, paved surface. (3) Is equipped or can readily be equipped with features customarily associated with practical street or highway use, such features including but not being limited to: A reverse gear and a differential, fifth wheel, cargo platform or cargo

enclosures, and (4) Does not exhibit features which render its use on a street or highway impractical, or highly unlikely, such features including, but not being limited to, tracked road means, an inordinate size or features ordinarily associated with combat or tactical vehicles. A

capacitor
A device for accumulating and holding a charge of electricity, consisting of conducting surfaces separated by a dielectric. Types of capacitors are as follows: (1) "Small Capacitor" means a capacitor which contains less than 1.36 kg (3 lbs.) of dielectric fluid. The following assumptions may be used if the actual weight of the dielectric fluid is unknown. A capacitor whose total volume is less than 1,639 cubic centimeters (100 cubic inches) may be considered to contain less than 1.36 kg (3 lbs.) of dielectric fluid and a capacitor whose total volume is more than 3,278 cubic centimeters (200 cubic inches) must be considered to contain more than 1.36 kg (3 lbs.) of dielectric fluid. A capacitor whose volume is between 1,639 and 3,278 cubic centimeters may be considered to contain less than 1.36 kg (3 lbs.) of dielectric fluid if the total weight of the capacitor is less than 4.08 kg (9 lbs.). (2) "Large high voltage capacitor" means a capacitor which contains 1.36 kg (3 lbs.) or more of dielectric fluid and which operates at 2000 volts (a.c. or d.c.) or above. (3) "Large low voltage capacitor" means a capacitor which contains 1.36 kg (3 lbs.) or more of dielectric fluid and which operates below 2000 volts (a.c. or d.c.). A

capacity factor
The ratio of the average load on a machine or equipment for the period of time considered to be the capacity rating of the machine or equipment. A

capillary
A vessel resembling a hair: fine, minute. Relating to a blood or lymphatic capillary vessel.

capillary fringe
A zone immediately above the water table in which water is drawn upward from the water table by capillary action. N

capital expenditure
An expenditure for a physical or operational change to an existing facility which exceeds the product of the applicable "annual asset guideline repair allowance percentage" specified in the latest edition of Internal Revenue Service Publication 534 and the existing facility's basis, as defined by section 1012 of the Internal Revenue Code. A

capture efficiency
The fraction of all organic vapors generated by a process that are directed to an abatement or recovery device. N

capture system
The equipment (including hoods, ducts, fans, dampers, etc.) used to capture or transport particulate matter generated by an affected electric submerged arc furnace to the control device. A

car coupling sound
A sound which is heard and identified by the observer as that of car coupling impact, and that causes a sound level meter indicator (FAST) to register an increase of at least ten decibels above the level observed immediately before hearing the sound. A

car line
A name denoting a group of vehicles within a make or car division which has a degree of commonality in construction (e.g., body, chassis). Car line does not consider any level of decor or opulence and is not generally distinguished by characteristics as roof line, number of doors, seats, or windows except for station wagons or light-duty trucks. Station wagons and light-duty trucks are considered to be different car lines than passenger cars. When applied to light trucks, the term "truck lines" will be used. A

carbon adsorber
An add-on control device which uses activated carbon to absorb volatile organic compounds from a gas stream. The VOCs are later recovered from the carbon. A

carbon dioxide recorder
An instrument that continuously monitors the volume concentration (in percent) of carbon dioxide in a flue gas.

carbon dioxide
CO_2. A colorless, odorless nonpoisonous gas normally part of ambient air; fossil fuel combustion produces significant quantities of CO_2. N

carbon monoxide
CO. A colorless, odorless, very toxic gas produced by any process that involves the incomplete combustion of carbon-containing substances. One of the major air pollutants, it is primarily emitted through the exhaust of gasoline-powered vehicles.

carbon sorption
The process in which a substance (the sorbate) is brought into contact with a solid (the sorbent) and held there either by chemical or physical means. It is used in hazardous waste treatment and often employs activated carbon as the sorbent.

carbon-nitrogen ratio
C/N. The ratio of the weight of carbon to the weight of nitrogen present in a compost or in materials being composted.

carbonaceous matter
Pure carbon or carbon compounds present in the fuel or residue of a combustion process.

carboxyhemoglobin
Hemoglobin in which the iron is associated with carbon monoxide (CO). The affinity of hemoglobin for CO is about 300 times greater than for oxygen. N

carcinogen
A material that has either been found to cause cancer in humans or to cause cancer in animals and therefore considered capable of causing cancer in humans. N

carcinogenic
Cancer producing. N

carcinoma
A malignant tumor or cancer; a new growth made up of epithelial cells tending to infiltrate other cells and give rise to metastases. N

carpool
A private motor vehicle occupied by two or more persons traveling together. A

carpool matching
Assembling lists of commuters whose daily travel plans indicate they might carpool with each other and making such lists available to such commuters to aid them in forming carpools. A

carrier
A common carrier by railroad, or partly by railroad and partly by water, within the continental United States, subject to the Interstate Commerce Act, as amended, excluding street, suburban, and interurban electric railways unless operated as a part of a general railroad system of transportation. A

carrying capacity
(1) In recreation management, the amount of use a recreation area can sustain without deterioration of its quality. (2) In wildlife management, the maximum number of animals an area can support during a given period of the year. N

carryout collection
Collection of solid waste from a

storage area proximate to the dwelling unit(s) or establishment. A

cartridge filter
A discrete filter unit containing both filter paper and activated carbon that traps and removes contaminants from petroleum solvent, together with the piping and ductwork used in the installation of this device. A

CAS
Chemical Abstract Service. N

CAS registration number
A number assigned by the Chemical Abstracts Service to identify a chemical.

CASAC
Clean Air Scientific Advisory Committee. N

casing
A pipe or tubing of appropriate material, of varying diameter and weight, lowered into a borehole during or after drilling in order to support the sides of the hole and thus prevent the walls from caving, to prevent loss of drilling mud into porous ground, or to prevent water, gas, or other fluid from entering or leaving the hole. A

cask
A thick-walled container (usually lead) used to transport radioactive material. Also called a coffin. N

catalytic combustion system
A process in which a substance is introduced into an exhaust gas stream to burn or oxidize vaporized hydrocarbons or odorous contaminants; the substance itself remains intact.

catalytic converter
An air pollution abatement device that removes organic contaminants by oxidizing them into carbon dioxide and water through chemical reaction. Can also be used to reduce nitrogen oxide emissions from motor vehicles. N

catalytic incinerator
A control device which oxidizes volatile organic compounds (VOCs) by using a catalyst to promote the combustion process. Catalytic incinerators require lower temperatures than conventional thermal incinerators, with resultant fuel and cost savings. N

catanadramous
Fish that swim downstream to spawn. N

catastrophic collapse
The sudden and utter failure of overlying strata caused by removal of underlying materials. A

categorical exclusion
A category of actions which do not individually or cumulatively have a significant effect on the human environment and which have been found to have no such effect in procedures adopted by a Federal agency in implementation of NEPA regulations (40 CFR §1507.3) and for which, therefore, neither an environmental impact statement is required. An agency may decide in its procedures or otherwise, to prepare environmental assessments for the reasons stated in 40 CFR § 1508.9 even though it is not required to do

so. Any procedures under this section shall provide for extraordinary circumstances in which a normally excluded action may have a significant environmental effect. A

categorical pretreatment standard
A technology-based effluent limitation for an industrial facility which discharges into a municipal sewer system. Analogous in stringency to Best Available Technology (BAT) for direct dischargers. N

category of chemical substances
A group of chemical substances the members of which are similar in molecular structure, in physical, chemical, or biological properties, in use, or in mode of entrance into the human body or into the environment, or the members of which are in some other way suitable for classification as such for purposes of the Toxic Substances Control Act, except that such term does not mean a group of chemical substances which are grouped together solely on the basis of their being new chemical substances. K

category of mixtures
A group of mixtures the members of which are similar in molecular structure, in physical, chemical, or biological properties, in use, or in the mode of entrance into the human body or into the environment, or the members of which are in some other way suitable for classification as such for the purposes of this [Toxic Substances Control] Act. K

cathode ray tubes
Electronic devices in which electrons focus through a vacuum to generate a controlled image on a luminescent surface. This definition does not include receiving and transmitting tubes. A

cathodic protection
A technique to prevent corrosion of a metal surface by making that surface the cathode of an electrochemical cell. N

cation exchange capacity
The sum of exchangeable cations a soil can absorb expressed in milliequivalents per 100 grams of soil as determined by sampling the soil to the depth of cultivation or solid waste placement, whichever is greater, and analyzing by the summation method for distinctly acid soils or the sodium acetate method for neutral, calcareous or saline soils ("Methods of Soil Analysis, Agronomy Monograph No. 9." C. A. Black, Ed., American Society of Agronomy, Madison, Wisconsin. pp. 891-901, 1965). A

CATS
Corrective Action Tracking System. N

CAU
Carbon Adsorption Unit. N

caustic soda
Sodium hydroxide (NaOH), a strong alkaline substance used as the cleaning agent in some detergents. N

C_{bi}
The concentration of VOC in each gas stream (i) for the time period entering

the emission control device, in parts per million by volume. A

CBI
Confidential Business Information. N

CBOD5
The amount of dissolved oxygen consumed in 5 days from the carbonaceous portion of biological processes breaking down in an effluent. The test methodology is the same as for BOD5, except that nitrogen demand is suppressed. N

cc.
Cubic centimeter.

CC/RTS
Chemical Collection/Request Tracking System. N

CCID
Confidential Chemicals Identification System. N

CCP
Composite Correction Plan (CWA). N

CCTP
Clean Coal Technology Program. N

Cd S
Cadmium sulfide.

CDC
Centers for Disease Control (HHS). N

CDM
Climatological Dispersion Model. N

CDNS
Climatological Data National Summary. N

CDS
Compliance Data System. N

CEA
(1) Council of Economic Advisors, White House staff office. (2) Cooperative Enforcement Agreement. N

CEAT
Contractor Evidence Audit Team. N

CEEM
Center for Energy and Environmental Management. N

CEI
Compliance Evaluation Inspection (CWA). N, I

cell height
The distance between the top and bottom of the compacted solid waste enclosed by natural soil or cover material in a sanitary landfill.

cell thickness
The perpendicular distance between the cover materials placed over the last working faces of two successive cells in a sanitary landfill.

cell-type incinerator
An incinerator whose grate areas are divided into cells, each of which has its own ash drop, underfire air control, and ash grate.

cells
In solid waste disposal, holes where

waste is dumped, compacted and covered with layers of dirt daily. N

CEM
Continuous Emission Monitoring (CAA). N

cementing
The operation whereby a cement slurry is pumped into a drilled hole and/or forced behind the casing. A

CEMS
Continuous Emission Monitoring System. N

center pivot irrigation machine
A multi-motored irrigation machine which revolves around a central pivot and employs alignment switches or similar devices to control individual motors. O

centrifugal collector
A mechanical system using centrifugal force to remove aerosols from a gas stream or to de-water sludge. N

CEQ
Council on Environmental Quality, a staff office of the Executive Office of the President. N

CERCLA
Comprehensive Environmental Response, Compensation and Liability Act of 1980. N (PL 96-510) ("Superfund").

CERI
Center for Environmental Research Information. N

certification
In pesticide regulation, the recognition by a certifying agency that a person is competent and thus authorized to use or supervise the use of restricted use of pesticides; also, a certification by [EPA] that a pesticide chemical is useful for the purpose for which a tolerance or exemption is sought under FIFRA. A A statement of professional opinion based upon knowledge and belief. A

certification vehicle
A vehicle which is selected by automobile manufacturers to be tested for compliance with new motor vehicle air pollutant emission limitations as a representative vehicle of that class of vehicle produced by that manufacturer. Test results from such vehicles determine whether EPA will issue a "certificate of conformity" necessary for the manufacturer to be able to market the vehicles.

certified
Equipment is "certified" if it (a) has been tested and found by a nationally recognized testing laboratory to meet nationally recognized standards or to be safe for use in a specified manner, or (b) is of a kind whose production is periodically inspected by a nationally recognized testing laboratory, and (c) it bears a label, tag, or other record of certification. O

certified applicator
Any individual who is certified under section 4 of FIFRA as authorized to use or supervise the use of any pesticide which is classifed for restricted use. Any applicator who holds or applies registered pesticides, or use dilutions of registered pesticides con-

sistent with section 2(ee) of FIFRA, only to provide a service of controlling pests without delivering any unapplied pesticide to any person so served is not deemed to be a seller or distributor of pesticides under this Act. A, C

certifying agency
The person or agency designated by the Governor of a State, by statute, or by other governmental act, to certify compliance with applicable water quality standards. If an interstate agency has sole authority to so certify for the area within its jurisdiction, such interstate agency shall be the certifying agency. Where a State agency and an interstate agency have concurrent authority to certify, the State agency shall be the certifying agency. A

cesium
Cs. A silver-white, soft ductile element of the alkali metal group that is the most electropositive element known. Used especially in photoelectric cells. N

CFCs
Chlorofluorocarbons. A family of inert, nontoxic, and easily liquified chemicals used in refrigeration, air conditioning, packaging, insulation, or as solvents and aerosol propellants. Because CFCs are not destroyed in the lower atmosphere, they drift into the upper atmosphere where their chlorine components destroy ozone. N

cfh.
Cubic feet per hour.

cfm.
Cubic feet per minute. A measure of the volume of a substance flowing through air within a fixed period of time. With regard to indoor air, refers to the amount of air, in cubic feet, that is exchanged with indoor air in a minute's time, or an air exchange rate. N (Also: cfm.)

CFR
Code of Federal Regulations. A codification of the general and permanent rules published in the Federal Register by the departments and agencies of the Federal government. The Code is divided into 50 titles which represent broad areas subject to Federal regulation. It is issued quarterly and revised annually. N

cfs.
Cubic feet per second, a measure of the amount of water passing a given point. N

cfv.
Critical flow venture.

CFV-CVS
Critical flow venture-constant volume sampler.

chain grate stoker
A stoker with a moving chain as a grate surface. The grate consists of links mounted on rods to form a continuous surface that is generally driven by a shaft with sprockets. B

chamber
An enclosed space inside an incinerator.

changed use pattern
A significant change from a use

pattern approved in connection with the registration of a pesticide product. Examples of significant changes include cude, but are not limited to, changes from nonfood to food use, outdoor to indoor use, ground to aerial application, terrestrial to aquatic use, and nondomestic to domestic use. A

channelization
To straighten and deepen streams so water will move faster, a flood reduction or marsh drainage tactic that can interfere with waste assimilation capacity and disturb fish habitat. N

characteristic
Any one of the four categories used in defining hazardous waste: ignitability, corrosivity, reactivity, and toxicity. N

charge
(1) The amount of solid waste introduced into a furnace at one time. (2) The addition of iron and steel scrap or other materials into the top of an electric arc furnace. A

charge chrome
An alloy containing 52 to 70 percent by weight chromium, 5 to 8 percent by weight carbon, and 3 to 6 percent by weight silicon. A

charging chute
An overhead passage through which waste materials drop into an incinerator.

charging equipment
The apparatus used to introduce refuse into an incinerator.

charging gate
A horizontal, movable cover that closes the opening on a top-charging furnace.

charging hopper
An enlarged opening at the top of a charging chute.

checker work
A pattern of multiple openings in a refractory structure through which the products of combustion pass to accelerate the turbulent mixing of gases.

chemical agents
Those elements, compounds, or mixtures that coagulate, disperse, dissolve, emulsify, foam, neutralize, precipitate, reduce, solubilize, oxidize, concentrate, congeal, entrap, fix, make the pollutant mass more rigid or viscous, or otherwise facilitate the mitigation of deleterious effects or removal of the pollutant from the water. A

chemical cartridge respirator
A respirator that uses various chemical substances to purify inhaled air of certain gases and vapors. This type respirator is effective for concentrations no more than ten times the TLV of the contaminant, if the contaminant has warning properties (odor or irritation) below the TLV. N

chemical coagulation
The destabilization and initial aggregation of colloidal and finely divided suspended matter by the addition of a floc-forming chemical.

chemical composition
The name and percentage of weight

of each compound in an additive and the name and percentage by weight of each element in an additive. A

chemical fixation
Any waste treatment process that involves reactions between the waste and certain chemicals, and results in solids that encapsulate, immobilize, or otherwise tie up hazardous components in the waste to minimize the leaching of such components and to render the waste nonhazardous and more suitable for disposal.

Chemical Hazards Response Information System/Hazard Assessment Computer System
CHRIS / HACS, developed by the U.S. Coast Guard. HACS is a computerized model of the four CHRIS manuals that contain chemical-specific data. Federal on scene coordinators (OSCs) use HACS to find answers to specific questions during a chemical spill/response. State and local officials and industry representatives may ask an OSC to request a HACS run for contingency planning purposes. N

chemical manufacturer
A person who imports, produces, or manufacturers a chemical substance. A person who extracts a component chemical substance from a previously existing chemical substance or a complex combination of substances is a manufacturer of that component chemical substance. A person who contracts with a manufacturer to manufacture or produce a chemical substance is also a manufacturer if (1) the manufacturer manufactures or produces the substance exclusively for

that person, and (2) that person specifies the identify of the substance and controls the total amount produced and the basic technology for the plant process. A

chemical metal cleaning waste
Any wastewater resulting from the cleaning of any metal process equipment with chemical compounds, including, but not limited to, boiler tube cleaning. A

chemical oxygen demand
COD. A measure of the oxygen required to oxidize all compounds in water, organic and inorganic. N

chemical precipitation
(1) Precipitation induced by addition of chemicals. (2) The process of softening water by the addition of lime or lime and soda ash as the precipitants. [See: precipitation].

chemical sensitivity
Health problems characterized by effects such as dizziness, eye and throat irritation, chest tightness, and nasal congestion that appear when certain individuals are exposed to certain chemicals. People may react to even trace amounts of chemicals to which they have become "sensitized." N

chemical structure
The molecular structure of a compound. A

chemical substance
Any organic or inorganic substance

of a particular molecular identity, including--(i) any combination of such substances occurring in whole or in part as a result of a chemical reaction or occurring in nature, and (ii) any chemical element or uncombined radical. Such term does not include--(i) any mixture, (ii) any pesticide (as defined in the Federal Insecticide, Fungicide, and Rodenticide Act) when manufactured, processed, or distributed in commerce for use as a pesticide, (iii) tobacco or any tobacco product, (iv) any source material, special nuclear material, or byproduct material (as such terms are defined in the Atomic Energy Act of 1954 and regulations issued under such Act), (v) any article the sale of which is subject to the tax imposed by section 4181 of the Internal Revenue Code of 1954 (determined without regard to any exemptions from such tax provided by section 4182 or 4221 or any other provision of such Code), any pistol, firearm, revolver, shells, or cartridges, and (vi) any food, food additive, drug, cosmetic, or device (as such terms are defined in section 201 of the Federal Food, Drug, and Cosmetic Act) when manufactured, processed, or distributed in commerce for use as a food, food additive, drug, cosmetic, or device. The term "food" as used in clause (vi) of this subparagraph includes poultry and poultry products (as defined in sections 4(e) and 4(f) of the Poultry Products Inspection Act), meat and meat food products (as defined in Section 1(j) of the Federal Meat Inspection Act), and eggs and egg products (as defined in section 4 of the Egg Products Inspection Act). K [Ed. This definition establishes the regulatory scope of TSCA].

Chemical Transportation Emergency Center
CHEMTREC. Operated by the Chemical Manufacturers Association this center provides information and/or assistance to emergency responders. CHEMTREC contacts the shipper or producer of the material for more detailed information, including on-scene assistance when feasible. Can be reached 24 hours a day by calling 800-424-9300. (See also: HIT). N

chemical treatment
Any one of a variety of technologies that use chemicals or a variety of chemical processes to treat waste. N

chemical waste
The waste generated by chemical, petrochemical, plastic, pharmaceutical, biochemical, or microbiological manufacturing processes.

chemical waste landfill
A landfill at which protection against risk of injury to health or the environment from migration of PCBs to land, water, or the atmosphere is provided from PCBs and PCB items deposited therein by locating, engineering, and operating the landfill as specified in 40 CFR § 761.75. A

CHEMNET
A mutual aid network of chemical shippers and contractors. CHEMNET has more than fifty participating companies with emergency teams, twenty-three subscribers (who receive services in an incident from a participant and then reimburse response and cleanup costs), and

several emergency response contractors. CHEMNET is activated when a member shipper cannot respond promptly to an incident involving that company's products(s) and requiring the presence of a chemical expert. If a member company cannot go to the scene of the incident, the shipper will authorize a CHEMNET-contracted emergency response company to go. Communications for the network are provided by CHEMTREC, with the shipper receiving notification and details about the incident from the CHEMTREC communicator. N

chemosterilant
A chemical that controls pests by preventing reproduction. N

CHEMTREC
Chemical Transportation Emergency Center. N

child-resistant packaging
Packaging that is designed and constructed to be significantly difficult for children under 5 years of age to open or obtain a toxic or harmful amount of the substance contained therein within a reasonable time, and that is not difficult for normal adults to use properly. A

chilling effect
The lowering of the earth's temperature because of increased particles in the air blocking the sun's rays. (Compare greenhouse effect). N

chilling effect
The lowering of the Earth's temperature because of increased particles in the air blocking the sun's rays. N

CHIP
Chemical Hazard Information Profile.

chipper
A size-reducing device with sharp blades attached to a rotating shaft (mandrel) that shaves or chips off pieces of objects such as tree branches or brush.

CHLOREP
Chlorine Emergency Plan.

chlorinated hydrocarbons
A class of persistent, broad-spectrum insecticides, notably DDT, that linger in the environment and accumulate in the food chain. Other examples are aldrin, dieldrin, heptachlor, chlordane, lindane, endrin, mirex, benzene, hexachloride, and toxaphene. N

chlorinated organic pesticides
A class of pesticides that include: Aldrin. BHC (benzene hexachloride). 1,1 - Bis(p-chlorophenyl) - 2, 2, 2-trichloroethanol. Chlorbenside (p-chlorobenzyl p-chlorophenyl sulfide). Chlordane. Chlorobenzilate (ethyl 4,4' - dichlorobenzilate). p-Chlorophenoxyacetic acid. p-Chlorophenyl-2, 4, 5-trichlorophenyl sulfide. 2,4-D (2,4-dichlorophenoxyacetic acid). DDD (TDE). DDT. 1,1 - Dichloro - 2,2-bis (p-ethyphenyl) ethane. 2,6 - Dichloro-4-nitroaniline. 2,4-Dichlorophenyl p-nitrophenyl ether. Dieldrin. Dodechachlorooctahydro - 1,3,4 metheno - 2H-cyclobuta [cd] pentalene. Endosulfan (6, 7, 8, 9, 10, 10- hexachloro- 1,5,5a,6,9,9a - hexahydro-6,9-methano - 2,4,3 - benzodioxathiepin - 3 - 0 oxide). Endosulfan sulfate (6,7,8,9,10,10-hexachloro- 1,5,5a,

,6,9,9a- hexahydro- 6,9 - methano-2,4,3-benzodioxathiepin-3,3-dioxide). Hepta-chlor (1,4,5,6,7,8,8 - heptachlor-3a, 4, 7, 7a- tetrahydro - 4, 7 - methanoindene). Heptachlor epoxide (1,4,5, 6,7,8,8-heptachloro -2,3 - epoxy-2,3,3a,4,7,7a-hexahydro-4,7-methanoindene). Hexachlorophene (2,2' - methylenebis (3,4,6-trichlorophenol) and its monosodium salt. Isopropyl 4,4'-dichlorobenzilate. Lindane. Methoxychlor. Oven (p-chlorophenyl p-chlorobenzenesulfonate). Sesone (sodium 2,4-dichlorophenoxyethyl sulfate, SES). Sodium 2,4-dichlorophenoxyacetate. Sodium trichloroacetate. Sulphenone (p-chlorophenyl phenyl sulfone). Terpene polychlorinates (chlorinated mixture of camphene, pinene, and related terpenes 65-66 percent chlorine). 2,3,5,6-Tetrachloronitrobenzene. Tetradifon (2,4,5,4'-tetrachlorodiphenyl sulfone). Toxaphene (chlorinated camphene). Trichlorobenzoic acid. Trichlorobenzyl chloride. A

chlorinated solvent
An organic solvent containing chlorine atoms, e.g., methylene chloride and 1,1,1-trichloromethane which are used in aerosol spray containers and in traffic paint. N

chlorination
The application of chlorine to drinking water, sewage, or industrial waste to disinfect or to oxidize undesirable compounds. N

chlorinator
A device that adds chlorine to water in gas or liquid form. N

Chlorine Emergency Plan
CHLOREP, operated by the Chlorine Institute is a 24-hour mutual aid program. Response is activated by a CHEMTREC call to the designated CHLOREP contact, who notifies the appropriate team leader, based upon CHLOREP's geographical sector assignment for teams. The team leader in turn calls the emergency caller at the incident scene and determines what advice and assistance are needed. The team lead then decides whether or not to dispatch his team to the scene. N

chlorine-contact chamber
That part of a waste treatment plant where effluent is disinfected by chlorine before being discharged. N

chlorosis
Discoloration of normally green plant parts, that can be caused by disease, lack of nutrients, or various air pollutants. N

cholinesterase-inhibiting pesticides
A class of pesticides.

CHRIS/HACS
Chemical Hazards Response Information System/Hazard Assessment Computer System.

chrome pigments
Chrome yellow, chrome orange, molybdate chrome orange, anhydrous and hydrous chromium oxide, chrome green, and zinc yellow. A

chrome tan
The process of converting hides into leather using a form of chromium. A

chromosomes
Thread-like bodies occurring in animal and plant cell nuclei; they contain genes, the material that makes possible the transfer of characteristics from parent to offspring.

chronic
Occurring over a long period of time, either continuously or intermittently; used to describe ongoing exposures and effects that develop only after a long exposure. Long-lasting or frequently recurring. N

chronic bronchitis
Inflammation of and anatomic changes in the bronchial tubes accompanied by persistent coughing and an excessive production of mucus.

chronic exposure
Long-term, low level exposure to a toxic chemical.

chronic health effect
An adverse effect on a human or animal body with symptoms that develop slowly over a long period of time or that recur frequently. N (Compare: acute health effect.)

chronic respiratory disease
A persistent or long-lasting intermittent disease of the respiratory tract.

chronic toxicity
The property of a substance or mixture of substances to cause adverse effects in an organism upon repeated or continuous exposure over a period of at least 1/2 the lifetime of that organism. A

chute-fed incinerator
An incinerator that is charged through a chute that extends two or more floors above it.

CIIT
Chemical Industry Institute of Toxicology.

cilia
Hair-like cells that line the airways and by their sweeping motion propel the dirt and germ-filled mucus out of the respiratory tract.

circuit
A conductor or system of conductors through which an electric current is intended to flow. O

circuit breaker
(i) (600 volts nominal, or less). A device designed to open and close a circuit by nonautomatic means and to open the circuit automatically on a predetermined overcurrent without injury to itself when properly applied within its rating. (ii) (Over 600 volts nominal). A switching device capable of making, carrying, and breaking currents under normal circuit conditions, and also making, carrying for a specified time, and breaking currents under specified abnormal circuit conditions, such as those of short circuit. O

city
A political subdivision of a State within a defined area over which a municipal corporation has been established to provide local government functions and facilities. A

city fuel economy
The fuel economy determined by operating a vehicle (or vehicles) over the driving schedule in the Federal Emission Test Procedure. A

cl.
Chemiluminescence.

claims-made policy
An insurance policy that provides coverage of an occurrence if a claim is filed during the term of a policy. A

clamshell bucket
A vessel used to hoist and convey materials; it has two jaws that clamp together when it is lifted by specially attached cables.

clarification
Clearing action that occurs during waste water treatment when solids settle out, often aided by centrifugal action and chemically induced coagulation. N

clarifier
A settling tank where solids are mechanically removed from waste water. N

class
A group of vehicles which are identical in all material aspects with respect to the parameters listed in 40 CFR § 205.155. A

class I, II and III
Geographical classification system for attainment areas under the Clean Air Act. Class I areas -- primarily national parks and wilderness areas--

allow virtually no emissions and therefore no economic development. Class II areas allow limited development and Class III areas the most development. N

Class P1
All aircraft piston engines, except radial engines. A

Class TF
All turbofan or turbojet aircraft engines except engines of Class T3, T8, and TSS. A

Class T1
Aircraft turbofan or turbojet engines except engines of Class T5 of rated power less than 8,000 pounds thrust. A

Class T2
All turbofan or turbojet aircraft engines except engines of Class T3, T4, and T5 of rated power of 8,000 pounds thrust or greater. A

Class T3
All aircraft gas turbine engines of the JT3D model family. A

Class T4
All aircraft gas turbine engines of the JT8D model family. A

Class T5
All aircraft gas turbine engines employed for propulsion of aircraft designed to operate at supersonic flight speeds. A

Class T8
All aircraft gas turbine engines of the JT8D model family. A

Class TP

All aircraft turboprop engines. A

Class TSS

All aircraft gas turbine engines employed for propulsion of aircraft designed to operate at supersonic flight speeds. A

classification

The separation and rearrangement of waste materials according to composition (organic or inorganic), size, weight, color, shape, and the like, using specialized equipment.

classification of railroads

The division of railroad industry operating companies by the Interstate Commerce Commission into three categories. As of 1978, Class I railroads must have annual revenues of $50 million or greater, Class II railroads must have annual revenues of between $10 and $50 million, and Class III railroads must have less than $10 million in annual revenues. A

classified information

Official information which has been assigned a security classification category in the interest of the national defense or foreign relations of the United States. A

classified material

Any document, apparatus, model, film, recording, or any other physical object from which classified information can be derived by study, analysis, observation, or use of the material involved. A

classified waste

Waste material that has been given security classification in accordance with 50 U.S.C. 401 and Executive Order 11652. A

Claus sulfur recovery plant

A process unit which recovers sulfur from hydrogen sulfide by a vapor-phase catalytic reaction of sulfur dioxide and hydrogen sulfide. A

Clean Air Act

CAA. 42 U.S.C § 7401 et seq.

clean air standards

Any enforceable rule, regulations, guidelines, standards, limitation, orders, controls, prohibitions, or other requirements which are contained in, issued under, or otherwise adopted pursuant to the Air Act or Executive Order 11738, an applicable implementation plan as adopted pursuant to section 110 of the Clean Air Act, an approved implementation procedure or plan under section 111(c) or section 111(d), (of the Clean Air Act), or an approved implementation procedure under section 112(d) of the Clean Air Act. A

clean water standards

Any enforceable limitation, control, condition, prohibition, standard, or other requirement which is promulgated pursuant to the Clean Water Act or contained in a permit issued to a discharger by EPA, or by a State under an approved program, as authorized by section 402 of the Clean Water Act, or by a local government to ensure compliance with pretreatment regulations as required by section 307 of the Clean Water Act. A

Clean Water Act

CWA. Clean Water Act (formerly referred to the Federal Water Pollution Control Act) Pub. L. 92-500, as amended by Pub. L. 95-217 and Pub. L. 95-576, 33 U.S.C. 1251 et seq. D

cleanup

Actions taken to deal with a release or threat of release of a hazardous substance that could affect humans and/or the environment. The term "cleanup" is sometimes used interchangeably with the terms remedial action, removal action, response action, or corrective action. N

clear cut

A forest management technique that involves harvesting all the trees in one area at one time. Under certain soil and slope conditions it can contribute sediment to water pollution. N

clinkers

Hard, sintered, or fused pieces of residue formed in a fire by the agglomeration of ash, metals, glass, and ceramics.

CLIPS

Chemical List Index and Processing System. N

cloning

In biotechnology, obtaining a group of genetically identical cells from a single cell. This term has assumed a more general meaning that includes making copies of a gene. N

closed container

A container so sealed by means of a lid or other device that neither liquid nor vapor will escape from it at ordinary temperatures. O

closed course competition event

An organized competition event covering an enclosed, repeated or confined route intended for easy viewing of the entire route by all spectators. Such events include short tract, dirt track, drag race, speedway, hillclimb, ice race, and the Bonneville Speed Trials. A

closed portion

That portion of a facility which an owner or operator has closed in accordance with the approved facility closure plan and all applicable closure requirements. A

closed-loop recycling

Reclaiming or reusing wastewater for non-potable purposes in an enclosed process. N

closed-vent system

A system that is not open to atmosphere and that is composed of piping, connections, and, if necessary, flow-inducing devices that transport gas or vapor from a piece or pieces of equipment to a control device. A

closing volume

CV. The lung volume at which the flow from the lower parts of the lungs becomes severely reduced or stops during expiration, presumably because of airway closure.

closure
The act of securing a "Hazardous Waste Management Facility" pursuant to the requirements of 40 CFR Part 264 (RCRA). A

clutch
The coupling mechanism used on a mechanical power press to couple the flywheel to the crankshaft, either directly or through a gear train. O

CMA
Chemical Manufacturers Association. N

CMB
Chemical Mass Balance. N

CME
Comprehensive (ground water) Monitoring Evaluation. N

CMEL
Comprehensive (ground water) Monitoring Evaluation Log. N

CN,A
Cyanide amenable to chlorination. A

CN,T
Cyanide, total. A

CO
Carbon monoxide.

co-product
A chemical substance produced for a commercial purpose during the manufacture, processing, use, or disposal of another chemical substance(s) or mixture(s). A

CO_2
Carbon dioxide.

coagulation
A clumping of particles in waste water to settle out impurities, often induced by chemicals such as lime or alum. N

coal
All solid fossil fuels classified as anthracite, bituminous, subbituminous, or lignite by the American Society for Testing and Materials. Designation D388-77. A

coal gasification
Any number of processes for converting coal to gas by adding hydrogen in the presence of steam at high temperature and pressure.

coal liquefaction
Any number of processes for converting coal to partially liquid form by heating it without oxygen but with other additives.

coal mine
An active mining area, including all land and property placed upon, under or above the surface of such land, used in or resulting from the work of extracting coal from its natural deposits by any means or method, including secondary recovery of coal from refuse or other storage piles derived from the mining, cleaning, or preparation of coal. A

coal pile runoff
The rainfall runoff from or through any coal storage pile. A

coal preparation plant
A facility where coal is subjected to cleaning, concentrating, or other processing or preparation in order to separate coal from its impurities and then is loaded for transit to a consuming facility. A

coal processing and conveying equipment
Any machinery used to reduce the size of coal or to separate coal from refuse, and the equipment used to convey coal to or remove coal and refuse from the machinery. This includes, but is not limited to, breakers, crushers, screens, and conveyor belts. A

coal refuse
Waste-products of coal mining, cleaning, and coal preparation operations (e.g., culm, gob, etc.) containing coal, matrix material, clay, and other organic and inorganic material. A

coal storage system
Any facility used to store coal except for open storage piles. A

coal treatment facility
All structures which contain, convey, and as necessary, chemically or physically treat coal mine drainage, coal preparation plant process wastewater, or drainage, from coal preparation plant associated areas, which remove pollutants regulated by this part from such waters. This includes all pipes, channels, ponds, basins, tanks and all other equipment serving such structures. A

coastal
(1) Any body of water landward of the territorial seas as defined in 40 CFR 125.1(gg), or (2) any wetlands adjacent to such waters. A

coastal waters
Generally, those U.S. waters navigable by deep draft vessels, the contiguous zone, the high seas and other waters subject to tidal influence. A

coastal zone
(1) Lands and waters adjacent to the coast that exert an influence on the uses of the sea and its ecology, or, inversely, whose uses and ecology are affected by the sea. N (2) All U.S. waters subject to the tide, U.S. water of the Great Lakes, specified ports and harbors on the inland rivers, waters of the contiguous zone, other waters of the high seas subject to this Plan, and the land surface or land substrata, ground waters, and ambient air proximal to those waters. The term coastal zone delineates an area of Federal responsibility for response action. Precise boundaries are determined by EPA/USCG agreements and identified in Federal regional contingency plans. A

coating
Any organic material that is applied to the surface of metal coil. A

coating application station
That portion of a large surface coating operation where a prime coat or a top coat is applied to products (e.g., dip tank, spray booth, or flow coating unit). That portion of the metal coil surface coating operation where the coating is applied to the

surface of the metal coil. Included as part of the coating application station is the flashoff area between the coating application station and the curing oven. A

coating blow
The process in which air is blown through hot asphalt flux to produce coating asphalt. The coating blow starts when the air is turned on and stops when the air is turned off. A

coating operations
All of the operations associated with preparation and application of the vitreous coating. Usually this includes ballmilling, slip transport, application of slip to the workpieces, cleaning and recovery of faulty parts, and firing (fusing) of the enamel coat. A

COCO
Contractor-Owned/Contractor-Operated. N

COD
Chemical Oxygen Demand.

codisposal
The technique in which sludge is combined with other combustible materials (e.g., refuse-derived fuels) to form a furnace feed with a higher heat value than pure sludge.

COE
Corps of Engineers.

Coefficient of Haze
COH. A measurement of visibility interference in the atmosphere. N

coffin
A thick-walled container (usually lead) used for transporting radioactive materials. N

COH
Coefficient of Haze.

coil coating
The process of converting basis material strip into coated stock. Usually cleaning, conversion coating, and painting are performed on the basis material. This regulation covers processes which perform any two or more of the three operations. A

coke
Bituminous coal from which the volatile components have been driven off by heat, leaving fixed carbon and ash fused together.

coke oven
An oven in which coal is changed to coke by destructive distillation. Coke is an essential component in pig iron and steel production.

coker feed (or fuel)
A special fuel oil used in a coker furnace, one of the operating elements of a refinery. A

cold drying hearth
A surface upon which unheated waste materials are placed to dry or to burn. Hot combustion gases are then passed over the materials.

coliform index
A rating of the purity of water based on a count of fecal bacteria. N

coliform organism
Microorganisms found in the intestinal tract of humans and animals. Their presence in water indicates fecal pollution and potentially dangerous bacterial contamination by disease-causing microorganisms. N

collection
The act of removing refuse from its point of generation or storage, loading it into a vehicle, and transporting it to a facility for processing.

collection center
An area or facility designated to accept particular waste materials (e.g., cans, glass bottles, newspapers) from the public; or a central receiving point for refuse collected by a municipal agency or private firm.

collection frequency
The number of times collection is provided in a given period of time. A

collector hauler
A person engaged in the collection of refuse and/or in its transport between storage and processing facilities.

collector ring
An assembly of slip rings for transferring electrical energy from a stationary to a rotating member. O

collector sewer
The common lateral sewers, within a publicly owned treatment system, which are primarily installed to receive wastewaters directly from facilities which convey wastewater from individual systems, or from private property, and which include service "Y" connec-

tions designed for connection with those facilities including: (i) Crossover sewers connecting more than one property on one side of a major street, road, or highway to a lateral sewer on the other side when more cost-effective than parallel sewers; and (ii) Pumping units and pressurized lines serving individual structures or groups of structures when such units are cost-effective and are owned and maintained by the grantee. (iii) This definition excludes other facilities which convey wastewater from individual structures, from private property to the public lateral sewer, or its equivalent and also excludes facilities associated with alternatives to conventional treatment works in small communities. A

colloidal matter
Finely divided solids which will not settle but may be removed by coagulation or biochemical action or membrane filtration.

color
(1) That color as measured by the testing method presented in the National Council for Air and Stream Improvement, (Inc.) "Technical Bulletin 253," December 1971. Color units are to be assumed equal to mg/1. (2) That color as measured by the modified tristimulus method as developed by the American Dye Manufacturers Institute and described in the Proceedings of the 28th Industrial Waste Conference, Purdue University, and in Appendix A in the "Development Document for Effluent Limitations Guidelines and New Source Per-

formance Standards for the Textile Mills Point Source Category." A

color sorting of glass
A technique for sorting glass recovered from solid waste by color. Two methods have been developed: (1) optical sorting, which compares the reflected light from each piece of glass with that of a standard and successively uses different light source filters and standards for color selectivity; and (2) magnetic sorting, which differentiates clear glass from colored by using high-intensity magnetic forces to attract the iron compounds found only in colored glass.

column dryer
Any equipment used to reduce the moisture content of grain in which the grain flows from the top to the bottom in one or more continuous packed columns between two perforated metal sheets. A

combined cycle gas turbine
A stationary turbine combustion system where heat from the turbine exhaust gases is recovered by a steam generating unit. A

combined cycle system
A system in which a separate source, such as a gas turbine, internal combustion engine, kiln, etc., provides exhaust gas to a heat recovery steam generating unit. A

combined fuel economy
The fuel economy value determined for a vehicle (or vehicles) by harmonically averaging the city and highway

fuel economy values, weighted 0.55 and 0.45 respectively, for gasoline-fueled and diesel vehicles. Four electric vehicles, the term means the equivalent petroleum-based fuel economy value as determined by the calculation procedure promulgated by the Secretary of Energy. A

combined sewers
A sewer system that carries both sewage and storm-water runoff. Normally, its entire flow goes to a waste treatment plant, but during a heavy storm, the storm water volume may be so great as to cause overflows. When this happens untreated mixtures of storm water and sewage may flow into receiving waters. Storm-water runoff may also carry toxic chemicals from industrial areas or streets into the sewer system. N

combustible liquids
Any liquid having a flash point at or above 140° F. (60° C.), and below 200° F. (93.4° C.). O

combustible waste
Waste materials that are burnable (e.g., paper, plastics, food, plant trimmings, wood).

combustibles
Materials that can be ignited at a specific temperature in the presence of air to release heat energy. A

combustion
(1) The production of heat and light energy through a chemical process-- usually oxidation. One of the three basic contributing processes of air pollution, the others being attrition

and vaporization. (2) Any chemical process that involves oxidation sufficient to produce light or heat. A

combustion air
The air used for burning a fuel.

combustion gases
The mixture of gases and vapors produced by burning.

commence
As applied to construction of a major stationary source or major modification, the owner or operator has all necessary preconstruction approvals or permits and either has: (i) Begun, or caused to begin, a continuous program of actual on-site construction of the source, to be completed within a reasonable time; or (ii) Entered into binding agreements or contractual obligations, which cannot be cancelled or modified without substantial loss to the owner or operator, to undertake a program of actual construction of the source to be completed within a reasonable time. [ed. The date construction commences often determines what air pollution requirements will be applicable to a new or modified facility]. A

commenced
As applied to construction of a major emitting facility, commenced means that the owner or operator has obtained all necessary preconstruction approvals or permits required by Federal, State, or local air pollution emissions and air quality laws or regulations and either has (i) begun, or caused to begin, a continuous program of physical on-site construction

of the facility or (ii) entered into binding agreements or contractual obligations, which cannot be canceled or modified without substantial loss to the owner or operator, to undertake a program of construction of the facility to be completed within a reasonable time. B

comment period
Time provided for the public to review and comment on proposed governmental action or rulemaking after it is published in the Federal Register. N

commerce
(1) Trade, traffic, commerce, or transportation, or communication among the several States, or between a State and any place outside thereof, or within the District of Columbia, or a possession of the United States (other than the Trust Territory of the Pacific Islands), or between points in the same State but through a point outside thereof. A, H (2) Trade, traffic or transportation (A) between any place in any State and any place outside thereof; and (B) commerce wholly within the District of Columbia. G, K

commercial aircraft engine
Any aircraft engine used or intended for use by an "air carrier," (including those engaged in "intrastate air transportation") or a "commercial operator" (including those engaged in "intrastate air transportation") as these terms are defined in the Federal Aviation Act and the Federal Aviation Regulations. A

commercial applicator
An applicator (whether or not he is private applicator with respect to some uses) who uses or supervises the use of any pesticide which is classified for restricted use for any purpose or on any property other than as provided by paragraph (2) [of FIFRA]. C

commercial asbestos
Any variety of asbestos which is produced by extracting asbestos from asbestos ore. A

commercial establishment
Stores, offices, restaurants, warehouses and other non-manufacturing activities. A

commercial item
(1) Any machine, manufacture, or composition of matter which, at the time of a request for a license has been sold, offered for sale or otherwise made available commercially to the public in the regular course of business, at terms reasonable in the circumstances, and (2) Any process which, at the time of a request for a license, is in commercial use, or is offered for commercial use, so the results of the process or the products produced thereby are or will be accessible to the public at terms reasonable in the circumstances. A

commercial parking facility
Any lot, garage, building or structure, or combination or portion thereof, on or in which motor vehicles are temporarily parked for a fee, excluding (i) a parking facility, the use of which is limited exclusively to residents (and guests of residents) of

a residential building or group of buildings under common control, and (ii) parking on public streets. A

commercial parking space
Any parking space in which the parking of a single motor vehicle is permitted for a fee. It includes on-street parking governed by parking meters, and excludes employee and residential parking spaces. A

commercial property
Any property that is normally accessible to the public and that is used for any of the purposes described in the following standard land use codes (reference Standard Land Use Coding Manual, U.S. DOT/FHWA, reprinted March 1977): 53-59, Retail Trade; 61-64, Finance, Insurance, Real Estate, Personal, Business and Repair Services; 652-659, Legal and other professional services; 671, 672, and 673 Governmental Services; 692 and 699, Welfare, Charitable and Other Miscellaneous Services; 712 and 719, Nature exhibitions and other Cultural Activities; 721, 723, and 729, Entertainment, Public and other Public Assembly; and 74-79, Recreational, Resort, Park and other Cultural Activities. A

commercial solid waste
All types of solid wastes generated by stores, offices, restaurants, warehouses, and other non-manufacturing activities, excluding residential and industrial wastes. A

commercial use request
Refers to a request from or on behalf of one who seeks information for a use or purpose that furthers the

commercial, trade or profit interests of the requestor or the person on whose behalf the request is made. In determining whether a requestor properly belongs in this category, EPA must determine the use to which a requestor will put the documents requested. Moreover, where EPA has reasonable cause to doubt the use to which a requestor will put the records sought, or where that use is not clear from the request itself, EPA may seek additional clarification before assigning the request to a specific category. <u>A</u>

commercial vessels
Those vessels used in the business of transporting property for compensation or hire, or in transporting property in the business of the owner, lessee, or operator of the vessel. <u>D</u>

comminuter
A machine that shreds or pulverizes solids to make waste treatment easier. <u>N</u>

comminution
Mechanical shredding or pulverizing of waste, used in solid waste management and waste water treatment. <u>N</u>

commission finishing
The finishing of textile materials, 50 percent or more of which are owned by others, in mills that are 51 percent or more independent (i.e., only a minority ownership by company(ies) with greige or integrated operations); the mills must process 20 percent or more of their commissioned production through batch, noncontinuous processing operations with 50 percent or

more of their commissioned orders processed in 5000 yard or smaller lots. <u>A</u>

commission scouring
The scouring of wool, 50 percent or more of which is owned by others, in mills that are 51 percent or more independent (i.e., only a minority ownership by company(ies) with greige or integrated operations); the mills must process 20 percent or more of their commissioned production through batch, noncontinuous processing operations. <u>A</u>

commitment of funds
Formal action by a program office (technically an "allowance holder") to set aside a specific portion of its allowance for a designated project. A document control register is maintained to record the commitments (Compare: obligation of funds.)

common carrier by motor vehicle
Any person who holds himself out to the general public to engage in the transportation by motor vehicle in interstate or foreign commerce of passengers or property or any class or classes thereof for compensation, whether over regular or irregular routes. <u>A</u>

common exposure route
A likely way (oral, dermal, respiratory) by which a pesticide may reach and/or enter an organism. <u>A</u>

common exposure route
A likely way (oral, dermal, respiratory) by which a pesticide may reach and/or enter an organism. <u>A</u>

Community Awareness and Emergency Response Program

CAER. Program developed by the Chemical Manufacturers Association, which provides guidance for chemical plant managers to assist them in taking the initiative in cooperating with local communities to develop integrated (community/industry) hazardous materials response plans. N

community water system

A public water system which serves at least 15 service connections used by year-round residents or regularly serves at least 25 year-round residents. N, A

compact cars

Interior volume index greater than or equal to 100 cubic feet but less than 110 cubic feet. A

compaction

The process of reducing the bulk of solid waste by rolling and tamping or compressing and crushing.

compaction pit transfer system

A transfer system in which solid waste is compacted in a storage pit by a crawler tractor before being pushed into an open-top transfer trailer.

compactor

(1) Any power-driven, mechanical device that reduces the volume of solid waste by compression and crushing. (2) A truck-mounted solid waste compactor, which comprises an engine powered truck cab and chassis or trailer, equipped with a compactor body and associated machinery for receiving, compacting, transporting and unloading solid waste. A

compactor collection vehicle

A vehicle with an enclosed body containing mechanical devices that convey solid waste into the main compartment of the body and compress it into a smaller volume of greater density. A

compartmentalized vehicle

A collection vehicle which has two or more compartments for placement of solid wastes or recyclable materials. The compartments may be within the main truck body or on the outside of that body as in the form of metal racks. A

compatibility

That property of a pesticide which permits its use with other chemicals without undesirable results being caused by the combination. A

compatible industrial wastewater

Wastewater that is produced by an industrial user, has a pollutant strength and other characteristics similar to those of domestic wastewater, and can be efficiently and effectively transported and treated with domestic wastewater. This definition includes wastewater from sanitary conveniences at an industrial user's facility. A

competent

Properly qualified to perform functions associated with pesticide application, the degree of capability required being directly related to the nature of the activity and the associated responsibility. A

competition motorcycle
Any motorcycle designed and marketed solely for use in closed course competition events. A

complainant
Any person authorized to issue a complaint on behalf of the EPA to persons alleged to be in violation of an Act. The complainant shall not be the Judicial Officer, Regional Judicial Officer, or any other person who will participate or advise in the decision. A

complete
In reference to an application for a PSD permit, this means the application contains all of the information necessary for processing the application. A

complete destruction
Alteration by physical or chemical processes to inorganic forms. A

complete waste treatment system
A complete waste treatment system consists of all the connected treatment works necessary to meet the requirements of Title III of the [Clean Water] Act and involved in: (a) The transport of wastewaters from individual homes or buildings to a plant or facility wherein treatment of the wastewater is accomplished; (b) the treatment of the wastewaters to remove pollutants; and (c) the ultimate disposal, including recycling or reuse, of the treated wastewaters and residues resulting from the treatment process. One complete waste treatment system would, normally, include one

treatment plant or facility, but in instances where two or more treatment plants are interconnected, all of the interconnected treatment works will be considered as one waste treatment system. A

completed project
A funded grant for which work has been completed and an acceptable final report received. The term has nothing to do with whether or not closeout has been effectuated.

compliance
Compliance with clean air or water standards. Also, compliance with a schedule or plan ordered or approved by a court of competent jurisdiction, the Environmental Protection Agency, or an air or water pollution control agency, in accordance with the requirements of the Air or Water Act and regulations issued pursuant thereto. A

compliance date period
The thirty day period immediately preceding the compliance date.

compliance date
The date upon which a source is required to meet applicable pollution control requirements.

compliance monitoring
Measuring and analyzing pollutant sources, review of reports and information obtained from dischargers, and all other activities conducted by the State to verify compliance with effluent limits and compliance schedules. A

compliance safety and health officer
CSHO. A person authorized by the Occupational Safety and Health Administration, U.S. Department of Labor, to conduct inspections. O

compliance schedule
A legally enforceable schedule specifying a date or dates by which a source or category of sources must comply with specific emission or effluent standards contained in a State implementation plan or NPDES permit or with any increments of progress to achieve such compliance. A

composite sample
A sample composed of no less than eight grab samples taken over the compositing period. A

compost
A mixture of garbage and degradable trash with soil in which certain bacteria in the soil break down the garbage and trash into organic fertilizer. N

composting
The natural biological decomposition of organic material in the presence of air to form a humus-like material. Controlled methods of composting include mechanical mixing and aerating, ventilating the materials by dropping them through a vertical series of aerated chambers, or placing the compost in piles out in the open air and mixing it or turning ir periodically. N

compound leachate collection
This system consists of a gravity flow drainfield installed under the waste disposal facility liner and above a secondary installed liner. This design is recommended for use when semiliquid or leachable solid wastes are placed in a lined pit excavated into relatively permeable soil. A

computer-aided carpool matching
A carpool matching system in which the work of assembling lists of commuters with similar daily travel patterns is done by computer. A

conc.
Concentration.

concealed
Rendered inaccessible by the structure or finish of the building. Wires in concealed raceways are considered concealed, even though they may become accessible by withdrawing them. O

concentrated animal feeding operation
(1) A relatively small confined area where large numbers of animals are fed before being sent to final markets. EPA establishes minimum number of animals that must be fed before a facility falls into this category of operation for water pollution regulatory purposes. (2) An animal feeding operation which meets the criteria set forth in either paragraphs (a)(2) (i) or (ii) of this section. (i) More than the numbers of animals specified in any of the following categories are confined: (a) 1,000 slaughter and feeder cattle, (b) 700 mature dairy cattle (whether milked or dry cows), (c) 2,500 swine weighing over 55 pounds, (d) 500 horses, (e) 10,000 sheep or lambs, (f) 55,000 turkeys, (g) 100,000 laying hens or broilers (if the facility has continu-

ous overflow watering), (h) 30,000 laying hens or broilers (if the facility has a liquid manure handling system), (i) 5,000 ducks, or (j) 1,000 animal units; or (ii) More than the following numbers and types of animals are confined: (a) 300 slaughter or feeder cattle, (b) 200 mature dairy cattle (whether milked or dry cows), (c) 750 swine weighing over 55 pounds, (d) 150 horses, (e) 3,000 sheep, (f) 16,500 turkeys, (g) 30,000 laying hens or broilers (if the facility has continuous overflow watering), (h) 9,000 laying hens or broilers (if the facility has a liquid manure handling system), (i) 1,500 ducks, or (j) 300 animal units; and either one of the following conditions are met: (k) Pollutants are discharged into navigable waters through a man-made ditch, flushing system or other similar man-made device; or (l) Pollutants are discharged directly into navigable waters which originate outside of and pass over, across, through or otherwise come into direct contact with the animals confined in the operation. Provided, however that no animal feeding operation is a concentrated animal feeding operation as defined above if such animal feeding operation discharges only in the event of a 25 year, 24-hour storm event.

concentration measurement system
The total equipment required for the continuous determination of SO_2 gas concentration in a given source effluent. A

concretion
A localized concentration of chemical compounds (e.g., calcium carbon-

ate and iron oxide) in the form of a grain or nodule of varying size, shape, hardness, and color, concretions of significance in hydric soils are usually iron oxides and manganese oxides occurring at or near the soil surface, which have developed under conditions of fluctuating water tables. N

concurrent
Acting in conjunction, and used to describe a situation wherein two or more controls exist in an operated condition at the same time. O

condensate
Hydrocarbon liquid separated from natural gas which condenses due to changes in the temperature and/or pressure and remains liquid at standard conditions. A

condensate stripper system
A column, and associated condensers, used to strip, with air or steam, TRS compounds from condensate streams from various processes within a kraft pulp mill. A

condenser stack gases
The gaseous effluent evolved from the stack of processes utilizing heat to extract mercury metal from mercury ore. A

conditional registration
Under special circumstances, the Federal Insecticide, Fungicide, and Rodenticide Act (FIFRA) permits registration of pesticide products that is "conditional" upon the submission of additional data. These special circumstances include a finding by the EPA Administrator that a new product

or use of an existing pesticide will not significantly increase the risk of unreasonable adverse effects. A product containing a new (previously unregistered) active ingredient may be conditionally registered only if the Administrator finds that such conditional registration is in the public interest, that a reasonable time for conducting the additional studies has not elapsed, and the use of the pesticide for the period of conditional registration will not present an unreasonable risk. N

conditioning
(1) Exposure of construction materials, test chambers, and testing apparatus to dilution water or to the test solution prior to the start of the test in order to minimize the sorption of test substance onto the test facilities or the leaching of substances from test facilities into the dilution water or the test solution. A (2) Pretreatment of a sludge to facilitate removal of water in a thickening or dewatering process. Methods are as follows: Chemical (inorganic and organic), Elutriation, Heat treatment.

conduction
The transfer of heat by physical contact between substances.

conductor
A material, usually in the form of a wire, cable, or bus bar suitable for carrying an electric current. O

configuration
(1) The mechanical arrangement, calibration, and condition of a test automobile, with particular respect to carburetion, ignition timing, and emission control systems. A (2) For automobile certification, a subclassification, if any, of a heavy-duty engine family for which a separate projected sales figure is listed in the manufacturer's Application for Certification and which can be described on the basis of emission control system, governed speed, injector size, engine calibration, and other parameters which may be designated by the Administrator, or a subclassification of a light-duty truck engine family-emission control system combination on the basis of engine code, inertia weight class, transmission type and gear ratios, rear axle ratio, and other parameters which may be designated by the Administrator. A

confined aquifer
An aquifer bounded above and below by impermeable beds or by beds of distinctly lower permeability than that of the aquifer itself; an aquifer containing confined ground water. A

confined space
Any area which has limited openings for entry and exit that would make escape difficult in an emergency, has a lack of ventilation, contains known and potential hazards, and is not intended nor designated for continuous human occupancy. N

confining bed
A body of impermeable or distinctly less permeable material stratigraphically adjacent to one or more aquifers. A

confining zone

A geological formation, group of formations, or part of a formation that is capable of limiting fluid movement above an injection zone. A

conical burner

A hollow, cone-shaped combustion chamber with an exhaust vent at its point and a door at its base through which waste materials are charged; air is delivered to the burning solid waste inside the cone. Also called teepee burner.

consent agreement

Any written document, signed by the parties, containing stipulations or conclusions of fact or law and a proposed penalty or proposed revocation or suspension acceptable to both complainant and respondent. A

consent decree

A legal document, approved by a judge, that formalizes an agreement reached between litigants. In Superfund cases it sets the terms by which potentially responsible parties (PRPs) will conduct all or part of a cleanup action at a Superfund site; cease or correct actions or processes that are polluting the environment; or otherwise comply with regulations where the PRP's failure to comply caused EPA to initiate regulatory enforcement actions. The consent decree describes the actions PRP's will take and may be subject to a public comment period. N

conservation

Avoiding waste of, and renewing when possible, human and natural resources. The protection, improvement, and use of natural resources according to principles that will assure their highest economic or social benefits. N

consistent POTW removal

Reduction in the amount of a pollutant or alteration of the nature of a pollutant in the influent to a POTW to a less toxic or harmless state in the effluent which is achieved by that POTW in 95 percent of the samples taken when measured according to specified procedures. The reduction or alteration can be obtained by physical, chemical or biological means and may be the result of specifically designed POTW capabilities or it may be incidental to the operation of the treatment system. Removal as used in this subpart shall not mean dilution of a pollutant in the POTW or its sewer system. The inability of monitoring equipment to detect pollutants in the influent to the POTW shall not by itself, constitute removal, except where the pollutant is shown by the POTW to be degradable during the time it is in the POTW or its sewer system. A

consolidated grants

A grant funded under more than one grant authority by EPA or a grant awarded in conjunction with one or more Federal agencies (e.g., Joint Funded Assistance). Application for and award and administration of a consolidated grant must conform to this subchapter, except as the Director, Grants Administration Division, may otherwise direct with respect to substatutory requirements. Those conditions and procedures will conform to this Subchapter to the greatest extent practicable. A

constant controls, control technology, and continuous emission reduction technology
Systems which limit the quantity, rate, or concentration of emissions of air pollutants on a continuous basis. A

construction
(1) Under the Water Pollution Act, any one or more of the following: preliminary planning to determine the feasibility of treatment works, engineering, architectural, legal, fiscal, or economic investigations or studies, surveys, designs, plans, working drawings, specifications, procedures, or other necessary actions, erection, building, acquisition, alteration, remodeling, improvement, or extension of treatment works, or the inspection or supervision of any of the foregoing items. D (2) Under the Clean Air Act, any physical change or change in the method of operation (including fabrication, erection, installation, demolition, or modification of an emissions unit) which would result in a change in actual emissions. [ed. The definition is used for determining whether a new source review under the CAA is required]. A (3) Under RCRA, (A) the erection or building of new structures and acquisition of lands or interests therein, or the acquisition, replacement, expansion, remodeling, alteration, modernization, or extension of existing structures, and (B) the acquisition and installation of initial equipment of, or required in connection with, new or newly acquired structures or the expanded, remodeled, altered, modernized or extended part of existing structures (including trucks and other motor vehicles, and tractors, cranes, and other machinery) necessary for the proper utilization and operation of the facility after completion of the project; and includes preliminary planning to determine the economic and engineering feasibility and the public health and safety aspects of the project, the engineering, architectural, legal, fiscal, and economic investigations and studies, and any surveys, designs, plans, working drawings, specifications, and other action necessary for the carrying out of the project, and (C) the inspection and supervision of the process of carrying out the project to completion. A, I (4) Under Superfund, erection, building, alternation, remodeling, improvement, or extension of buildings, structures or other property; construction also includes remedial actions in response to a release, or a threat of a release, of a hazardous substance into the environment as determined by CERCLA. A, L

construction and demolition waste
The waste building materials, packaging, and rubble resulting from construction, remodeling, repair, and demolition operations on pavements, houses, commercial buildings and other structures. A

construction material
Any article, material, or supply brought to the construction site for incorporation in the building or work. A

construction runoff

The point source rainfall runoff from any construction activity and any earth surface disturbed by such activity from the inception of the construction until construction is complete and any disturbed earth is returned to a vegetative or other cover commensurate with the intended land use. A

construction work

The construction, rehabilitation, alteration, conversion, extension, demolition or repair of buildings, highways, or other changes or improvements to real property, including facilities providing utility services. The term also includes the supervision, inspection, and other on-site functions incidental to the actual construction. A

consumer waste

Materials used and discarded by the buyer, or consumer, as opposed to waste created and discarded in-plant during the manufacturing process.

contact cooling water

(1) Any wastewater which contacts the metal workpiece or the raw materials used in forming metals for the purpose of removing heat from the metal. A (2) Water used to reduce temperature which comes into contact with a raw material, intermediate product, waste product other than heat, or finished product. N

contact pesticide

A chemical that kills pests when it touches them, rather than by being eaten (stomach poison). Also, soil that contains the minute skeletons of certain algae that scratches and dehydrates waxy-coated insects. N

container

Any package, can, bottle, bag, barrel, drum, tank, or other containing-device (excluding spray applicator tanks) used to enclose a pesticide or pesticide-related waste. A

container glass

Glass made of soda-lime recipe, clear or colored, which is pressed and /or blown into bottles, jars, ampoules, and other products listed in Standard Industrial Classification 3221 (SIC 32-21). A

container train

Small trailers, hitched in series, that are pulled by a motor vehicle and used to collect and transport solid waste.

containerized refuse

Solid waste that has been deposited into a receptacle for storage or transport.

contaminant

Any physical, chemical, biological, or radiological substance or matter that has an adverse affect on air, water, or soil. A, J, N [ed. Used for FWPCA].

contaminate

Introduce a substance that would cause (a) The concentration of that substance in the ground water to exceed the maximum contaminant level or (b) An increase in the concentration of that substance in the ground water where the existing concentration of that substance exceeds the maximum contaminant level. A

contaminated non-process wastewater

Any water including precipitation runoff which, during manufacturing or processing, comes into incidental contact with any raw material, intermediate product, finished product, by-product or waste product by means of: (1) Precipitation runoff; (2) accidental spills; (3) accidental leaks caused by the failure of process equipment and which are repaired or the discharge of pollutants therefrom contained or terminated within the shortest reasonable time which shall not exceed 24 hours after discovery or when discovery should reasonably have been made, whichever is earliest; and (4) discharges from safety showers and related personal safety equipment, and from equipment washings for the purpose of safe entry, inspection and maintenance; provided that all reasonable measures have been taken to prevent, reduce, eliminate and control to the maximum extent feasible such contact and provided further that all reasonable measures have been taken that will mitigate the effects of such contact once it has occurred. **A**

contiguous zone

The zone of the high seas, established by the United States under Article 24 of the Convention on the Territorial Sea and Contiguous Zone, which is contiguous to the territorial sea and which extends nine miles seaward form the outer limit of the territorial sea. **A, D**

contingency plan

A document setting out an organized, planned, and coordinated course of action to be followed in case of a fire, explosion, or release of hazardous waste or hazardous waste constituents which could threaten human health or the environment. **A**

continuing planning process

The continuing planning process, including any revision thereto, required by sections 208 and 303(e) of the [Clean Water] Act for State agencies and section 208(b) of the [Clean Water] Act for designated areawide agencies. **A**

continuing resolution

Legislation enacted by Congress to provide budget authority for specific ongoing activities when a regular appropriation for such activities has not been enacted by the beginning of the fiscal year.

continuous casting

The production of sheet, rod, or other long shapes by solidifying the metal while it is being poured through an open-ended mold. **A**

continuous discharge (NPDES)

A "discharge" which occurs without interruption throughout the operating hours of the facility, except for infrequent shutdowns for maintenance, process changes, or other similar activities. **A**

continuous feed incinerator

An incinerator into which solid waste is charged almost continuously to maintain a steady rate of burning.

continuous monitoring

The taking and recording of

measurements at regular and frequent intervals during operation of a facility. A

continuous operations
The introduction of by an industrial user of regulated wastewaters to a POTW throughout the operating hours of the facility, except for infrequent shut-downs for maintenance, process changes, or other similar activities. A

contour plowing
Farming methods that break ground following the shape of the land in a way that discourages erosion. N

contract
An award of funds or other assistance by means of a written contractual agreement under Federal Procurement Regulations.

contract authority
Statutory authority, not necessarily provided through the appropriations process, that permits Federal agencies to enter into contracts or incur other obligations in advance of an appropriation.

contract carrier by motor vehicle
Any person who engages in transportation by motor vehicle of passengers or property in interstate or foreign commerce for compensation under continuing contracts with one person or a limited number of persons either (1) for the furnishing of transportation services through the assignment of motor vehicles for a continuing period of time to the exclusive use of each person served or (2) for the furnishing of transportation services designed to meet the distinct need of each individual customer. A

contract collection
Refuse collection performed in accordance with a written agreement in which the rights and duties of the contractual parties are set forth.

contract specifications
The set of specifications prepared for an individual construction project which contains design, performance, and material requirements for that project. A

contrails
Long, narrow clouds caused when high-flying jet aircraft disturb the atmosphere. N

control
(Including the terms "controlling," "controlled by," and "under common control with") means the power to direct or cause the direction of the management and policies of a person or organization, whether by the ownership of stock, voting rights, by contract, or otherwise. [ed. Relevant to determining what entities may be liable for polluting activities]. A

control device
The air pollution control equipment used to remove particulate matter generated by an EAF(s) from the effluent gas stream. A

control efficiency
The ratio of the amount of a pollutant removed from effluent gases by a control device to the total amount of pollutant without control.

control strategy

A combination of measures designated to achieve the aggregate reduction of emissions necessary for attainment and maintenance of a national standard, including, but not limited to, measures such as: (1) Emission limitations. (2) Federal or State emission charges or taxes or other economic incentives or disincentives. (3) Closing or relocation of residential, commercial, or industrial facilities. (4) Changes in schedules or methods of operation of commercial or industrial facilities or transportation systems, including, but not limited to, short-term changes made in accordance with standby plans. (5) Periodic inspection and testing of motor vehicle emission control systems, at such time as the Administrator determines that such programs are feasible and practicable. (6) Emission control measures applicable to in-use motor vehicles, including, but not limited to, measures such as mandatory maintenance, installation of emission control devices, and conver-sion to gaseous fuels. (7) Measures to reduce motor vehicle traffic, including, but not limited to, measures such as commuter taxes, gasoline rationing; parking restrictions, or staggered working hours. (8) Expansion or promotion of the use of mass transportation facilities through measures such as increases in the frequency, convenience, and passenger-carrying capacity of mass transportation systems or providing for special bus lanes on major streets and highways. (9) Any land use or transportation control measures not specifically delineated herein. (10) Any variation of, or alternative to, any measure delineated herein. (11) Control or prohibition of a fuel or fuel additive used in motor vehicles, if such control or prohibition is necessary to achieve a national primary or secondary air quality standard and is approved by the Administrator under section 211(c)(4)(C) of the Clean Air Act. [ed. A necessary part of an approvable State implementation plan under § 110 of the Clean Air Act]. A

control system

Equipment and/or procedures intended to reduce the amount of a pollutant, or pollutants, in effluent gases.

control techniques guidelines

Technology assessments prepared by EPA to provide guidance on the best controls available for use by categories of existing sources; used to establish RACT.

controlled area

(1) A surface location, to be identified by passive institutional controls, that encompasses no more than 100 square kilometers and extends horizontally no more than five kilometers in any direction from the outer boundary of the original location of the radioactive wastes in a disposal system; and (2) the subsurface underlying such a surface location. A

controlled surface mine drainage

Any surface mine drainage that is pumped or siphoned from the active mining area. A

controlled vehicles

Light-duty vehicles sold nationally (except in California) in the 1968 model-year and later and light-duty vehicles sold in California in the 1966 model-year and later. A

controlled-air incinerator
An incinerator with two or more combustion areas in which the amounts and distribution of air are controlled. Partial combustion takes place in the first zone, and gases are burned in a subsequent zone or zones.

conventional mine
An open pit or underground excavation for the production of minerals. A

conventional pollutants
Statutorily listed pollutants which are understood well by scientists. These may be in the form of organic waste, sediment, acid, bacteria and viruses, nutrients, oil and grease, or heat. N

conventional sewage treatment system
A collection and treatment system consisting of minimum size (six or eight inch) gravity collector sewers normally with manholes, force mains, pumping and lift stations, and interceptors leading to a central treatment plant. A

conventional technology
Wastewater treatment processes and techniques involving the treatment of wastewater at a centralized treatment plant by means of biological or physical/chemical unit processes followed by direct point source discharge to surface waters. A

conversion
A resource recovery method that uses biological, chemical, or mechanical processes to transform solid waste materials into usable forms. See bioconversion, recycling, reprocessing, and transformation.

coolant
A liquid or gas used to reduce the heat generated by power production in nuclear reactors, electric generators, various industrial and mechanical processes, and automobile engines. N

cooling air
Ambient air that is added to hot combustion gases to cool them. Also called tempering air.

cooling lake
Any manmade water impoundment which impedes the flow of a navigable stream and which is used to remove waste heat from heated condenser water prior to recirculating the water to the main condenser. A

cooling pond
Any manmade water impoundment which does not impede the flow of a navigable stream and which is used to remove waste heat from heated condenser water prior to returning the recirculated cooling water to the main condenser. A

cooling sprays
Water sprays directed into flue gases to cool them and, in most cases, to remove some fly ash.

cooling tower
A device that aids in heat removal

from water used as a coolant in electric power generating plants. N

cooling water intake structure
The total structure used to direct water into the components of the cooling systems wherein the cooling function is designed to take place, provided that the intended use of the major portion of the water so directed is to absorb waste heat rejected from the process or processes employed or from auxiliary operations on the premises, including air conditioning. A

cooperating agency
Any Federal agency other than a lead agency which has jurisdiction by law or special expertise with respect to any environmental impact involved in a proposal (or a reasonable alternative) for legislation or other major Federal action significantly affecting the quality of the human environment. The selection and responsibilities of a cooperating agency are described in 40 CFR §1501.6. A State or local agency of similar qualifications or, when the effects are on a reservation, an Indian Tribe, may by agreement with the lead agency become a cooperating agency. A

cooperator
Any person who grants permission to a permittee or a permittee's designated participant to use an experimental-use pesticide at an application site owned or controlled by the cooperator. N

core
The uranium-containing heart of a

nuclear reactor, where energy is released. N

core wall
In a battery wall, those center courses of brick, none of which are exposed on either side.

corrosion
The gradual wearing away of a substance by chemical action.

corrosion expert
A person who, by reason of his knowledge of the physical sciences and the principles of engineering and mathematics, acquired by a professional education and related practicable experience, is qualified to engage in the practice of corrosion control on buried or submerged metal piping systems and metal tanks. Such a person must be certified as being qualified by the National Association of Corrosion Engineers (NACE) or be a registered professional engineer who has certification or licensing that includes education and experience in corrosion control on buried or submerged metal piping systems and metal tanks. A

corrosive
A chemical agent that reacts with the surface of a material causing it to deteriorate or wear away. N

corrosivity
A characteristic of hazardous waste which identifies waste that must be segregated because of its ability to extract and solubilize toxic contaminants (especially heavy metals) from other waste; identifies waste that re-

quires the use of corrosion-resistant containers for disposal.

cosmic radiation

Radiation of many sorts but mostly atomic nuclei (protons) with very high energies, originating outside the earth's atmosphere. Cosmic radiation is part of the natural background radiation. Some cosmic rays are more energetic than any manmade forms of radiation.

cost per ton per minute

A unit that is often used in cost comparisons between transfer (in which there is an intermediate step between refuse collection and processing or disposal in a sanitary landfill) and direct-haul (in which collected refuse is transported directly to processing plants or sanitary landfills) operations.

cost recovery

A legal process by which potentially responsible parties who contributed to contamination at a Superfund site can be required to reimburse the Trust Fund for money spent during any cleanup actions by the federal government. N

cost-effective alternative

An alternative control or corrective method identified after analysis as being the best available in terms of reliability, permanence, and economic considerations. Although costs are one important consideration, when regulatory and compliance methods are being considered, such analysis does not require EPA to choose the least expensive alternative. For example, when selecting a method for cleaning up a site on the Superfund National Priorities List, the Agency balances costs with the long-term effectiveness of the various methods proposed. N

cost-effectiveness analysis

An analysis performed to determine which waste treatment management system or component part thereof will result in the minimum total resources costs over time to meet the Federal, State, or local requirements. A

cost-sharing

(1) Participation by a grantee in the costs of conducting the project. For EPA grants, cost-sharing is mandatory at a minimum of five percent of allowable actual project costs, unless otherwise required by statute. (2) The portion of allowable project costs that a recipient contributes toward completing its project (i.e., non-Federal share, matching share). A

cotton fiber furnish subdivision mills

Mills where significant quantities of cotton fibers (equal to or greater than 4 percent of the total product) are used in the production of fine papers. A

cost/benefit analysis

A quantitative evaluation of the costs which would be incurred versus the overall benefits to society of a proposed action such as the establishment of an acceptable dose of a toxic chemical. N

cost of production

For a car line, this is the aggregate

of the products of: (1) The average U.S. dealer wholesale price for such car line as computed from each official dealer price list effective during the course of a model year, and (2) The number of passenger automobiles within the car line produced during the part of the model year that the price list was in effect. A

counterbalance
The mechanism that is used to balance or support the weight of the connecting rods, slide, and slide attachments. O

cover material
Soil used to cover compacted solid waste in a sanitary landfill. N

covered
A conductor encased within material of composition or thickness that is not recognized as electrical insulation. O

CPSC
Consumer Product Safety Commission. N

crankcase emissions
Airborne substances emitted to the atmosphere from any portion of the engine crankcase ventilation or lubrication systems. A

crawler-dozer
One of the most commonly used machines on sanitary landfills because of its capacity to perform a variety of operations: site preparation, spreading, compacting, covering, construction and maintenance of access roads and because of its excellent flotation and tractive abilities.

criteria
(1) Descriptive factors taken into account by EPA in setting standards for various pollutants. These factors are used to determine limits on allowable concentration levels, and to limit the number of violations per year. When issued by EPA, the criteria provide guidance to the states on how to establish their standards. N (2) As used in the Clean Air Act, information on adverse effects of air pollutants on human health or the environment at various concentrations. The information is collected pursuant to section 108 of the Clean Air Act and used to set national ambient air quality standards.

criteria pollutants
The 1970 amendments to the Clean Air Act required EPA to set National Ambient Air Quality Standards for certain pollutants known to be hazardous to human health. EPA has identified and set standards to protect human health and welfare for six pollutants: ozone, carbon monoxide, total suspended particulates, sulfur dioxide, lead, and nitrogen oxide. The term, "criteria pollutants" derives from the requirement that EPA must describe the characteristics and potential health and welfare effects of these pollutants. It is on the basis of these criteria that standards are set or revised. N

critical organ
The most exposed human organ or tissue exclusive of the integumentary system (skin) and the cornea. A

critical pollutant
The pollutant or pollutant combination (TSP x SO_2) with the highest subindex during the reporting period. [ed. for the PSD areas]. A

cross grain
Cross grain (slope of grain) is a deviation of the fiber direction from a line parallel to the sides of the piece. O

cross recovery furnace
A furnace used to recover chemicals consisting primarily of sodium and sulfur compounds by burning black liquor which on a quarterly basis contains more than 7 weight percent of the total pulp solids from the neutral sulfite semichemical process and has a green liquor sulfidity of more than 28 percent. A

crude oil
Petroleum as it is extracted from the earth. There may be several thousands of different substances in crude oil, some of which evaporate quickly while others persist indefinitely. The physical characteristics of crude oils may vary widely. Crude oils are often identified in trade jargon by their regions of origin. This identification may not relate to the apparent physical characteristics of the oil. Commercial gasoline, kerosene, heating oils, diesel oils, lubricating oils, waxes, and asphalts are all obtained by refining crude oil. A

crusher
A machine used to crush any metallic mineral and includes feeders or conveyors located immediately below the crushing surfaces. Crushers include, but are not limited to, the following types: jaw, gyratory, cone, and hammermill. A

Cs
Cesium.

ct.
Closed throttle.

cu.
Cubic.

cu.ft.
Cubic feet.

cu.in.
Cubic inch(es).

Cubic Feet Per Minute
CFM. A measure of the volume of a substance flowing through air within a fixed period of time. With regard to indoor air, refers to the amount of air, in cubic feet, that is exchanged with indoor air in minute's time, or an air exchange rate. N

cullet
Clean, color-sorted, crushed-glass that is used in glassmaking to expedite the melting of silica sand.

cullet water
That water which is exclusively and directly applied to molten glass in order to solidify the glass. A

cultivating
Physical methods of soil treatment employed within established farming, ranching and silviculture lands upon planted farm, ranch, or forest crops to

aid and improve their growth, quality or yield. A

cultural eutrophication
Increasing rate at which water bodies "die" by pollution from human activities. N

cumulative impact
The impact on the environment which results from the incremental impact of the action when added to the other past, present, and reasonably foreseeable future actions regardless of what agency (Federal or non-Federal) or person undertakes such other actions. Cumulative impacts can result from individually minor but collectively significant actions taking place over a period of time. A

Cumulative Working Level Months
CWLM. The sum of lifetime exposure to radon working levels expressed in total working level months. N

curb collection
Collection of solid waste placed adjacent to a street. A

curb mass
The actual or manufacturer's estimated mass of the vehicle with fluids at nominal capacity and with all equipment specified by the Administrator. A

curb-idle
(1) For manual transmission code light-duty trucks, the engine speed with the transmission in neutral or with the clutch disengaged and with the air conditioning system, if present, turned off. For automatic transmission code light-duty trucks, curb-idle means the engine speed with the automatic transmission in the Park position (or the Neutral position if there is no Park position), and with the air conditioning system, if present, turned off. (2) For manual transmission code heavy-duty engines, the manufacturer's recommended engine speed with the transmission in neutral or with the clutch disengaged. For automatic transmission code heavy-duty engines, curb-idle means the manufacturer's recommended engine speed with the automatic transmission in gear and the output shaft stalled. A

curie
(1) A measure of radioactivity. N (2) The amount of radioactive material which produces 37 billion nuclear transformations per second. One pico-curie (pCi) = 10^{-12} Ci. A

curing oven
A device that uses heat or radiation to dry or cure the coating(s) applied to metal parts or products. A

current assets
Cash or other assets or resources commonly identified as those which are reasonably expected to be realized in cash or sold or consumed during the normal operating cycle of the business. A

current liabilities
Obligations whose liquidation are reasonably expected to require the use of existing resources properly classifiable as current assets or the creation of other current liabilities. A

curtain wall
A refractory construction or baffle that deflects combustion gases downward.

custody transfer
The transfer of produced petroleum and/or condensate, after processing and/or treating in the producing operations, from storage tanks or automatic transfer facilities to pipelines or any other forms of transportation. A

custom blend
A mixture of pesticide and another compound (usually herbicides with fertilizers), which is prepared to the order of the end user and not held in inventory. N

custom blender
Any pesticide-producing establishment whose production is totally confined to custom blend products. N

custom-molded device
A hearing protective device that is made to conform to a specific ear canal. This is usually accomplished by using a moldable compound to obtain an impression of the ear and ear canal. The compound is subsequently permanently hardened to retain this shape. A

customs territory of the United States
The 50 States, Puerto Rico, and the District of Columbia. A

cut
The portion of a land surface from which earth or rock is excavated; the distance between an original ground surface and an excavated surface.

cutback asphalts
Asphalts diluted with solvents to reduce viscosity for low temperature applications. A

cutie-pie
An instrument used to measure radiation levels. N

cutout or by-pass
Devices which vary the exhaust system gas flow so as to discharge the exhaust gas and acoustic energy to the atmosphere without passing through the entire length of the exhaust system, including all exhaust system sound attenuation components. A

cvs.
Constant volume sampler.

CWA
Clean Water Act (formerly referred to the Federal Water Pollution Control Act) Pub. L. 92-500, as amended by Pub. L. 95-217 and Pub. L. 95-576, 33 U.S.C. 1251 et seq.

CWA and regulations
The Clean Water Act (CWA) and applicable regulations promulgated thereunder. In the case of an approved State program, it includes State program requirements. A

CWLM
Cumulative Working Level Months. The sum of lifetime exposure to radon working levels expressed in total working level months. N

cwt.
Hundred weight.

CWTC
Chemical Waste Transportation Council. N

cyclone collector
(1) An incinerator collector in which an inlet gas stream is made to move vortically; its centrifugal force tends to drive suspended particles to the cyclone wall, where they fall to the bottom and are collected. (2) A device that uses centrifugal force to pull large particles from polluted air. N

cyclone separator
A separator that uses a swirling air flow to sort mixed materials according to the size, weight, and density of the pieces.

cyclonic flow
A spiraling movement of exhaust gases within a duct or stack. A

cylinder
A pressure vessel for the storage of gases. O

cytology
The scientific study of cells. N

D

daily cover

Cover material that is spread and compacted on the top and side slopes of compacted solid waste at least at the end of each compacting day in order to control vectors, fire, moisture, and erosion and to assure an aesthetic appearance. A

daily discharge

NPDES. The "discharge of a pollutant" measured during a calendar day or any 24-hour period that reasonably reports the calendar day for purposes of sampling. For pollutants with limitations expressed in units of mass, the "daily discharge" is calculated as the total mass of the pollutant discharged over the day. For pollutants with limitations expressed in other units of measurement, the "daily discharge" is calculated as the average measurement of the pollutant over the day. A

dairy waste

The waste generated by dairy plants in their processing of milk to produce cream, butter, cheese, ice cream, and other dairy products; it consists primarily of organic materials and suspended solids.

damper

A manually or automatically controlled valve or plate in a breeching, duct, or stack that is used to regulate a draft or the rate of flow of air or other gases.

Dano biostabilizer system

An aerobic, thermophilic composting process in which optimum conditions of moisture, air, and temperature are maintained in a single, slowly revolving cylinder that retains the compostable solid waste for 1 to 5 days; the material is later windrowed.

DASHO
Designed Agency Safety and Health Official. The executive official of a Federal Department or Agency who is responsible for safety and occupational health matters within a Federal agency, and is so designated or appointed by the head of the agency. N

data call-in
A part of the Office of Pesticide Programs (OPP) process of developing key required test data, especially on the long-term, chronic effects of existing pesticides, in advance of scheduled Registration Standard reviews. Data Call-In is an adjunct of the Registration Standards program intended to expedite reregistration and involves the "calling-in" of data from manufacturers. N

data fleet
A fleet of automobiles tested at "zero device-miles" in "baseline configuration," the "retrofitted configuration," and in some cases the "adjusted configuration," in order to determine the changes in fuel economy and exhaust emissions due to the "retrofitted configuration," and where applicable the changes due to the "adjusted configuration," as compared to the fuel economy and exhaust emissions of the "baseline configuration." A

data gap
The absence of any valid study or studies in the Agency's files that would satisfy a specific data requirement for a particular pesticide product. A

data submitters list
The current Agency list, entitled "Pesticide Data Submitters by Chemical," of persons who have submitted data to the Agency. A

daughter
A nuclide formed by the radioactive decay of another nuclide, which in this context is called the parent.

dB(A)
The standard abbreviation for A-weighted sound levels in decibels. A

DBCP
Dibromo Chloropropane.

dcf.
Dry cubic feet.

dcm.
Dry cubic meter.

DDT
The first chlorinated hydrocarbon insecticide (chemical name: 1,1,1-trichlorous-2, 2-bis (p-chloriphenyl)-ethane). It has a half-life of 15 years and can collect in fatty tissues of certain animals. EPA banned registration and interstate sale of DDT for virtually all but emergency uses in the U.S. in 1972 because of its persistence in the environment and accumulation in the food chain. N

DDT formulator
A person who produces, prepares or processes a formulated product comprising a mixture of DDT and inert materials or other diluents into a product intended for application in any use registered under the Federal Insecticide, Fungicide and Rodenticide

Act, as amended (7 U.S.C. 135, et seq.). A

DDT manufacturer
A manufacturer, excluding any source which is exclusively a DDT formulator, who produces, prepares or processes technical DDT, or who uses DDT as a material in the production, preparation or processing of another synthetic organic substance. A

dead (deenergized)
Free from any electrical connection to a source of potential difference and from electrical charges: not having a potential difference from that of earth. Note: The term is used only with reference to current-carrying parts which are sometimes alive (energized). O

deadweight tonnage
The actual weight in tons of cargo, stores, etc., required to bring a vessel down to her load line, from the light condition. Cargo deadweight is, as its name implies, the actual weight in tons of the cargo when loaded, as distinct from stores, ballast, etc. A

dealer
(1) A person who resides or is located in the United States, any territory of the United States or the District of Columbia and who is engaged in the sale or distribution of new automobiles to the ultimate purchaser. [ed. Used for provisions of CAA that prevent tampering with pollution control equipment in automobiles]. A (2) Any person who is engaged in the sale or the distribution of new motor vehicles or new motor vehicle engines to the ultimate purchaser. B

debarment
An action taken by the Director, Grants Administration Division, U.S. EPA under 40 CFR Part 32 to deny an individual, organization or unit of government the opportunity to participate in EPA grant agreements or to receive subagreements. A

decel.
Deceleration.

dechlorination
Removal of chlorine from a substance by chemically replacing it with hydrogen or hydroxide ions in order to detoxify the substances involved. N

decibel
dB. The unit measurement of sound level calculated by taking ten times the common logarithm of the ratio of the magnitude of the particular sound pressure to the standard reference sound pressure of 20 micropascals and its derivatives. A

declared value
For imported components, the value at which components are declared by the importer to the U.S. Customs Service at the date of entry into the customs territory of the United States, or, with respect to imports into Canada, the declared value of such components as if they were declared as imports into the United States at the date of entry into Canada. A

decommissioning
The process of removing a facility or area from operation and decontaminating and/or disposing of it or placing it in a condition of standby with appropriate controls and safeguards.

decomposition
The breakdown of matter by bacteria. It changes the chemical make-up and physical appearance of materials. N

decontamination/detoxification
(1) Processes which will convert pesticides into nontoxic compounds. A
(2) The selective removal of radioactive material from a surface or from within another material. A

deep-well disposal
The deposition of raw or treated, filtered hazardous waste by pumping it into deep wells, where it is contained in the pores of permeable subsurface rock and separate, stores, etc.

defeat device
An AECD [air emission control device] that reduces the effectiveness of the emission control system under conditions which may reasonably be expected to be encountered in normal urban vehicle operation and use, unless (1) such conditions are substantially included in the Federal emission test procedure, or (2) the need for the AECD is justified in terms of protecting the vehicle against damage or accident, or (3) the AECD does not go beyond the requirements of engine starting. A

defoliant
All substances or mixtures of substances intended for causing the leaves or foliage to drop from plants. Defoliants include, but are not limited to, harvest-aid agents intended for defoliating plants (such as cotton) to facilitate harvesting. C

degradation
The process by which a chemical is reduced to a less complex form. N

degradation product
A substance resulting from the transformation of a pesticide by physicochemical or biochemical means. A

degreasing
(1) The removal of oils and greases from the surface of the metal workpiece. This process can be accomplished with detergents as in alkaline cleaning or by the use of solvents. A
(2) The operation of using an organic solvent as a surface cleaning agent. A

deinking
A process in which most of the ink, filler, and other extraneous material is removed from printed paper waste or broke. The result is a pulp that can be used in the manufacture of new paper.

delayed compliance order
An order issued by a state or by the administrator to a stationary source which postpones the date by which the source is required to comply with any requirement contained in the applicable state implementation plan. O

delegated state
A state (or other governmental entity) which has applied for, and received authority to administer, within its territory, its state regulatory program as the federal program required under a particular federal statute. As used in connection with NPDES, UIC, and PWS programs, the

term does not connote any transfer of federal authority to a state. N

delist
Use of the petition process to have a facility's toxic designation rescinded. N

demolition
The wrecking or taking out of any load-supporting structural member of a facility together with any related handling operations. A

demonstration
The initial exhibition of a new technology process or practice or a significantly new comination or use of technologies, processes or practices, subsequent to the development stage, for the purpose of proving technological feasibility and cost effectiveness. I

demulsibility
The resistance of an oil to emulsification, or the ability of an oil to separate from any water with which it is mixed. The better the demulsibility rating, the more quickly the oil separates from water. A

denitrification
The anaerobic biological reduction of nitrate nitrogen to nitrogen gas. N

densified refuse-derived fuel
d-RDF. A refuse-derived fuel that has been compressed to improve certain handling or burning characteristics. B

density
(1) The mass of a unit volume; its numerical expression varies with the units selected. A (2) The mass of a unit volume of liquid, expressed as grams per cubic centimeter, kilograms per liter, or pounds per gallon, at a specified temperature. A

denuder
A horizontal or vertical container which is part of a mercury chlor-alkali cell and in which water and alkali metal amalgam are converted to alkali metal hydroxide, mercury, and hydrogen gas in a shortcircuited, electrolytic reaction. A

Deoxyribonucleic Acid
DNA. The molecule in which the genetic information for most living cells is encoded. Viruses, too, can contain RNA. N

departure angle
The smallest angle, in a plan side view of an automobile, formed by the level surface on which the automobile is standing and a line tangent to the rear tire static loaded radius arc and touching the underside of the automobile rearward of the rear tire. A

depletion curve
In hydraulics, a graphical representation of water depletion from storage-stream channels, surface soil, and ground water. A depletion curve can be drawn for base flow, direct runoff, or total flow. N

deposit
The sum paid to the dealer by the consumer when beverages are purchased in returnable beverage containers, and which is refunded when the beverage container is returned. A

depressurization
A condition that occurs when the air pressure inside a structure is lower than the air pressure outside. Depressurization can occur when household appliances that consume or exhaust house air, such as fireplaces or furnaces, are not supplied with enough makeup air. Radon-containing soil gas may be drawn into a house more rapidly under depressurized conditions. N

dermal exposure
Contact between a chemical and the skin. N

dermal toxicity
The ability of a pesticide or toxic chemical to poison people or animals by contact with the skin. (See: contact pesticide). N

DES
Diethylstilbestrol. A synthetic estrogen used as a growth stimulant in food animals. Residues in meat are thought to be carcinogenic. N

desalinization
Removing salt from ocean or brackish water. N

desiccant
(1) Chemical agents that absorb moisture; some desiccants are capable of drying out plants or insects, causing death. N (2) All substances or mixtures of substances intended for artificially accelerating the drying of plant tissue. Desiccants include, but are not limited to, harvest-aid agents whose use is intended to cause sufficient foliage injury so as to result in accelerated drying and death (maturation) of certain crop plants, such as cotton and soybeans. O

design value
EPA-computed statistic that characterizes air quality and determines the nature of pollution controls. In non-attainment areas, the design value is the fourth highest daily reading at the "worst case" monitor--the monitor with the highest pollutant readings during any one of three consecutive years. N

designated areawide planning area
All areas designated pursuant to section 208 (a) (2), (3), or (4) of the [Clean Water] Act and [40 CFR] §130.13. A

designated areawide planning agency
That agency designated in accordance with section 208(a)(2),(3), or (4) of the [Clean Water] Act. A

designated employee
A qualified person delegated to perform specific duties under the conditions existing. O

designated facility
A hazardous waste treatment, storage, or disposal facility which has received an EPA permit (or a facility with interim status) or a permit from a State that has been designated on the manifest by the generator. A

designated high-altitude location
Certain counties which have substantially all of their area located above 1,219 meters (4,000 feet). A

designated liability area
The geographic area within which emissions from a source may significantly affect the ambient air quality. A

designated pollutant
(1) An air pollutant which is neither a criteria nor hazardous pollutant, as described in the Clean Air Act, but for which new sources performance standards exist. The Clean Air Act requires states to control these pollutants, which include acid mist, total reduced sulfur (TRS), and fluorides. N (2) Any air pollutant, emissions of which are subject to a standard of performance for new stationary sources but for which air quality criteria have not been issued, and which is not included on a list published under section 108(a) or section 112(b)(1)(A) of the [Clean Air] Act. A

designated uses
Those water uses identified in state water quality standards which must be achieved and maintained as required under the Clean Water Act. Uses can include cold water fisheries, public water supply, agriculture, etc. N

Designed Agency Safety and Health Official
DASHO. The executive official of a Federal Department or Agency who is responsible for safety and occupational health matters within a Federal agency, and is so designated or appointed by the head of the agency. N

designer bugs
Popular term for microbes developed through biotechnology that can degrade specific toxic chemicals at their source in toxic waste dumps or in ground water. N

destructive distillation
The airless heating of organic matter that results in the evolution of volatile substances and produces a solid char consisting of fixed carbon and ash. See Lantz process.

desulfurization
Removal of sulfur from fossil fuels to reduce pollution. N

detergent
Synthetic washing agent that helps to remove dirt and oil. Some contain compounds which kill useful bacteria and encourage algae growth when they are in wastewater that reaches receiving waters. N

developer
A person, government unit, or company that proposes to build a hazardous waste treatment, storage, or disposal facility. N

deviation
A formal exception to a Section or Sections of EPA grant regulations or the EPA Grants Administration Manual based on written justification, and provided for by a grant amendment.

device
Any instrument or contrivance (other than a firearm) which is intended for trapping, destroying, repelling, or mitigating any pest or any other form of plant or animal life (other than man and other than bacteria, virus, or other microorganism on or in living man or other living

animals); but not including equipment used for the application of pesticides when sold separately therefrom. A, C

device integrity
The durability of a device and effect of its malfunction on vehicle safety or other parts of the vehicle system. A

dewatering
The removal of water by such processes as filtration, centrifugation, pressing, and coagulation to prepare sewage sludge for disposal by burning or landfill. The term also applies to the removal of water from pulp or other materials.

DHEW
Former U.S. Department of Health, Education and Welfare, now Department of Health and Human Services. A

diagnostic-feasibility study
A two part study to determine a lake's current condition and to develop possible methods for lake restoration and protection. (a) The diagnostic portion of the study includes gathering information and data to determine the limnological, morphological, demographic, socio-economic, and other pertinent characteristics of the lake and its watershed. This information will provide recipients an understanding of the quality of the lake, specifying the location and loading characteristics of significant sources polluting the lake. (b) The feasibility portion of the study includes: (1) Analyzing the diagnostic information to define methods and procedures for controlling the sources of pollution; (2) Determining the most energy and cost

efficient procedures to improve the quality of the lake for maximum public benefit; (3) Developing a technical plan and milestone schedule for implementing pollution control measures and in-lake restoration procedures; and (4) If necessary, conducting pilot scale evaluations. A

dialysis
A process by which various substances in solution with widely differing molecular weights may be separated by solute diffusion through semipermeable membranes. It is a suitable means of separation for hazardous wastes that form aqueous solutions.

diathermy
The generation of heat in tissues for medical or surgical purposes by electric currents.

diatomaceous earth
Diatomite. A chalk-like material (fossilized diatoms) used to filter out solid waste in waste-water treatment plants; also used as an active ingredient in some powdered pesticides. N

diazinon
An insecticide. In 1986, EPA banned its use on open areas such as sod farms and golf courses because it posed a danger to migratory birds who gathered on them in large numbers. The ban did not apply to its use in agriculture, or on lawns of homes and commercial establishments. N

dicofol
A pesticide used on citrus fruits. N

die

The tooling used in a press for cutting or forming material. An upper and a lower die make a complete set. O

diesel engine

A type of internal combustion engine that uses a fuel injector and produces combustion temperatures by compression.

dietary LC$_{50}$

A statistically derived estimate of the concentration of a test substance in the diet that would cause 50 percent mortality to the test population under specified conditions. A

differentiation

The process by which single cells grow into particular forms of specialized tissue, e.g., root, stem, leaf. N

diffused air

A type of aeration that forces oxygen into sewage by pumping air through perforated pipes inside a holding tank and bubbling it through the sewage. N

diffusion

The movement of suspended or dissolved particles from a more concentrated to a less concentrated region as a result of the random movement of individual particles; the process tends to distribute them uniformly throughout the available volume. N

digester

In wastewater treatment, a closed tank; in solid waste conversion, a unit in which bacterial action is induced and accelerated in order to break down organic matter and establish the proper carbon to nitrogen ratio. N

digestion

The biochemical decomposition of organic matter. Digestion of sewage sludge occurs in tanks where it breaks down into gas, liquid, and mineral matter. N

dike

(1) An embankment or ridge of either natural or man-made materials used to prevent the movement of liquids, sludges, solids, or other materials. A (2) A low wall that can act as a barrier to prevent a spill from spreading. N

diluent

The material added to a pesticide by the user or manufacturer to reduce the concentration of active ingredient in the mixture. A

dilution ratio

The relationship between the volume of water in a stream and the volume of incoming waste. It can affect the ability of the stream to assimilate waste. N

dilution ventilation

Air flow designed to dilute contaminants to acceptable levels. (See: general ventilation or exhaust.) N

dinocap

A fungicide used primarily by apple growers to control summer diseases. EPA, in 1986, proposed restrictions on its use when laboratory tests found it caused birth defects in rabbits. N

dinoseb

A herbicide that is also used as a fungicide and insecticide. It was banned by EPA in 1986 because it posed the risk of birth defects and sterility. N

dioxin

Any of a family of compounds known chemically as dibenzo-p-dioxins. Concern about them arises from their potential toxicity and as contaminants in commercial products. Tests on laboratory animals indicate that it is one of the more toxic man-made chemicals known. N

direct costs

Those costs which can be identified specifically with the grant project or which can be directly assigned to it with a high degree of accuracy.

direct discharge

The discharge of a pollutant. A

direct discharger

(1) A source that places pollutants directly into navigable waters. Sources that dispose of pollutants into a sewer system and non-point sources, that add pollutants to uncontrolled runoff, are not direct dischargers. (2) A municipal or industrial facility which introduces pollution through a defined conveyance or system; a point source. N

direct drive

The type of driving arrangement wherein no clutch is used; coupling and decoupling of the driving torque is accomplished by energization and de-energization of a motor. Even though not employing a clutch, direct drives

match the operational characteristics of "part revolution clutches" because the driving power may be disengaged during the stroke of the press. O

direct feed incinerator

An incinerator that accepts solid waste directly into its combustion chamber.

direct photolysis

The direct absorption of light by a chemical followed by a reaction which transforms the parent chemical into one or more products. A

disaggregation

The result of breaking down a sum total of population or economic activity for a State or other jurisdiction (i.e., designated 208 area or SMSA) into portions, each representing a smaller area or jurisdiction. A

disallowed costs

Those charges to a grant which EPA or its representative determine to be unallowable.

discharge

(1) [For purposes of Section 311 of the CWA], includes, but is not limited to, any spilling, leaking, pumping, pouring, emitting, emptying or dumping, but excludes (A) discharges in compliance with a permit under section 402 of this [Federal Water Pollution Control] Act, (B) discharges resulting from circumstances identified and reviewed and made a part of the public record with respect to a permit issued or modified under section 402 of this Act, and subject to a condition in such permit, and (C) continuous or

anticipated intermittent discharges from a point source, identified in a permit or permit application under section 402 of this Act, which are caused by events occurring within the scope of relevant operating or treatment systems. D (2)(A) [In connection with activities under the Outer Continental Shelf Lands Act or the Deepwater Port Act of 1974, or which may affect natural resources belonging to, appertaining to, or under the exclusive management authority of the United States including resources under the Fishery Conservation and Management Act of 1976]. A discharge into any waters beyond the contiguous zone from any vessel or onshore or offshore facility, which vessel or facility is subject to or is engaged in activities under the Outer Continental Shelf Lands Act or the Deepwater Port Act of 1974, and (B) any discharge into any waters beyond the contiguous zone which contain, cover, or support any natural resource belonging to, appertaining to, or under the exclusive management authority of the United States (including resources under the Fishery Conservation and Management Act of 1976). A (3) When used without qualification includes a discharge of a pollutant, and a discharge of pollutants. D

Discharge Monitoring Report
DMR. The EPA uniform national form, including any subsequent additions, revisions, or modifications, for the reporting of self-monitoring results by NPDES permitees. DMRs must be used by "approved States" as well as by EPA. EPA will supply DMRs to any approved State upon request. The EPA national forms may be modi-

fied to substitute the state agency name, address, logo, and other similar information, as appropriate, in place of EPA's. A

discharge of a pollutant
(1)(a) Any addition of any "pollutant" or combination of pollutants to "waters of the United States" from any "point source," or (b) any addition of any pollutant or combination of pollutants to the waters of the "contiguous zone" or the ocean from any point source other than a vessel or other floating craft which is being used as a means of transportation. (2) This definition includes additions of pollutants into waters of the United States from: surface runoff which is collected or channelled by man; discharges through pipes, sewers, or other conveyances owned by a State, municipality, or other person which do not lead to a treatment works; and discharges through pipes, sewers, or other conveyances leading into privately owned treatment works. This term does not include an addition of pollutants by any "indirect discharger." A

discharge of fill material
The addition from any "point source" of "fill material" into "waters of the United States." The term includes the following activities in waters of the United States: Placement of fill that is necessary for the construction of any structure; the building of any structure or impoundment requiring rock, sand, dirt, or other materials for its construction; site-development fills for recreational, industrial, commercial, residential, and other uses; causeways

or road fills; dams and dikes; artificial islands; property protection and/or reclamation devices such as riprap, groins, seawalls, breakwaters, and revetments; beach nourishment; levees; fill for structures such as sewage treatment facilities, intake and outfall pipes associated with power plants and subaqueous utility lines, and artificial reefs. A

**discharge of pollutant
or discharge of pollutants**
Each means (1) any addition of any pollutant to navigable waters other than the territorial sea, from any point source, (2) any addition of any pollutant to the waters of the territorial sea, the contiguous zone or the ocean from any point source other than a vessel or other floating craft. A, D

discharge of dredged material
Any addition from any "point source" of "dredge material" into "waters of the United States." The term includes the addition of dredged material into waters of the United States and the runoff or overflow from a contained land or water dredged material disposal area. Discharges of pollutants into waters of the United States resulting from the subsequent onshore processing of dredged material are not included within this term and are subject to the NPDES program even though the extraction and deposit of such material may also require a permit from the Corps of Engineers or the State section 404 program [of the FWPCA]. A

discharge of pollutants associated with an aquaculture project
The addition or discharge of specific pollutants in a controlled manner from a point source to an aquaculture project to enhance the growth or propagation of the species under culture. A

disconnecting (or isolating) switch
(Over 600 volts, nominal.) A mechanical switching device used for isolating a circuit or equipment from a source of power. O

disinfectant
(1) Any oxidant, including but not limited to chlorine, chlorine dioxide, chloramines, and ozone added to water in any part of the treatment or distribution process, that is intended to kill or inactivate pathogenic microorganisms. A (2) A chemical or physical process that kills pathogenic organisms in water. Chlorine is often used to disinfect sewage treatment effluent, water supplies, wells, and swimming pools. N

dispenser
The permanent (intended to be refilled) or disposable (discarded when empty) container designed to hold more than one complete set of hearing protector(s) for the express purpose of display to promote sale or display to promote use or both. A

dispersant
(1) A chemical agent used to break up concentrations of organic material such as spilled oil. M (2) An agent that emulsifies, disperses, or solubilizes oil into the water column or promotes the surface spreading of

oil slicks to facilitate dispersal of the oil into the water column. A

dispersion technique
(1) The use of dilution to attain ambient air quality levels including any intermittent or supplemental control of air pollutants varying with atmospheric conditions. B Increase in stack height is an example of a dispersion technique. (2) Any technique which attempts to affect the concentration of a pollutant in the ambient air by using that portion of a stack which exceeds good engineering practice stack height, varying the rate of emission of a pollutant according to atmospheric conditions or ambient concentrations of that pollutant, or by addition of a fan or reheater to obtain a less stringent emission limitation. The preceding sentence does not include: (a) The reheating of a gas stream, following use of a pollution control system, for the purpose of returning the gas to the temperature at which it was originally discharged from the facility generating the gas stream; (b) the use of smoke management in agricultural or silvicultural programs; or (c) combining the exhaust gases from several stacks into one stack. A

disposable device
A hearing protective device that is intended to be discarded after one period of use. A

disposal
(1) The planned release or placement of waste in a manner that precludes recovery. (2) The discharge, deposit, injection, dumping, spilling, leaking, or placing of any solid waste or hazardous waste into or on any land or water so that such solid waste or hazardous waste or any constituent thereof may enter the environment or be emitted into the air or discharged into any waters, including ground waters. I (3) Final placement or destruction of toxic, radioactive, or other wastes; surplus or banned pesticides or other chemicals; polluted soils; and drums containing hazardous materials from removal actions or accidental releases. Disposal may be accomplished through use of approved secure landfills, surface impoundments, land farming, deep well injection, ocean dumping, or incineration. N

disposal facility
A facility or part of a facility at which "hazardous waste" is intentionally placed into or on the land or water, and at which hazardous waste will remain after closure. A

disposal site
That portion of the "waters of the United States" enclosed within fixed boundaries consisting of a bottom surface area and any overlaying volume of water. In the case of "wetland" on which water is not present, the disposal site consists of the wetland surface area. Fixed boundaries may consist of fixed geographic point(s) and associated dimensions, or of a discharge point and specific associated dimensions. A

disposal well
A well used for the disposal of waste into a subsurface stratum. A

dissolved chromium, dissolved nickel or dissolved iron
That portion of chromium, nickel or iron, respectively, determined utilizing the approved method for total chromium, total nickel or total iron, respectively, following preliminary treatment as described in paragraph 4.1.1, page 86, of the *Methods for Chemical Analysis of Water and Wastes*, 1971, EPA, Analytical Quality Control Laboratory, Cincinnati, Ohio. A

dissolved iron
That portion of iron determined utilizing the approved method for total iron following preliminary treatment as described in paragraph 4.1.1, Page 86, of the *Methods for Chemical Analysis of Water and Waste*, 1971, EPA, Analytical Quality Control Laboratory, Cincinnati, Ohio. A

Dissolved Oxygen
DO. 1) A measure of the amount of oxygen available for biochemical activity in a given amount of water. Adequate levels of DO are needed to support aquatic life. Low dissolved oxygen concentrations can result from inadequate waste treatment. N (2) The oxygen freely available in water. Dissolved oxygen is vital to fish and other aquatic life and for the prevention of odors. Traditionally, the level of dissolved oxygen has been accepted as the single most important indicator of a water body's ability to support desirable aquatic life. Secondary and advanced waste treatment are generally designed to protect DO in waste-receiving waters. N

dissolved solids
(1) The total of disintegrated organic and inorganic material contained in water. Excesses can make water unfit to drink or use in industrial processes. N (2) Disintegrated organic and inorganic material contained in water. N

distillate oil
Fuel oils that contain 0.05 weight percent nitrogen or less and comply with the specifications for fuel oil numbers 1 and 2, as defined by the American Society of Testing and Materials in ASTM D396-78, Standard Specifications for Fuel Oils (incorporated by reference--see [40 CFR] § 60.17). A

distillation
The act of purifying liquids through boiling, so that the steam condenses to a pure liquid and the pollutants remain in a concentrated residue. N

distribute in commerce
(1) Sell in, offer for sale in, or introduce or deliver for introduction into, commerce. A (2) When used to describe an action taken with respect to a chemical substance or mixture or article containing a substance or mixture, to sell, or the sale of, the substance, mixture, or article in commerce; to introduce or deliver for introduction into commerce, or the introduction or delivery for introduction into commerce of, the substance, mixture, or article; or to hold, or the holding of, the substance, mixture, or article after its introduction into commerce. K (3) To sell in commerce,

to introduce or deliver for introduction into commerce, or to hold after introduction into commerce. A

distributor
Any person who transports or stores or causes the transportation of storage of gasoline at any point between any gasoline refinery and any retail outlet or wholesale-purchaser-consumer's facilities. A

district engineer
The District Engineer for the U.S. Army Corps of Engineers District in which dredged or fill material is proposed to be discharged or such other individual as may be designated by the Secretary of the Army to issue or deny permits under section 404 of the [Clean Water] Act. A

diurnal breathing loss
Fuel evaporative emissions as a result of the daily range in temperature to which the fuel system is exposed. A

DMR
Discharge Monitoring Reports (EPA).

DNA
Deoxyribonucleic Acid. The molecule in which the genetic information for most living cells is encoded. Viruses, too, can contain RNA. N

DNA hybridization
Use of a segment of DNA, called a DNA probe, to identify its complementary DNA; used to detect specific genes. This process takes advantage of the ability of a single strand of DNA to combine with a complimentary strand. N

DO
Dissolved Oxygen.

DOC
Department of Commerce.

DOD
Department of Defense.

DOE
Department of Energy.

DOI
Department of the Interior.

DOJ
Department of Justice.

DOL
Department of Labor.

domestic application
Application of a pesticide directly to humans or pets, or application of a pesticide in, on or around all structures, vehicles or areas associated with the household or home life, patient care areas of health related institutions, or areas where children spend time including but not limited to: (1) Gardens, non-commercial greenhouses, yards, patios, houses, pleasure marine craft, mobile homes, campers and recreational vehicles, non-commercial campsites, home swimming pools and kennels; (2) Articles, objects, devices or surfaces handled or contacted by humans or pets in all structures, vehicles or areas listed above; (3) Patient care areas of nursing homes, mental institutions, hospitals, and convalescent homes; (4) Educational, lounging and recreational areas of preschools, nurseries and day camps. A

domestic construction material

An unmanufactured construction material which has been mined or produced in the United States, or manufactured construction material which has been manufactured in the United States if the cost of its components which are mined, produced, or manufactured in the United States exceeds 50 percent of the cost of all its components. A

domestic wastewater

Wastewater of the type commonly introduced into a treatment works by residential users. A

DOS

Department of State.

dose

(1) The quantity of a chemical to which an organism is exposed. N (2) A general term denoting the quality of radiation or energy absorbed. For special purposes it must be appropriately qualified. If unqualified, it refers to absorbed dose. (3) In radiology, the quantity of energy or radiation absorbed. N

dose equivalent

The product of the absorbed dose from ionizing radiation and such factors as account for differences in biological effectiveness due to the type of radiation and its distribution in the body as specified by the International Commission on Radiological Units and Measurements (ICRU). The unit of the dose equivalent is the rem. A

dose rate

Absorbed dose delivered per unit time.

dosimeter

An instrument that measures exposure to radiation. N

DOT

Department of Transportation.

downpass

A chamber or gas passage placed between two combustion chambers to carry the products of combustion downward.

draft

The difference between the pressure in an incinerator, or any component part, and that in the atmosphere; it causes air or the products of combustion to flow from the incinerator to the atmosphere.

draft controller

An automatic device that maintains a uniform furnace draft by regulating a damper.

Draft Environmental Impact Statement

DEIS. The document prepared by EPA, or under EPA guidance, which attempts to identify and analyze the environmental impacts of a proposed EPA action and feasible alternatives, and is circulated for public comment prior to preparation of the final environmental impact statement (final EIS). A

draft permit

A document prepared under 40 CFR

§124.6 indicating the Director's tentative decision to issue or deny, modify, revoke and reissue, terminate, or reissue a "permit." A notice of intent to terminate a permit, and a notice of intent to deny a permit, as discussed in 40 CFR §124.5 are types of "draft permits." A denial of a request for modification, revocation and reissuance, or termination, as discussed in 40 CFR §124.5, is not a "draft permit." A "proposed permit" is not a "draft permit." A

drag conveyor
A conveyor that uses vertical steel plates fastened between two continuous chains to drag material across a smooth surface.

drag plate
A plate beneath a traveling or chain grate stoker used to support the returning grates.

dragline
A revolving shovel that carries a bucket attached only by cables and digs by pulling the bucket toward itself.

dredged material
(1) Any material excavated or dredged from the navigable waters of the United States. (2) [ed. Dredged material often contains high levels of toxic and other pollutants that have precipitated into bottom sediments. Disposal of dredged material can cause serious environmental problems. Disposal in navigable waters requires a permit under Section 404 of CWA]. (3) Material that is excavated or dredged from "waters of the United States." A

dredging
Removal of mud from the bottom of water bodies using a scooping machine. This disturbs the ecosystem and causes silting that can kill aquatic life. Dredging of contaminated mud can expose aquatic life to heavy metals and other toxics. Dredging activities may be subject to regulation under Section 404 of the Clean Water Act. N

drift
Movement of a pesticide during or immediately after application or use through air to a site other than the intended site of application or use. A

drilling and production facility
All drilling and servicing equipment, wells, flow lines, separators, equipment, gathering lines, and auxiliary nontransportation - related equipment used in the production of petroleum but does not include natural gasoline plants. A

drilling mud
A heavy suspension used in drilling an "injection well," introduced down the drill pipe and through the drill bit. A

drinking water supply
Any raw or finished water source that is or may be used by a public water system (as defined in the Safe Drinking Water Act) or as drinking water by one or more individuals. L

drivetrain configuration
A unique combination of engine code, transmission configuration and axle ratio. A

dross reverberatory furnace
Any furnace used for the removal or refining of impurities from lead bullion. A

drum mill
A long, inclined steel drum that rotates and grinds solid wastes in its rough interior; finer ground material falls through holes near the end of the drum and coarser material drops out of the end. The drum mill is used in some composting operations.

dry cleaning operation
That process by which an organic solvent is used in the commercial cleaning of garments and other fabric materials. A

dry limestone process
An air pollution control method that uses limestone to absorb the sulfur oxides in furnaces and stack gases. N

dryer
A unit in which the moisture content of a substance is reduced by contact with a heated gas stream. A

drying hearth
A solid surface in an incinerator upon which wet waste materials, liquids, or waste matter that may turn to liquid before burning are placed to dry or to burn with the help of hot combustion gases.

dscf.
Dry cubic feet at standard conditions.

dscm.
Dry cubic meter at standard conditions.

duct burner
A device that combusts fuel and that is placed in the exhaust duct from another source, such as a stationary gas turbine, internal combustion engine, kiln, etc., to allow the firing of additional fuel to heat the exhaust gases before the exhaust gases enter a heat recovery steam generating unit. A

dump
A site used to dispose of solid wastes without environmental controls. N

dump plate
A hinged plate in an incinerator that supports residue and from which residue may be discharged by rotating the plate.

dumping
[As used in regulation of ocean disposal] a disposition of material: Provided, That it does not mean a disposition of any effluent from any outfall structure to the extent that such disposition is regulated under the provisions of the Federal Water Pollution Control Act, as amended, under the provisions of [33 USC § 407], or under the provisions of the Atomic Energy Act of 1954, as amended, nor

does it mean a routine discharge of effluent incidental to the propulsion of, or operation of motor-driven equpment on, vessels: Provided further, That it does not mean the construction of any fixed structure or artificial island nor the intentional placement of any device in ocean waters or on or in the submerged land beneath such waters, for a purpose other than disposal, when such construction or such placement is otherwise regulated by Federal or State law or occurs pursuant to an authorized Federal or State program: And provided further, That it does not include the deposit of oyster shells, or other materials when such deposit is made for the purpose of developing, maintaining, or harvesting fisheries resources and is otherwise regulated by Federal or State law or occurs pursuant to an authorized Federal or State program. A, E

durability fleet
A fleet of automobiles operated for mileage accumulation used to assess deterioration effects associated with the retrofit device. A

dust
Fine grain particles light enough to be suspended in air. N

dust loading
The amount of dust in a gas; usually expressed in grains per cubic foot or pounds per thousand pounds of gas.

dust-handling equipment
Any equipment used to handle particulate matter collected by the air pollution control device (and located at or near such device) serving any electric submerged arc furnace subject to this subpart. A

dustfall jar
An open container used to collect large particles from the air for measurement and analysis. N

dye penetrant testing
A nondestructive method for finding discontinuities that are open to the surface of the metal. A dye is applied to the surface of metal and the excess is rinsed off. Dye that penetrates surface discontinuities will not be rinsed away, thus marking these discontinuities. A

dynamometer-idle
For automatic transmission code heavy-duty engines, the manufacturer's recommended engine speed without a transmission that simulates recommended engine speed with a transmission and with the transmission in neutral. A

dystrophic lakes
Shallow bodies of water that contain much humus and/or organic matter, that contain many plants but few fish, and are highly acidic. N

E

E

The VOC emission reduction efficiency (as a fraction) of the emission control device during performance testing. A

EAP

Environmental Action Plan. N

ear insert device

A hearing protective device that is designed to be inserted into the ear canal, and to be held in place principally by virtue of its fit inside the ear canal. A

ear muff device

A hearing protective device that consists of two acoustic enclosures which fit over the ears and which are held in place by a spring-like headband to which the enclosures are attached. A

early life stage toxicity test

A test to determine the minimum concentration of a substance which produces a statistically significant observable effect on hatching, survival, development and/or growth of a fish species continuously exposed during the period of their early development. A

ecological impact

The effect that a man-made or natural activity has on living organisms and their non-living (abiotic) environment. N

ecology

(1) The relationship of living things to one another and their environment, or the study of such relationships. (2) The study of the interrelationships between living organisms and their environment, both physical and biological. N

economic poisons

Chemicals used to control pests and to defoliate cash crops such as cotton. N

ecosphere

(1) The layer of earth and troposphere inhabited by or suitable for the existence of living organisms. (2) The "bio-bubble" that contains life on earth, in surface waters, and in the air. (Compare: biosphere). N

ecosystem
The interacting system of a biological community and its nonliving surroundings. N

ecotoxicological studies
Measurement of effects of environmental toxicants on indigenous populations of organisms. N

ECRA
Environmental Cleanup and Responsibility Act, effective December 31, 1983 in New Jersey.

ECSL
Enforcement Compliance Schedule Letters.

EDA
Economic Development Administration.

EDB
Ethylene Dibromide. A chemical used as an agricultural fumigant and in certain industrial processes. Extremely toxic and found to be a carcinogen in laboratory animals. EDB has been banned for most agricultural uses in the United States. N

EDD
Enforcement Decision Document.

eddy current separator
A separator that uses an alternating current to temporarily magnetize a piece of metal making it possible to deflect it and separate it out. This is used to sort out aluminum and other nonmagnetic metals. Also called alumnum magnet and electrodynamic separator.

EDF
Environmental Defense Fund.

education
Planned and organized activity by a consultant to impart information to employers and employees to enable them to establish and maintain employment and a place of employment which is safe and healthful. O

EEC
European Economic Community, headquartered in Brussels.

EEI
Edison Electric Institute. N

EENET
Emergency Education Network (FEMA). N

EER
Excess Emission Report. N

effective dose equivalent
The sum of the products of the dose equivalents to individual organs and tissues and appropriate weighing factors representing the risk relative to that for an equal dose to the whole body. A

effectively grounded
Intentionally connected to earth through a ground connection or connections of sufficiently low impedance and having sufficient current-carrying capacity to prevent buildup of voltages which may result in undue hazard to connected equipment or to persons. O

effects
(a) Direct effects, which are caused

by the action and occur at the same time and place. (b) Indirect effects, which are caused by the action and are later in time or farther removed in distance, but are still reasonably foreseeable. Indirect effects may include growth inducing effects and other effects related to induced changes in the pattern of land use, population density or growth rate, and related effects on air and water and other natural systems, including ecosystems. Effects and impacts as used in these regulations are synonymous. Effects includes ecological (such as the effects on natural resources and on the components, structures, and functioning of affected ecosystems), aesthetic, historic, cultural, economic, social, or health, whether direct, indirect, or cumulative. Effects may also include those resulting from actions which may have both beneficial and detrimental effects, even if on balance the agency believes that the effect will be beneficial. [ed. Used for determining the application of NEPA]. A

effects on welfare
All language referring to effects on welfare includes, but is not limited to, effects on soils, water, crops, vegetation, man-made materials, animals, wildlife, weather, visibility, and climate, damage to and deterioration of property, and hazards to transportation, as well as effects on economic values and on personal comfort and well being. B

efficacy
The capacity of a pesticide product when used according to label directions to control, kill, or induce the desired action in the target pest. A

efficiency rating
The degree to which a desired effect takes place. The efficiency rating of a piece of control equipment is based on the proportion of pollution it can remove.

effluent
Wastewater--treated or untreated--that flows out of a treatment plant, sewer, or industrial outfall. Generally refers to wastes discharged into surface waters. N

effluent limitation
Any restriction established by a State or the Administrator on quantities, rates, and concentrations of chemical, physical, biological, and other constituents which are discharged from point sources into navigable waters, the waters of the contiguous zone, or the ocean, including schedules of compliance. D

effluent limitation guideline
A regulation published by the Administrator under Section 304(b) of the Clean Water Act to adopt or revise effluent limitations. N

EGR
Exhaust Gas Recirculation. N

EHS
Extremely Hazardous Substances.

EI
Emissions Inventory. N

EIA
(1) Environmental Impact Assessment. (2) Economic Impact Assessment. N

EIL
Environmental Impairment Liability.
N

EIR
Environmental Impact Report. (2) En
dangerment Information Report. N

EIS/AS
Emissions Inventory System/Area
Source. N

EIS/PS
Emissions Inventory System/Point
Source. N

EKMA
Empirical Kinetic Modeling Approach.
N

electric arc furnace
A steel-making furnace in which the
heat is obtained by an electric arc
formed between the material to be
heated and electrodes. The charge for
this furnace consists almost entirely of
scrap.

electric sign
A fixed, stationary, or portable self-
contained, electrically illuminated utilization equipment with words or symbols
designed to convey information or
attract attention. O

electric submerged arc furnace
Any furnace wherein electrical energy
is converted to heat energy by transmission of current between electrodes
partially submerged in the furnace
charge. A

electric supply lines
Those conductors used to transmit
electric energy and their necessary
supporting or containing structures.
Signal lines of more than 400 volts to
ground are always supply lines within
the meaning of the rules, and those of
less than 400 volts to ground may be
considered as supply lines, if so run
and operated throughout. O

electric traction motor
An electrically powered motor which
provides tractive energy to the wheels
of a vehicle. A

**electric utility combined cycle gas
turbine**
Any combined cycle gas turbine used
for electric generation that is constructed for the purpose of supplying
more than one-third of its potential
electric output capacity and more than
25 MW electrical output to any utility
power distribution system for sale.
Any steam distribution system that is
constructed for the purpose of providing steam to a steam electric generator that would produce electrical
power for sale is also considered in
determining the electrical energy output capacity of the affected facility. A

electric utility steam generating unit
Any steam electric generating unit
that is constructed for the purpose of
supplying more than one-third of its
potential electric output capacity and
more than 25 MW electrical output to
any utility power distribution system
for sale. Any steam supplied to a
steam distribution system for the
purpose of providing steam to a
steam-electric generator that would
produce electrical energy for sale is
also considered in determining the

electrical energy output capacity of the affected facility. A

electric utility company

The largest interconnected organization, business or governmental entity that generates electric power for sale (e.g., a holding company with operating subsidiary companies). A

electric utility stationary gas turbine

Any stationary gas turbine constructed for the purpose of supplying more than one-third of its potential electric output capacity to any utility power distribution system for sale. A

electrical charging system

A device to convert 60 Hz alternating electric current, as commonly available in residential electric service in the United States, to a proper form for recharging the energy storage device. A

electrocoating

The electrodeposition of a metallic or nonmetallic coating onto the surface of a workpiece. A

electrodeposition

EDP. A method of applying a prime coat by which the automobile or light-duty truck body is submerged in a tank filled with coating material and an electrical field is used to effect the deposition of the coating material on the body. A

electrodialysis

A process that uses electrical current applied to permeable membranes to remove minerals from water. Often used to desalinize salty or brackish water. N

electron volt

(eV). A unit of energy equivalent to the energy gained by an electron in passing through a potential difference of one volt. Larger multiples of the electron volt are frequently used: KeV for thousand or kilo electron volts: MeV for million or mega electron volts ($1 \text{ eV} = 1.6 \times 10^{-12} \text{ erg}$).

electronic crystals

Crystals or crystalline material which because of their unique structural and electronic properties are used in electronic devices. Examples of these crystals are crystals comprised of quartz, ceramic, silicon, gallium arsenide, and idium arsenide. A

Electrostatic Precipitator (ESP)

An air pollution control device that removes particles from a gas stream (smoke) after combustion occurs. The ESP imparts an electrical charge to the particles, causing them to adhere to metal plates inside the precipitator. Rapping on the plates causes the particles to fall into a hopper for disposal. N

electrostatic spray application

A spray application method that uses an electrical potential to increase the transfer efficiency of the coating solids. Electrostatic spray application can be used for prime coat, guide coat, or topcoat operations. A

elementary neutralization unit

(1) Is used for neutralizing wastes which are hazardous wastes only because they exhibit the corrosivity characteristic defined in 40 CFR 261.22 of this chapter, or are listed in

Subpart D of Part 261 of Title 40 only for this reason; and (2) Meets the definition of tank, container, transport vehicle, or vessel in 40 CFR §260.10.

eligible costs

The construction costs for wastewater treatment works upon which EPA grants are based. N

elutriation

A process for separating lighter particles from heavier particles by washing solid waste with a slowly moving upward stream of fluid that carries the lighter particles with it. It is used in sludge conditioning to reduce the need for conditioning chemicals and to improve sedimentation and filtration by removing excess alkalinity and dissolved solids.

embryo cup

A small glass jar or similar container with a screened bottom in which the embryos of some species (i.e., minnow) are placed during the incubation period and which is normally oscillated to ensure a flow of water through the cup. A

emergency

Any occurrence such as, but not limited to, equipment failure, rupture of containers, or failure of control equipment which may result in a release of--which is (insert appropriate quantitative or qualitative level of release which constitutes an emergency). O

emergency (chemical)

A situation created by an accidental release or spill of hazardous chemicals which poses a threat to the safety of workers, residents, the environment, or property. N

emergency action plan

A plan for a workplace, or parts thereof, describing what procedures the employer and employees must take to ensure employee safety from fire or other emergencies. O

emergency condition

That period of time when: (a) The electrical output of an affected facility with a malfunctioning flue gas desulfurization system cannot be reduced or electrical output must be increased because: (1) All available system capacity in the principal company interconnected with the affected facility is being operated, and (2) All available purchase power interconnected with the affected facility is being obtained, or (b) The electric generation demand is being shifted as quickly as possible from an affected facility with a malfunctioning flue gas desulfurization system to one or more electrical generating units held in reserve by the principal company or by a neighboring company, or (c) An affected facility with a malfunctioning flue gas desulfurization system becomes the only available unit to maintain a part or all of the principal company's system emergency reserves and the unit is operated in spinning reserve at the lowest practical electric generation load consistent with not causing significant physical damage to the unit. If the unit is operated at a higher load to meet load demand, an emergency condition would not exist unless the conditions under (a) of this definition apply. A

emergency episode
(See: air pollution episode.) N

emergency escape route
The route that employees are directed to follow in the event they are required to evacuate the workplace or seek a designated refuge area. O

emergency fuel
A fuel fired by a gas turbine only during circumstances, such as natural gas supply curtailment or breakdown of delivery system, that makes it impossible to fire natural gas in the gas turbine. A

emergency gas turbine
Any stationary gas turbine which operates as a mechanical or electrical power source only when the primary power source for a facility has been rendered inoperable by an emergency situation. A

emergency level
For air quality contingency plans, the emergency level indicates that air quality is continuing to degrade toward a level of significant harm to the health of persons and that the most stringent control actions are necessary. An emergency will be declared when any one of the following levels is reached at any monitoring site: (1) SO_2--2,100 ug/m^3 (0.08 ppm), 24-hour average. (2) Particulate--875 ug/m^3, 24-hour average. (3) SO_2 and particulate combined--product of SO_2 ug/m^3, 24-hour average and particulate ug/m^3, 24-hour average equal to 393 x 10^3. (4) CO--46 mg/m^3 (40 ppm), 8-hour average. (5) Ozone (O_3)--1,000 ug/m^3 (0.05 ppm), 1-hour average. (6)

NO_2--3,000 ug/m^3 (1.6 ppm), 1-hour average; 750 ug/m^3 (0.04 ppm), 24-hour average and meteorological conditions are such that pollutant concentrations can be expected to remain at the above levels for twelve (12) or more hours or increase, or in the case of ozone, the situation is likely to reoccur within the next 24 hours unless control actions are taken. A

Emergency Management Institute
EMI is a component of FEMA's National Emergency Training Center located in Emmitsburg, Maryland. It conducts resident and nonresident training activities for Federal, State, and local government officials, managers in the private economic sector, and members of professional and volunteer organizations on subjects that range from civil nuclear preparedness systems to domestic emergencies caused by natural and technological hazards. Nonresident training activities are also conducted by State Emergency Management Training Offices under cooperative agreements that offer financial and technical assistance to establish annual training programs that fulfill emergency management training requirements in communities throughout the nation. N

EMS
Enforcement Management System, database under NPDES program.

Emergency Planning and Community Right-to-Know Act of 1986
Title III of Superfund Amendments and Reauthorization Act of 1986 (SARA). N

EMI
Emergency Management Institute.

eminent domain
Government taking--or forced acquisition--of private land for public use, with compensation paid to the landowner. N

emission
Pollution discharged into the atmosphere from smokestacks, other vents, and surface areas of commercial or industrial facilities; from residential chimneys; and from motor vehicle, locomotive, or aircraft exhausts. N

emission factor
The relationship between the amount of pollution produced and the amount of raw material processed. For example, an emission factor for a blast furnace making iron would be the number of pounds of particulates per ton of raw materials. N

emission inventory
A listing, by source, of the amount of air pollutants discharged into the atmosphere of a community. It is used to establish emission standards. N

emission limitation
A requirement established by a State, local government, or the Administrator which limits the quantity, rate, or concentration of emissions of air pollutants on a continuous basis, including any requirements which limit the level of opacity, prescribe equipment, set fuel specifications, or prescribe operation or maintenance procedures for a source to assure continuous emission reduction. A

emission measurement system
All of the equipment necessary to transport and measure the level of emissions. This includes the sample system and the instrumentation system. A

emission outlet pathlength
The depth of effluent at the location emissions are released to the atmosphere. A

emission rate
The amount of pollutant emitted per unit of time.

emission short test
Any test prescribed under 40 CFR 85.2201 et seq., and meeting all of the requirements thereunder. A

emission standard
(1) The maximum amount of a pollutant that is permitted to be discharged from a single polluting source; e.g., the number of pounds of fly ash per cubic foot of air that may be emitted from a coal-fired boiler. (2) The maximum amount of air polluting discharge legally allowed from a single source, mobile or stationary. N

emission-critical parameters
Those critical parameters and tolerances which, if equivalent from one part to another, will not cause the vehicle to exceed applicable emission standards with such parts installed. A

emission-related maintenance
That maintenance which does substantially affect emissions or which is likely to affect the deterioration of the vehicle or engine with respect to

emissions, even if the maintenance is performed at some time other than that which is recommended. A

emission-related standards
Those critical parameters and tolerances which, if equivalent from one part to another, will not cause the vehicle to exceed applicable emission standards with such parts installed. A

emissions trading
EPA policy that allows a plant complex with several facilities to decrease pollution from some facilities while increasing it from others, so long as total results are equal to or better than previous limits. Facilities where this is done are treated as if they exist in a bubble in which total emissions are averaged out. Complexes that reduce emissions substantially may "bank" their "credits" or sell them to other industries. N

emissions unit
Any part of a stationary source which emits or would have the potential to emit any pollutant subject to regulation under the Clean Air Act. A

employee
An employee of an employer who is employed in a business of that employer which affects commerce. O

employer
A person engaged in a business affecting commerce who has employees, but does not include the United States or any State or political subdivision of a State. H

EMS
Enforcement Management System under NPDES program. D

EMTS
Exposure Monitoring Test Site. N

emulsified asphalts
Asphalts dispersed in water with an emulsifying agent. A

emulsion
A mechanical mixture of two liquids which do not naturally mix as oil and water. Water-in-oil emulsions have the water as the internal phase and oil as the external. Oil-in-water emulsions have water as the external phase and the internal phase is oil. A

encapsulate
To seal a pesticide, and its container if appropriate, in an impervious container made of plastic, glass, or other suitable material which will not be chemically degraded by the contents. This container then should be sealed within a durable container made from steel, plastic, concrete, or other suitable material of sufficient thickness and strength to resist physical damage during and subsequent to burial or storage. A

encapsulation
The treatment of ACBM with a material that surrounds or embeds asbestos fibers in an adhesive matrix to prevent the release of fibers, as the encapsulant creates a membrane over the surface (bridging encapsulant) or penetrates the material and binds its components together (penetrating encapsulant). A

enclosed
Surrounded by a case, cage, or fence, which will protect the contained equipment and prevent accidental contact of a person with live parts. O

end use product
A pesticide product whose labeling (1) includes directions for use of the product (as distributed or sold, or after combination by the user with other substances) for controlling pests or defoliating, desiccating, or regulating the growth of plants, and (2) Does not state that the product may be used to manufacture or formulate other pesticide products. A

endangered species
Animals, birds, fish, plants, or other living organisms threatened with extinction by man-made or natural changes in their environment. Requirements for declaring a species endangered are contained in the Endangered Species Act. N

endangerment assessment
(1) A site-specific risk assessment of the actual or potential danger to human health or welfare and the environment from the release of hazardous substances or waste. The endangerment assessment document is prepared in support of enforcement actions under CERCLA or RCRA. N (2) A study conducted to determine the nature and extent of contamination at a site on the National Priorities List and the risks posed to public health of the environment. EPA or the state conduct the study when a legal action is to be taken to direct potentially responsible parties to clean up a site or pay for the cleanup. An endangerment assessment supplements a remedial investigation. N

endpoint
A biological effect used as an index of the effect of a chemical on an organism. N

energy
The capacity to do work. It may take a number of forms, among them mechanical, chemical, and radiant, and can be transformed from one form to another, but cannot be created or destroyed.

energy average level
A quantity calculated by taking ten times the common logarithm of the arithmetic average of the antilogs of one-tenth of each of the levels being averaged. The levels may be of any consistent type, e.g. maximum sound levels, sound exposure levels, and day-night sound levels. A

energy storage device
A rechargeble means of storing tractive energy on board a vehicle such as storage batteries or a flywheel. A

energy summation of levels
A quantity calculated by taking ten times the common logarithm of the sum of the antilogs of one-tenth of each of the levels being summed. The levels may be of any consistent type, e.g., day-night sound level or equivalent sound level. A

enforceable requirements of the Act

Those conditions or limitations of section 402 or 404 [FWPCA] permits which, if violated, could result in the issuance of a compliance order or initiation of a civil or criminal action under section 309 of the Act. If a permit has not been issued, the term shall include any requirement which, in the Regional Administrator's judgment, would be included in the permit when issued. Where no permit applies, the term shall include any requirement which the Regional Administrator determines is necessary to meet applicable criteria for best practicable waste treatment technology (BPWTT). A

enforcement

EPA, state, or local legal actions to obtain compliance with environmental laws, rules, regulations, or agreements and/or obtain penalties or criminal sanctions for violations. Enforcement procedures may vary, depending on the specific requirements of different environmental laws and related implementing regulatory requirements. Under CERCLA, for example, EPA will seek to require potentially responsible parties to clean up a Superfund site, or pay for the cleanup, whereas under the Clean Air Act the agency may invoke sanctions against cities failing to meet ambient air quality standards that could prevent certain types of construction or federal funding. In other situations, if investigations by EPA and state agencies uncover willful violations, criminal trials and penalties are sought. N

Enforcement Decision Document

EDD. A document that provides an explanation to the public of EPA's selection of the cleanup alternative at enforcement sites on the National Priorities List. Similar to a Record of Decision. N

Enforcement Division Director

One of the Directors of the Enforcement Divisions within the Regional offices of the Environmental Protection Agency or the designated representative of the Enforcement Division Director. A

engine code

A unique combination, within an engine-system combination (as defined in Part 86), of displacement, carburetor (or fuel injection) calibration, distributor calibration, choke calibration, auxiliary emission control devices and other engine and emission control system components specified by the Administrator of EPA. A

engine configuration

A subclassification of an engine-system combination on the basis of engine code, inertia weight class, transmission type and gear ratios, final drive ratio, and other parameters which may be designated by the Administrator of EPA. A

engine displacement

Volumetric engine capacity as defined in 40 CFR § 205.153. A

engine family

The basic classification unit of a manufacturer's product line used for the purpose of test fleet selection. A

engine family group
A combination of engine families for the purpose of determining a minimum deterioration factor under the Alternative Durability Program. A

engine malfunction
Not operating according to specifications (e.g., those specifications listed in the application for [motor vehicle] certification). A

engine sidescreen
A rugged screen that fits on the engine housing of a vehicle used at a sanitary landfill to prevent paper and other objects from accumulating and damaging the engine.

engine-system combination
An engine family-exhaust emission control system combination. A

engineered storage
This disposal method is considered a last alternative for those wastes for which no adequate disposal methods exist (particularly radioactive wastes). A facility would temporarily store harmful substances until a permanent disposal site is developed. Engineered storage facilities must provide safe keeping for solidified hazardous wates for long periods of time and the wastes must be retrievable at any point in time. This method is being proposed as an option for long term storage of high-level radioactive wastes.

enrichment
The addition of nutrients (e.g., nitrogen, phosphorous, carbon compounds) from sewage effluent or agricultural runoff to surface water. This process greatly increases the growth potential for algae and aquatic plants. N

environment
(1) Water, air, land, and all plants and man and other animals living therein, and the interrelationships which exist among these. C (2) (a) The navigable waters, the waters of the contiguous zone, and the ocean waters of which the natural resources are under the exclusive management authority of the United States under the Fishery Conservation and Management Act of 1976, and (b) any other surface water, ground water, drinking water supply, land surface or subsurface strata, or ambient air within the United States or under the jurisdiction of the United States. L (3) The sum of all external conditions affecting the life, development and survival of an organism. N

environmental assessment
(1) A written environmental analysis which is prepared pursuant to the National Environmental Policy Act to determine whether a federal action would significantly affect the environment and thus require preparation of a more detailed environmental impact statement. N (2) A concise public document for which a Federal agency is responsible that serves to: (a) Briefly provide sufficient evidence and analysis for determining whether to prepare an environmental impact statement or a finding of no significant impact. (b) Aid an agency's compliance with the Act when no environmental impact statement is necessary.

(c) Facilitate preparation of a statement when one is necessary. (3) Shall include brief discussions of the need for the proposal, of alternatives as required by sec. 102(2)(E) of NEPA, of the environmental impacts of the proposed action and alternatives, and a listing of agencies and persons consulted. A

environmental audit
(1) An independent assessment of the current status of a company's compliance with applicable environmental requirements. (2) An independent evaluation of a company's environmental compliance policies, practices, and controls. N

environmental fate
The destiny of a chemical after release to the environment; involves considerations such as transport through air, soil and water, bioconcentration, degradation, etc. N

environmental impact appraisal
An environmental review supporting a negative declaration [i.e., the action is not a major Federal action significantly affecting the environment]. It describes a proposed EPA action, its expected environmental impact, and the basis for the conclusion that no significant impact is anticipated [and no NEPA Statement is required]. A

environmental impact statement
EIS. A document required of federal agencies by the National Environmental Policy Act for major projects or legislative proposals significantly affecting the environment. A tool for decision making, it describes the positive and negative effects of the undertaking and lists alternative actions. N

environmental impact assessment
EIA. The report, prepared by the applicant for an NPDES permit to discharge as a new source, which identifies and analyzes the environmental impacts of the applicant's proposed source and feasible alternatives.

environmental information document
Any written analysis prepared by an applicant, grantee or contractor describing the environmental impacts of a proposed action. This document will be of sufficient scope to enable the responsible official to prepare an environmental assessment as described in the remaining subparts of this regulation. A

environmental noise
The intensity, duration, and the character of sounds from all sources. A

Environmental Protection Agency
EPA. An independent agency of the Federal government formed in 1970 and responsible for pollution abatement and control programs, including programs in air and water pollution control, water supply and radiation protection, solid and toxic waste management, pesticides control, and noise abatement.

environmental response team
EPA experts located in Edison, NJ, and Cincinnati, OH, who can provide around-the-clock technical assistance to EPA regional offices and states

during all types of emergencies involving hazardous waste sites and spills of hazardous substances. N

environmental review

A formal evaluation undertaken by EPA to determine whether a proposed EPA action may have a significant impact on the environment. The environmental assessment is one of the major sources of information used in this review. A

environmental transformation product

Any chemical substance resulting from the action of environmental processes on a parent compound that changes the molecular identity of the parent compound. A

environmentally sensitive areas

Areas having beneficial qualities or termed "natural assets" by the Environmental Protection Agency, which include wetlands, floodplains, permafrost areas, critical habitats of endangered species, and recharge zones of sole-source aquifers.

enzyme

Any of numerous substances produced by living cells that affect or bring about chemical changes in the body without being changed themselves.

E.O.

Executive Order. A Presidential directive to executive agencies that is promulgated under Constitutional or statutory authority. For certain E.O.'s, independent agencies may voluntarily comply. E.O.'s are published in the Federal Register and in Title 3 of the Code of Federal Regulations.

EP

(1) Extraction Procedure. (2) End point.

EPA

The U.S. Environmental Protection Agency, established in 1970 by Presidential Executive Order, bringing together parts of various government agencies involved with the control of pollution. N

EPA enforcement officer

Any officer or employee of the Environmental Protection Agency so designated in writing by the Administrator (or by his designee). A

EPA identification number

The number assigned by EPA to each generator, transporter, and treatment, storage, or disposal facility. A

EPA legal office

The EPA General Counsel and any EPA office over which the General Counsel exercises supervisory authority, including the various Offices of Regional Counsel. A

EPA record

Any document, writing, photograph, sound or magnetic recording, drawing, or other similar thing by which information has been preserved, from which the information can be retrieved and copied, and which is, was, or is alleged to be possessed by EPA and used to support an EPA decision or action. The term includes informal writings (such as handwritten notes, drafts, and the like), and also includes information preserved in a form which must be translated or deciphered by machine in order to be intelligible to humans. The term includes documents and the like which were created or acquired by EPA, its predecessors, its officers, and employees by use of Government funds or in the course of transacting official business. However, the term does not include materials which are legally owned by an EPA officer or employee in his or her purely personal capacity. Nor does the term include materials published by non-Federal organizations which are readily available to the public, such as books, journals, and periodicals available through reference libraries, even if such materials are in EPA's possession.

EPA region
The states and territories found in any one of the following ten regions:

Region I-Maine, Vermont, New Hampshire, Massachusetts, Connecticut, and Rhode Island.

Region II - New York, New Jersey, Commonwealth of Puerto Rico, and the U.S. Virgin Islands.

Region III - Pennsylvania, Delaware, Maryland, West Virginia, Virginia, and the District of Columbia.

Region IV - Kentucky, Tennessee, North Carolina, Mississippi, Alabama, Georgia, South Carolina, and Florida.

Region V - Minnesota, Wisconsin, Illinois, Michigan, Indiana, and Ohio.

Region VI - New Mexico, Oklahoma, Arkansas, Louisiana, and Texas.

Region VII - Nebraska, Kansas, Missouri, and Iowa.

Region VIII - Montana, Wyoming, North Dakota, South Dakota, Utah, and Colorado.

Region IX - California, Nevada, Arizona, Hawaii, Guam, American Samoa, Commonwalth of the Northern Mariana Islands.

Region X - Washington, Oregon, Idaho, and Alaska. N

EPA share
That portion of allowable project costs provided by EPA under EPA grant programs. A

EPA-approved emission test
Any test prescribed under 40 CRF§ 85.2201 et seq., and meeting all of the requirements thereunder. A

epidemic
Widespread outbreak of a disease, or a large number of cases of a disease in a single community or relatively small area. N

epidemiology
The study of diseases as they affect population, including the distribution of disease, or other health-related states and events in human populations, the factors (e.g. age, sex, occupation, economic status) that influence this distribution, and the application of this study to control health problems. N

episode (pollution)
An air pollution incident in a given

area caused by a concentration of atmospheric pollution reacting with meteorological conditions that may result in a significant increase in illnesses or deaths. Although most commonly used in relation to air pollution, the term may also be used in connection with other kinds of environmental events such as a massive water pollution situation. N

epithelial cells
Cells that make up the tissue--epithelium--covering the skin and various organs and cavities of the body.

EPR
Engine Pressure Ratio.

EPTC
Extraction Procedure Toxicity Characteristic Test. N

eq.
Equivalent.

equilibrium
In relation to radiation, the state at which the radioactivity of consecutive elements within a radioactive series is neither increasing nor decreasing. N

equipment
This is a general term which includes fittings, devices, appliances, fixtures, apparatus, and the like, used as part of, or in connection with, a system or systems. O

equivalence data
Chemical data or biological test data intended to show that two substances or mixtures are equivalent. A

equivalent method
Any method of sampling and analyzing for pollution which has been demonstrated to the EPA Administrator's satisfaction to be, under specific conditions, an acceptable alternative to the normally used reference methods. N

equivalent petroleum-based fuel economy value
A number which represents the average number of miles traveled by an electric vehicle per gallon of gasoline. A

equivalent sound level
The level, in decibels, of the mean-square A-weighted sound pressure during a stated time period, with reference to the square of the standard reference sound pressure of 20 micropascals. It is the level of the sound exposure divided by the time period and is abbreviated as L_{eq}. A

ERA
(1) Economic Regulatory Administration of the U.S. Department of Energy. (2) Expedited Response Action. N

erase stack
An expanding connection on the outlet of a fan or in an airflow passage to convert kinetic energy into static pressure.

erosion
The wearing away of land surface by wind or water. Erosion occurs naturally from weather or runoff but can be intensified by land-clearing practices related to farming, residential or

industrial development, road building, or timber-cutting. N

ERP
Enforcement Response Policy, at EPA, aimed at high priority violators under RCRA.

ERT
Environmental Response Team.

ESP
Electrostatic Precipitator.

established federal standard
Any operative occupational safety and health standard established by any agency of the United States and presently in effect, or contained in any Act of Congress in force on the date of enactment of [OSHA]. H

establishment
(1) Each site where a pesticide, as defined by FIFRA, or a device is produced, regardless of whether such site is independently owned or operated and regardless of whether such site is domestic and producing any pesticide or device for export only or whether the site is foreign and producing any pesticide or device for import into the United States. A (2) Any place where a pesticide or device or active ingredient used in producing a pesticide is produced, or held, for distribution or sale. C

estuarine zones
An environmental system consisting of an estuary and those transitional areas which are consistently influenced or affected by water from an estuary such as, but not limited to, salt marshes, coastal and intertidal areas, bays, harbors, lagoons, inshore waters, and channels, and the term "estuary" means all or part of the mouth of a river or stream or other body of water having unimpaired natural connection with open sea and within which the sea water is measurably diluted.

estuary
Region of interaction between rivers and nearshore ocean waters, where tidal action and river flow create a mixing of fresh and salt water. These areas may include bays, mouths of rivers, salt marshes, and lagoons. These brackish water ecosystems shelter and feed marine life, birds, and wildlife. (See: wetlands). N

Ethylene Dibromide
EDB. A chemical used as an agricultural fumigant and in certain industrial processes. Extremely toxic and found to be a carcinogen in laboratory animals. EDB has been banned for most agricultural uses in the United States. N

etiology
All of the factors that contribute to the cause of a disease or an abnormal condition; a branch of medical science concerned with the causes and origins of disease. N

eutrophic lakes
(1) Shallow, murky bodies of water that have excessive concentrations of plant nutrients causing excessive algal production. (See: dystrophic lakes). N (2) A lake that exhibits any of the following characteristics: (a) Excessive biomass accumulations of primary pro-

ducers; (b) rapid organic and/or inorganic sedimentation and shallowing; or (c) seasonal and/or diurnal dissolved oxygen deficiencies that may cause obnoxious odors, fish kills, or a shift in the composition of aquatic fauna to less desirable forms. A

eutrophication
The slow aging process during which a lake, estuary, or bay evolves into a bog or marsh and eventually disappears. During the later stages of eutrophication the water body is choked by abundant plant life as the result of increased amounts of nutritive compounds such as nitrogen and phosphorus. Human activities that add nutrients to a water body can accelerate the process. N

evap.
Evaporative.

evaporation
The physical transformation of a liquid to a gas at any temperature below its boiling point.

evaporation ponds
Areas where sewage sludge or other wastes are dumped and allowed to dry out. N

evaporation rate
The rate at which a material will vaporize (evaporate) when compared to the known rate of vaporization of a standard material. The evaporation rate can be useful in evaluating the health and fire hazards of a material. The designated standard material is usually normal butyl acetate (NBUAC or n-BuAc), with a vaporization rate

designated as 1.0. Vaporization rates of other solvents or materials are then classified as:

- FAST evaporating if greater than 3.0. Examples: Methyl Ethyl Ketone = 3.8, Acetone = 5.6, Hexane = 8.3.

- MEDIUM evaporating if 0.8 to 3.0 Examples: 190 proof (95%) Ethyl Alcohol = 1.4, VM&P Naphtha = 1.4, MIBK = 1.6.

- SLOW evaporating if less than 0.8. Examples: Xylene = 0.6, Isobutyl Alcohol = 0.6, Normal Butyl Alcohol = 0.4, Water = 0.3, Mineral Spirits = 0.1. N

evaporative emission code
A unique combination in an evaporative emission family on a vehicle--evaporative emission control system combination, of purge system calibrations, fuel tank and carburetor bowl vent calibrations and other fuel system and evaporative emission control system components and calibrations specified by the Administrator of EPA. A

evaporative emissions
Hydrocarbons emitted into the atmosphere from a motor vehicle, other than exhaust and crankcase emissions. A

evapotranspiration
The loss of water from the soil both by evaporation and by transpiration from the plants growing in the soil. N

exceedance
Violation of environmental protec-

tion standards by exceeding allowable limits or concentration levels. N

excess combustion air
The quantity of air in excess of theoretical air, and usually expressed as a percentage of the theoretical air.

excess emissions
An [air pollutant] emission rate which exceeds any applicable emission limitation. The averaging time and test procedures for determining such excess emissions shall be as specified as part of the applicable emission limitation. A

excessive concentrations
For the purpose of determining good engineering practice stack height in a fluid model or field study, a maximum concentration due to downwash wakes, or eddy effects produced by structures or terrain features which is at least 40 percent in excess of the maximum concentration experienced in the absence of such downwash, wakes or eddy effects. A

excessive infiltration/inflow
The quantities of infiltration/inflow which can be economically eliminated from a sewer system as determined in a cost-effectiveness analysis that compares the costs for correcting the infiltration/inflow conditions to the total costs for transportation and treatment of the infiltration/inflow. A

exclusionary
Any form of zoning ordinance that tends to exclude specific classes of persons or businesses from a particular district or area. N

exclusive bus lane
A lane on a street or highway for the exclusive use of buses, whether constructed especially for that purpose or converted from an existing lane. A

exclusive use study
A study that meets each of the following requirements: (1) The study pertains to a new active ingredient (new chemical) or new combination of active ingredients (new combination) first registered after September 30, 1978; (2) The study was submitted in support of, or as a condition of approval of, the application resulting in the first registration of a product containing such new chemical or new combination (first registration), or an application to amend such registration to add a new use; and (3) The study was not submitted to satisfy a data requirement imposed under FIFRA section 3(c)(2)(B); Provided that, a study is an exclusive study only during the 10-year period following the date of the first registration. A

exempt solvent
Specific organic compounds that are not subject to requirements of regulation because they have been deemed by EPA to be of negligible photochemical reactivity. N

exempted aquifer
Underground bodies of water defined in the Underground Injection Control program as aquifers that are sources of drinking water (although they are not being used as such) and that are exempted from regulations barring underground injection activities. N

exemption category

A category of chemical substances for which a person(s) has applied for or been granted an exemption under section 5(h)(4) of the Toxic Substances Control Act. A

exemption certification

A certified statement delineating those actions specifically exempted from NEPA compliance by existing legislation. A

exhaust emissions

Substances emitted to the atmosphere from any opening downstream from the exhaust port of a motor vehicle engine. A

exhaust gas recirculation-air bleed

EGR. A system or device (such as modification of the engine's carburetor or positive crankcase ventilation system) that results in engine operation at an increased air-fuel ratio so as to achieve reductions in exhaust emissions of hydrocarbons and carbon monoxide. A

exhaust system

The system comprised of a combination of components which provides for enclosed flow of exhaust gas from engine exhaust port to the atmosphere. A

existing facility

With reference to a stationary source, any apparatus of the type for which a new source performance standard is promulgated and the construction or modification of which was commenced before the date of proposal of that standard; or any apparatus

which could be altered in such a way as to be of that type. A

existing hazardous waste management (HWM) facility (existing facility)

A facility which was in operation or for which construction commenced on or before November 19, 1980. A facility has commenced construction if: (1) The owner or operator has obtained the Federal, State and local approvals or permits necessary to begin physical construction; and either (2)(i) A continuous on-site, physical construction program has begun; or (ii) The owner or operator has entered into contractual obligations--which cannot be cancelled or modified without substantial loss--for physical construction of the facility to be completed within a reasonable time. A

existing injection well

An injection well other than a new injection well. N

existing source

Any stationary source which is not a new source. A

existing vessel

Includes every description of watercraft or other artificial contrivance used, or capable of being used, as a means of transportation on the navigable waters, the construction of which is initiated before promulgation of standards and regulations under [§ 312 of FWPCA]. D

expedited hearing

A hearing commenced as the result of the issuance of a notice of intention to suspend or the suspension of a registration of a pesticide by an emergency order, and is limited to a consideration as to whether a pesticide presents an imminent hazard which justifies such suspension. A

expendable personal property
Expendable personal property refers to all tangible personal property (including consumable materials) other than nonexpendable personal property. A

experimental animals
Individual animals or groups of animals, regardless of species, intended for use and used solely for research purposes and does not include animals intended to be used for any food purposes. A

experimental use permit review
Review of an application for a permit pursuant to section 5 of FIFRA to apply a limited quantity of a pesticide in order to accumulate information necessary to register the pesticide. The application may be for a new chemical or for a new use of an old chemical. The fee applies to such experimental uses of a single unregistered active ingredient (no limit on the number of other active ingredients, in a tank mix, already registered for the crops involved) and no more than three crops. This fee does not apply to experimental use permits required for small-scale field testing of microbial pest control agents (40 CFR 172.3). A

expiratory (maximum) flow rate
The maximum rate at which air can be expelled from the lungs.

export exemption
An exemption from the prohibitions of Section 10(a)(3) and (4) of FIFRA; this type of exemption is granted by statute under Section 10(b)(2) of FIFRA for the purpose of exporting regulated products. A

exporter
The person who, as the principal party in interest in the export transaction, has the power and responsibility for determining and controlling the sending of the chemical substance or mixture to a destination out of the customs territory of the United States. A

exposure
Contact with a chemical or physical agent. N (2) The amount of radiation or pollutant present in an environment which represents a potential health threat to the living organisms in that environment. N

exposure assessment
The determination or estimation (qualitative or quantitative) of the magnitude, frequency, duration, route, and extent (number of people) of exposure to a chemical. N

external radiation
Radiation from a source outside the body.

extinguishing media
The fire fighting substance to be used to control a material in the event of a fire. It is usually named by its generic name, such as fog, foam, water, etc. N

extraction test procedure
A series of laboratory operations and analyses designed to determine whether, under severe conditions, a solid waste, stabilized waste or landfilled material can yield a hazardous leachate.

extrapolation
Estimation of unknown values by extending or projecting from known values. N

extremely hazardous substances
Any of 406 chemicals identified by EPA on the basis of toxicity, and listed under SARA Title III. The list is subject to revision. N

extrusion
The application of pressure to a billet of metal, forcing the metal to flow through a die orifice. A

F

F
Fahrenheit.

FAA
Federal Aviation Administration.

fabric filter
A cloth device that catches dust and particles from industrial emissions. N

facilities plan
A preliminary plan prepared as the basis for construction of publicly owned waste treatment works under Title II of FWPCA, as amended. A

facility
(1) An identifiable piece of process equipment. A source is composed of one or more [air] pollutant-emitting facilities. A (2) (a) Any building, structure, installation, equipment, pipe or pipeline (including any pipe into a sewer or publicly owned treatment works), well, pit, pond, lagoon, impoundment, ditch, landfill, storage container, motor vehicle, rolling stock, or aircraft, or (b) any site or area where a hazardous substance has been deposited, stored, disposed of, or placed, or otherwise come to be located; but does not include any consumer product in consumer use or any vessel. L (3) Any HWM facility, UIC underground injection well, NPDES point source, PSD stationary source, or any other facility or activity (including land or appurtenances thereto) that is subject to regulation under the RCRA, UIC, NPDES, or PSD programs. N

facultative bacteria
Those bacteria able to live and grow under more than one set of conditions, with or without oxygen.

facultative species
Species that can occur both in wetlands and uplands; there are three subcategories of facultative species: (1) Facultative Wetland Plants (FACW) that usually occur in wetlands (estimated probability 67-99%), but occasionally are found in nonwetlands, (2) Facultative Plants (FAC) that are equally likely to occur in wetlands or nonwetlands (estimated probability 34-66%), and (3) Facultative Upland Plants (FACU) that usually occur in

nonwetlands (estimated probability 67-99%); occasionally are found in wetlands (estimated probability 1-33%). N

failing vehicle
The measured emissions of the vehicle, when measured in accordance with the applicable procedure, exceeds the applicable standard. A

fair market value
The price at which property would change hands between a willing buyer and a willing seller, neither being under any compulsion to buy or to sell and both having reasonable knowledge or relevant facts. O

fall time
The time interval between initial response and 95 percent of final response after a step decrease in input concentration. A

family NO$_x$ emission limit
The NO$_x$ emission level to which an engine family is certified in the light-duty truck NO$_x$ averaging program, expressed to one-tenth of a gram per mile accuracy. A

farm field equipment
Tractors or implements, including self-propelled implements, or any combination thereof used in agricultural operations. O

fast meter response
The "fast" response of the sound level meter shall be used. The fast dynamic response shall comply with the meter dynamic characteristics in paragraph 5.3 of the American National Standard Specification for Sound Level

Meters. ANSI S1.4-1971. This publication is available from the American National Standards Institute, Inc., 1430 Broadway, New York, New York 10018. A

fault
A surface or zone of rock fracture along which there has been displacement. A

fault-tree analysis
A means of analyzing hazards. Hazardous events are first identified by other techniques such as HAZOP. Then all combinations of individual failures that can lead to that hazardous event are shown in the logical format of the fault tree. By estimating the individual failure probabilities, and then using the appropriate arithmetical expressions, the top-event frequency can be calculated. N

FCC
Federal Communications Commission.

FCs
(1) Fluorocarbons. A gas used as a propellant in aerosols, thought to be modifying the ozone layer in the stratosphere thereby allowing more harmful solar radiation to reach the Earth's surface. N (2) Any of a number of organic compounds analogous to hydrocarbons in which one or more hydrogen atoms are replaced by flourine. Once used in the United States as a propellant in aerosols, they are now primarily used in coolants and some industrial processes. FCs containing chlorine are

called chlorofluorocarbons (CFCs). They are believed to be modifying the ozone layer in the stratosphere, thereby allowing more harmful solar radiation to reach the Earth's surface. **N**

FD&CA
Food, Drug and Cosmetic Act.

FDA
Food and Drug Administration. **N**

FDAA
Federal Disaster Assistance Administration.

FDF
Fundamentally Different Factors. **N**

FE
Fugitive Emissions. **N**

feasibility study
(1) A process undertaken by the lead agency (or responsible party if the responsible party will be developing a cleanup proposal) for developing, evaluating, and selecting remedial actions which emphasizes data analysis. The feasibility study is generally performed concurrently and in an interdependent fashion with the remedial investigation. In certain situations, the lead agency may require potentially responsible parties to conclude initial phases of the remedial investigation prior to initiation of the feasibility study. The feasibility study process uses data gathered during the remedial investigation. These data are used to define the objectives of the response action and to broadly develop remedial action alternatives. Next, an

initial screening of these alternatives is required to reduce the number of alternatives to a workable number. Finally, the feasibility study involves a detailed analysis of a limited number of alternatives which remain after the initial screening stage. The factors that are considered in screening and analyzing the alternatives are public health, economics, engineering practicality, environmental impacts, and institution issues. **A** (2) Analysis of the practicability of a proposal; e.g., a description and analysis of the potential cleanup alternatives for a site or alternatives for a site on the National Priorities List. The feasibility study usually recommends selection of a cost-effective alternative. It usually starts as soon as the remedial investigation is underway; together, they are commonly referred to as the "RI/FS." The term can apply to a variety of proposed corrective or regulatory actions. (3) In research, a small-scale investigation of a problem to ascertain whether or not a proposed research approach is likely to provide useful data. **N**

fecal coliform bacteria
Those organisms associated with the intestines of warm-blooded animals that are commonly used to indicate the presence of fecal material and the potential presence of organisms capable of causing human disease. **A**

federal agency
(1) Any department, agency, or other instrumentality of the federal government, and any independent agency or establishment of the federal

government including any government corporation and the Government Printing Office. A, I, J (2) All agencies of the Federal Government. It does not mean the Congress, the Judiciary, or the President, including the performance of staff functions for the President in his Executive Office. It also includes, for purposes of these regulations, States and units of general local government and Indian tribes assuming NEPA responsibilities under section 104(h) of the Housing and Community Development Act of 1974. A

federal assistance
The entire Federal contribution to a project, including, but not limited to, the EPA grant amount.

federal delayed compliance order
A delayed compliance order issued by the administrator under section 113(d) (1), (3), (4) or (5) of the Act. O

federal emission test procedure
The dynamometer driving schedule, dynamometer procedure, and sampling and analytical procedures described in [40 CFR] Part 86 for the respective model year, which are used to derive city fuel economy data. A

Federal Environmental Impact Statement
FEIS. The document prepared by a Federal agency or department or under Federal guidance which identifies and analyzes in detail the environmental impacts of a proposed Federal action and incorporates comments made on the draft EIS. A

federal facility
Any building, installation, structure, land, or public work owned by or leased to the Federal Government. A

federal financial assistance
Any financial benefits provided directly as aid to a project by a department, agency, or instrumentality of the Federal government in any form including contracts, grants, and loan guarantees. Actions or programs carried out by the Federal government itself such as dredging performed by the Army Corps of Engineers do not involve Federal financial assistance. Actions performed for the Federal government by contractors, such as construction of roads on Federal lands by a contractor under the supervision of the Bureau of Land Management, should be distinguished from contracts entered into specifically for the purpose of providing financial assistance, and will not be considered programs or actions receiving Federal financial assistance. Federal financial assistance is limited to benefits earmarked for a specific program or action and directly awarded to the program or action. Indirect assistance, e.g., in the form of a loan to a developer by a lending institution which in turn receives Federal assistance not specifically related to the project in question is not Federal financial assistance.

federal highway fuel economy test procedure
The dynamometer driving schedule, dynamometer procedure, and sampling and analytical procedures used to derive highway fuel economy data.

Federal Implementation Plan

FIP. A plan developed by EPA pursuant to §110(c) of the Clean Air Act and imposed on a State that fails to produce its own plan to comply with the Act by a certain date. N

federal land manager

With respect to any lands in the United States, the Secretary of the department with authority over such lands. A

Federal Register

A daily federal government publication that announces all proposed and final federal regulations. It also contains notices of public meetings and other events the agency may schedule. Most major libraries carry the Federal Register. A

federal, state and local approvals or permits necessary to begin physical construction

Permits and approvals required under federal, state or local hazardous waste control statutes, regulations or ordinances. A

federally assisted construction contract

Any agreement or modification thereof between any applicant and any person for construction work which is paid for in whole or in part with funds obtained from the Agency or borrowed on the credit of the Agency pursuant to any Federal program involving a grant, contract, loan, insurance, or guarantee, or undertaken pursuant to any Federal program involving such grant, contract, loan, insurance, or guarantee, or any application or modification thereof approved by the Agency for a grant, contract, loan, insurance, or guarantee under which the applicant itself participates in the construction work. A

federally enforceable

[For purposes of the Clean Air Act] all limitations and conditions which are enforceable by the Administrator, including requirements developed pursuant to 40 CFR Parts 60 and 61, requirements within any applicable State Implementation Plan, and any permit requirements established pursuant to 40 CFR 52.21 or under regulations approved pursuant to this section, 40 CFR 51.18, or 51.24. A

federally permitted release

(A) Discharges in compliance with a permit under section 402 of the Federal Water Pollution Control Act, (B) discharges resulting from circumstances identified and reviewed and made part of the public record with respect to a permit issued or modified under section 402 of the Federal Water Pollution Control Act and subject to a condition of such permit, (C) continuous or anticipated intermittent discharges from a point source, identified in a permit or permit application under section 402 of the Federal Water Pollution Control Act, which are caused by events occurring within the scope of relevant operating or treatment systems, (D) discharges in compliance with a legally enforceable permit under section 404 of the Federal Water Pollution Control Act, (E) releases in compliance with a legally enforceable final permit issued pursuant to section 3005 (a) through (d) of the Solid Waste Disposal Act from a hazardous waste treatment, storage, or disposal facility when such permit specifically identifies the hazardous substances and makes such substances subject to a standard of practice, control procedure or bioassay limitation or condition, or other control on the hazardous substances in such releases, (F) any release in compliance with a legally enforceable permit issued under section 102 of section 103 of the Marine Protection, Research, and Sanctuaries Act of 1972, (G) any injection of fluids authorized under Federal underground injection control programs or State programs submitted for Federal approval (and not disapproved by the Administrator of the Environmental Protection Agency) pursuant to part C of the Safe Drinking Water Act, (H) any emission into the air subject to a permit or control regulation under section 111, section 112, title I part C, title I part D, or State implementation plans submitted in accordance with section 110 of the Clean Air Act (and not disapproved by the Administrator of the Environmental Protection Agency), including any schedule or waiver granted, promulgated, or approved under these sections, (I) any injection of fluids or other material authorized under applicable State law (i) for the purpose of stimulating or treating wells for the production of crude oil, natural gas, or water, (ii) for the purpose of secondary, tertiary, or other enhanced recovery of crude oil or natural gas, or (iii) which are brought to the surface in conjunction with the production of crude oil or natural gas and which are reinjected, (J) the introduction of any pollutant into a publicly owned treatment works when such pollutant is specified in and in compliance with applicable pretreatment standards of section 307(b) or (c) of the Clean Water Act and enforceable requirements in a pretreatment program submitted by a State or municipality for Federal approval under section 402 of such Act, and (K) any release of source, special nuclear, or byproduct material, as those terms are defined in the Atomic Energy Act of 1954, in compliance with a legally enforceable license, permit, regulation, or order issued pursuant to the Atomic Energy Act of 1954. [ed. Used to create exclusions from the reporting requirements of Superfund]. L

feedlot
A concentrated, confined animal or poultry growing operation for meat, milk or egg production, or stabling, in pens or houses wherein the animals or poultry are fed at the place of confinement and crop or forage growth or production is not sustained in the area of confinement. A

feedlot waste
High concentrations of animal excrement that result from raising large numbers of animals on a relatively small, confined area of land. The soil cannot handle the excessive amounts of excrement, as it does under open-range conditions, so run-off from feedlots contributes excessive quantities of nitrogen, phosphorus, and potassium to nearby waterways.

feedstock
(1) The raw materials supplied to manufacturing or processing plants for use in the production of goods or for treatment, respectively. Waste from one industry may be the feedstock for another industry. (2) The crude oil and natural gas liquids fed to the topping units. A

fen
(1) Low-lying land partly covered with water. N (2) A type of wetland that accumulates peat deposits. Fens are less acidic than bogs, deriving most of their water from groundwater rich in calcium and magnesium. (See: wetlands.) N

FEPCA
Federal Environmental Pesticide Control Act.

FERC
Federal Energy Regulatory Commission.

fermentation
Chemical reactions accompanied by living microbes that are supplied with nutrients and other critical conditions such as heat, pressure, and light that are specific to the reaction at hand. N

ferrofluid systems
A means of separating nonmagnetic materials or immersing them in a ferrofluid held within a magnetic field. The "apparent density" for the ferrofluid thus created causes separation of any two substances differing in density by 5 to 10 percent or more according to a float/sink technique.

ferromanganese silicon
That alloy containing 63 to 66 percent by weight manganese, 28 to 32 percent by weight silicon, and a maximum of 0.08 percent by weight carbon. A

ferrosilicon
That alloy as defined by ASTM Designation A100-69 (Reapproved 1974) (incorporated by reference-see § 60.17) grades A, B, C, D, and E, which contains 50 or more percent by weight silicon. A

ferrous
Describes those metals that are predominantly composed of iron and are most commonly magnetic.

fertilizer
Materials such as nitrogen and phosphorous that provide nutrients for plants. Commercially sold fertilizers may contain other chemicals or may be in the form of processed sewage sludge. N

FGD
Flue Gas Desulfurization. N

FHA
Federal Housing Administration.

FHLBB
Federal Home Loan Bank Board.

FHWA
Federal Highway Administration.

fibrosis
A condition marked by the formation of thread-like tissue.

FID
Flame Ionization Detector. N

field capacity of solid waste
The amount of water retained in solid waste after it has been saturated and has drained freely. Also called moisture-holding capacity.

field testing
Practical and generally small-scale testing of innovative or alternative technologies directed to verifying performance and/or refining design parameters not sufficiently tested to resolve technical uncertainties which prevent the funding of a promising improvement in innovative or alternative treatment technology. A

FIFRA
Federal Insecticide, Fungicide and Rodenticide Act. C

fill material
Any "pollutant" which replaces portions of the "waters of the United States" with dry land or which changes the bottom elevation of a water body for any purpose. A

filling
(1) Depositing dirt and mud, often raised by dredging, into marshy areas to create stable land generally for development. It can destroy the marsh ecology. N (2) Depositing dirt and mud or other materials into aquatic areas to create more dry land, usually for agricultural or commercial development purposes. Such activities often damage the ecology of the area. N

film badge
A piece of masked photographic film worn by nuclear workers to monitor their exposure to radiation. Nuclear radiation darkens the film. N

film wet mixture
A water or organic solvent-based suspension, solution, dispersion, or emulsion used in the manufacture of an instant photographic or peel-apart film article. A

filter
A porous device through which a gas or liquid is passed to remove suspended particles or dust.

filter collector
A mechanical filtration system for removing particulate matter from a gas stream, for measurement, analysis, or control; also called bag collector. Filters are designed in a variety of sizes and materials for specific purposes.

filtration
The physical removal of the solid constituents from aqueous waste streams by means of a filter medium. Most aqueous waste streams that contain solids are treated by this process.

final closure
(1) The measures which must be taken by a facility to render the landfill portion environmentally innocuous when it determines that it will no longer accept waste for treatment, storage, or disposal on the entire facility. (2) The closure of all

hazardous waste management units at the facility in accordance with all applicable closure requirements so that hazardous waste management activities under 40 CFR Parts 264 and 265 are no longer conducted at the facility unless subject to the provisions in § 262.34. A

final cover
Cover material at a landfill that serves the same functions as daily cover but, in addition, may be permanently exposed on the surface. A

Final Environmental Impact Statement
FEIS. The document prepared by a Federal agency or department or under Federal guidance which identifies and analyzes in detail the environmental impacts of a proposed Federal action and incorporates comments made on the draft EIS. A

final order
(a) An order issued by the Administrator after an appeal of an initial decision, accelerated decision, decision to dismiss, or default order, disposing of a matter in controversy between the parties, or (b) an initial decision which becomes a final order. A

final printed labeling
(1) The printed label and the labeling which will appear on or will accompany the pesticide product. A (2) The label or labeling of the product when distributed or sold. Final printed labeling does not include the package of the product, unless the labeling is an integral part of the package. A

finding of no significant impact
A document by a Federal agency briefly presenting the reasons why an action, not otherwise excluded (40 CFR § 1508.4), will not have a significant effect on the human environment and for which an environmental impact statement therefore will not be prepared. It shall include the environmental assessment or a summary of it and shall note any other environmental documents related to it (40 CFR § 1501.7(a)(5)). If the assessment is included, the finding need not repeat any of the discussion in the assessment but may incorporate it by reference. A

FINDS
Facility Index System (OIRM). N

fines
Fine particulates; aerosols.

finish coat operation
The coating application station, curing oven, and quench station used to apply and dry or cure the final coating(s) on the surface of the metal coil. Where only a single coating is applied to the metal coil, that coating is considered a finish coat. A

FIP
Federal Implementation Plan.

FIPS
Federal Information Procedures System. N

FIT
Field Investigation Team. N

fire point
The lowest temperature at which an oil vaporizes rapidly enough to burn for at least 5 seconds after ignition, under standard conditions. A

fire-fighting turbine
Any stationary gas turbine that is used solely to pump water for extinguishing fires. A

firebrick
Refractory brick made from fireclay.

fireclay
A sedimentary clay containing only small amounts of fluxing impurities. It is high in hydrous aluminum silicates and is, therefore, capable of withstanding high temperatures.

first aid
Any one-time treatment, and any followup visit for the purpose of observation, of minor scratches, cuts, burns, splinters, and so forth, which do not ordinarily require medical care. Such one-time treatment, and followup visit for the purpose of observation, is considered first aid even though provided by a physician or registered professional personnel. O

first attempt at repair
Rapid action taken for the purpose of stopping or reducing leakage of organic material to atmosphere using best practices. A

first food use
Refers to the use of a pesticide on a food or in a manner which otherwise would be expected to result in residues in a food, if no permanent

tolerance, exemption from the requirement of a tolerance, or food additive regulation for residues of the pesticide on any food has been established for the pesticide under section 408 (d) or (e) or 409 of the Federal Food, Drug, and Cosmetic Act. A

first-order half-life
t1/2. The time required for the concentration of the chemical to be reduced to one-half its initial value. A

first-order reaction
A reaction in which the rate of disappearance of a chemical is directly proportional to the concentration of the chemical and is not a function of the concentration of any other chemical present in the reaction mixture. A

fiscal year
A budget term. The federal fiscal year runs from October to September 30 as opposed to the calendar year which runs from January 1 to December 31.

fish poisons and repellents
All substances or mixtures of substances intended for destroying, repelling, or mitigating fish declared to be pests under 40 CFR §162.14. Fish poisons and repellents include, but are not limited to: (i) Toxicants intended to kill fish in lakes, ponds, or streams; (ii) Repellents intended to repel species dangerous to man or injurious to aquatic organisms which man wishes to protect; and (iii) Sex influence agents intended to control sexual development of fish, such as to

cause young to develop into all-female populations. A

fission
The splitting of atomic nuclei into smaller nuclei, accompanied by the release of great quantities of energy.

fixed capital cost
The capital needed to provide all the depreciable components. A

fixed carbon
The ash-free carbonaceous material that remains after volatile matter is driven off during the proximate analysis of a dry solid waste sample.

fixed grate
A grate without moving parts; also called a stationary grate. A stationary grate through which no air passes is called a dead plate.

fixed station monitoring
The repeated, long-term sampling or measurement of parameters at representative points for the purpose of determining air or water quality trends and characteristics. A

FL
Full Load.

flammable
A chemical that includes one of the following categories:
(a) Aerosol, flammable. An aerosol that, when tested by the method described in 16 CFR 1500.45, yields a flame projection exceeding 18 inches at full valve opening, or a flashback (a flame extending back to the valve) at any degree of valve opening; (b) Gas, flammable. (1) A gas that, at ambient temperature and pressure, forms a flammable mixture with air at a concentration of 13 percent by volume or less; or (2) A gas that, at ambient temperature and pressure, forms a range of flammable mixtures with air wider than 12 percent by volume, regardless of the lower limit; (c) Liquid, flammable. Any liquid having a flashpoint below 100° F (37.8° C), except any mixture having components with flashpoints of 100° F (37.8° C) or higher, the total of which make up 99 percent or more of the total volume of mixture. (d) Solid, flammable. A solid, other than a blasting agent or explosive as defined in 1910.109(a), that is liable to cause fire through friction, absorption of moisture, spontaneous chemical change, or retained heat from manufacturing or processing, or which can be ignited readily and when ignited burns so vigorously and persistently as to create a serious hazard. A solid is a flammable solid if, when tested by the method described in 16 CFR 1500.44, it ignites and burns with a self-sustained flame at a rate greater than one tenth of an inch per second along its major axis. N

flash drying
The process of drying a wet organic material by passing it through a high temperature zone at such a rate that the water is rapidly evaporated but the organic material, protected by the boiling point of water, is not overheated.

flash point

(1) The minimum temperature at which a liquid gives off a vapor in sufficient concentration to ignite when tested by the following methods: (a) Tagliabue Closed Tester (see American National Standard Method of Test for Flash Point by Tag Closed Tester, Z11.24 1979 [ASTM D56-79]). (b) Pensky-Martens Closed Tester (see American National Standard Method of Test for Flash Point by Pensky-Martens Closed Tester, Z11.7-1979 [ASTM D93-79]). (c) Setaflash Closed Tester (see American National Standard Method of Test for Flash Point by Setaflash Closed Tester [ASTM D 3278-78]). N (2) The minimum temperature at which a liquid or solid gives off sufficient vapor to form an ignitable vapor-air mixture near the surface of the liquid or solid.

flash-off area

The structure on automobile and light-duty truck assembly lines between the coating application system (dip tank or spray booth) and the bake oven. A

flat glass

Glass made of soda-lime recipe and produced into continuous flat sheets and other products listed in SIC 3211. A

fleet vehicle

Any of 5 or more light duty vehicles operated by the same person(s), business, or governmental entity and used principally in connection with the same or related occupations or uses. This definition shall also include any taxicab (or other light duty vehicle-for-hire) owned by any individual or business. A

flight conveyor

A drag conveyor that uses rollers interspersed in its pull chains to reduce friction.

floating roof

A storage vessel cover consisting of a double deck, pontoon single deck, internal floating cover or covered floating roof, which rests upon and is supported by the petroleum liquid being contained, and is equipped with a closure seal or seals to close the space between the roof edge and tank wall. A

floc

A clump of solids formed in sewage by biological or chemical action. N

flocculation

Separation of suspended solids during waste water treatment by chemical creation of clumps of flocs. N

floor sweep

A vapor collection designed to capture vapors which are heavier than air and which collect along the floor. N

flotation

The rising of suspended matter to the surface of the liquid in a tank as scum by aeration, the evolution of gas, chemicals, electrolysis, heat, or bacterial decomposition and the subsequent removal of the scum by skimming.

flow coating

A method of applying coatings in which the part is carried through a chamber containing numerous nozzles which direct unatomized streams of coatings from many different angles onto the surface of the part. A

flow rate

The volume per time unit given to the flow of gases or other fluid substance which emerges from an orifice, pump, turbine or passes along a conduit or channel. A

flow through

Refers to the continuous or very frequent passage of fresh test solution through a test chamber with no recycling. A

flowmeter

(1) A gauge that shows the speed of waste water moving through a treatment plant. N (2) Also used to measure the speed of liquids moving through various industrial processes. N

FLPMA

Federal Land Policy and Management Act. N

flue

Any passage designed to carry combustion gases and entrained particulates.

flue dust

Solid particles (smaller than 100 microns) carried in the products of combustion.

flue gas desulfurization

Any pollution control process which treats stationary source combustion flue gas to remove sulfur oxides. A

flue gas scrubber

A type of equipment that removes fly ash or other objectionable materials from flue gas by using sprays, wet baffles, or other means that require water as the primary separation mechanism. Also called flue gas washer, gas scrubber, and gas washer. B

flue gas

The air and pollutants emitted to the atmosphere after a production process or combustion takes place; al-so called stack gas.

flue-fed incinerator

An incinerator that is charged through a shaft that functions as a chute for charging waste and has a flue to carry the products of combustion.

fluid

Any material or substance which flows or moves whether in a semisolid, liquid, sludge, gas, or any other form or state. A

fluidized bed technique

A combustion process in which heat is transferred from finely divided particles, such as sand, to combustible materials in a fluid bed incinerator. In one such incinerator, combustion is confined within a bed of waste and sand that is fluidized by an upward-controlled flow of air with enough velocity to float some of the solids. Volatile gases are collected above the bed.

fluidized-bed combustion
The burning of pulverized coal kept in motion by a current of air so that the mass appears to be boiling.

flume
A natural or man-made channel that diverts water. N

fluorescent light ballast
A device which electrically controls fluorescent light fixtures and includes a capacitor containing 0.1 kg or less of dielectric. A

fluorides
Gaseous, solid, or dissolved compounds containing fluorine that result from industrial processes. N

fluorocarbons
(1) FCs. A gas used as a propellant in aerosols, thought to be modifying the ozone layer in the stratosphere thereby allowing more harmful solar radiation to reach the Earth's surface. N (2) Any of a number of organic compounds analogous to hydrocarbons in which one or more hydrogen atoms are replaced by flourine. Once used in the United States as a propellant in aerosols, they are now primarily used in coolants and some industrial processes. FCs containing chlorine are called chlorofluorocarbons (CFCs). They are believed to be modifying the ozone layer in the stratosphere, thereby allowing more harmful solar radiation to reach the Earth's surface. N

fluorosis
An abnormal condition caused by excessive intake of fluorine,

characterized chiefly by mottling of the teeth. N

flush
(1) To open a cold-water tap to clear out all the water which may have been sitting for a long time in the pipes. In new homes, to flush a system means to send large volumes of water gushing through the unused pipes to remove loose particles of solder and flux. (2) To force large amounts of water through liquid to clean out piping or tubing, storage or process tanks. N

flux density (neutron)
A term used to express the number of neutrons entering a sphere of unit cross-sectional area in unit time. For neutrons of given energy, the product of neutron density and speed.

fluxing
The use of a substance to promote fusion of metals or minerals by removing impurities.

fly ash
(1) The component of coal which results from the combustion of coal, and is the finely divided mineral residue which is typically collected from boiler stack gases by electrostatic precipitator or mechanical collection devices. (2) The ash that is carried out of the furnace by the gas stream and collected by mechanical precipitators, electrostatic precipitators, and/or fabric filters. Economizer ash is included when it is collected with fly ash. A

fly ash collector
The equipment used to remove fly ash from incinerator combustion gases.

FMC
Federal Maritime Commission.

FMD
EPA's Financial Management Division.

FMSHRC
Federal Mine Safety and Health Review Commission.

fog
Suspended liquid particles formed by condensation of vapor. N

fogging
Applying a pesticide by rapidly heating the liquid chemical so that it forms very fine droplets that resemble smoke. It is used to destroy mosquitoes and blackflies. N

FOIA
Freedom of Information Act N

fomite
An inanimate object that can harbor or transmit pathogenic organisms.

FONSI
Finding of No Significant Impact (NEPA). N

food-chain crops
Tobacco, crops grown for human consumption, and crops grown for feed for animals whose products are consumed by humans. A

food chain
A sequence of organisms, each of which uses the next lower member of the sequence as a food source. N

food-processing waste
The waste resulting from operations that alter the form or composition of agricultural products for marketing purposes.

food waste
The organic residues generated by the handling, storage, sale, preparation, cooking, and serving of foods, commonly called garbage. A

forced draft
The positive pressure created by the action of a fan or blower, which supplies the primary or secondary combustion air in an incinerator.

forced expiratory volume
FEV. The maximum volume of air that can be forcibly expired when starting from maximal-inspiration. Can also be expressed for a specific time interval, e.g., FEV (one second).

foreseeable emergency
Any potential occurrence such as, but not limited to, equipment failure, rupture of containers, or failure of control equipment which could result in an uncontrolled release of a hazardous chemical into the workplace. N

forging
Deforming metal, usually hot, with compressive force into desired shapes, with or without dies. Where dies are used, the metal is forced to take the shape of the die. A

formaldehyde

CH_2O. (1) A pungent, irritating gas formed by the oxidation of hydrocarbons. (2) A colorless, pungent, irritating gas, CH_2O, used chiefly as a disinfectant and preservative and in synthesizing other compounds and resins. N

formation

UIC. A body of consolidated or unconsolidated rock characterized by a degree of lithologic homogeneity which is prevailingly, but not necessarily, tabular and is mappable on the earth's surface or traceable in the subsurface. A

formation fluid

Fluid present in a formation under natural conditions as opposed to introduced fluids, such as drilling mud. A

formulation

(1) The process of mixing, blending, or dilution of one or more active ingredients with one or more other active or inert ingredients, without an intended chemical reaction, to obtain a manufacturing use product or an end use product, or (2) The repackaging of any registered product. A (3) The substance or mixture of substances which is comprised of all active and inert ingredients in a pesticide. N

fossil fuel and wood residue fired steam generating unit

A furnace or boiler used in the process of burning fossil fuel and wood residue for the purpose of producing steam by heat transfer. A

fossil fuel

Natural gas, petroleum, coal, and any form of solid, liquid, or gaseous fuel derived from such materials for the purpose of creating useful heat. A

fossil-fuel fired steam generating unit

A furnace or boiler used in the process of burning fossil fuel for the purpose of producing steam by heat transfer. A

fouling

The impedance to the flow of gas or heat that results when material accumulates in gas passages or on heat-absorbing surfaces in an incinerator or other combustion chamber.

four-wheel drive general utility vehicle

A four-wheel drive, general purpose automobile capable of off-highway operation that has a wheelbase not more than 110 inches and that has a body shape similar to a 1977 Jeep CJ-5 or CJ-7, or the 1977 Toyota Land Cruiser, as defined by the Secretary of Transportation at 49 CFR 533.4. A

FR

See Federal Register.

FRA

Federal Railroad Administration.

fraction

Refinery term for a product of fractional distillation having a restricted boiling range. A

franchise collection

Refuse collection by a private firm that is given exclusive rights to collect, for a fee paid by customers, in a specific territory or from specific types of customers.

free liquids
Liquids which readily separate from the solid portion of a waste under ambient temperature and pressure. A

free moisture
Liquid that will drain freely by gravity from solid materials. A

free stall barn
Specialized facilities wherein producing cows are permitted free movement between resting and feeding areas. A

freeboard
The vertical distance between the top of a tank or surface impoundment dike, and the surface of the waste contained therein. A

frequency
Number of cycles, revolutions, or vibrations completed in a unit of time [See: Hertz].

fresh water
Water that generally contains less than 1,000 milligrams-per-liter of dissolved solids. N

freshwater lake
Any inland pond, reservoir, impoundment, or other similar body of water that has recreational value, that exhibits no oceanic and tidal influences, and that has a total dissolved solids concentration of less than 1 percent. A

friable
Material, which when dry, may be crumbled, pulverized, or reduced to powder by hand pressure, and includes previously nonfriable material after such previously nonfriable material becomes damaged to the extent that when dry it may be crumbled, pulverized, or reduced to powder by hand pressure. A

friable asbestos material
Any material that contains more than 1 percent asbestos by weight and that can be crumbled, pulverized, or reduced to powder, when dry, by hand pressure. A

friable material
Any material applied onto ceilings, walls, structural members, piping, ductwork, or any other part of the building structure which, when dry, may be crumbled, pulverized, or reduced to powder by hand pressure. A

front panel
That portion of the label of a pesticide product that is ordinarily visible to the purchaser under the usual conditions of display for sale. A

frontend loader
A collection vehicle with mechanical arms in the front that engage a refuse container, lift it up over the cab, empty it into the vehicle's body, where it is compressed, and return it to the ground.

frontend recovery system
Nontechnical term for any process that separates and recovers valuable

resources from inorganic solid waste. Examples are air classification, flotation, grinding, magnetic separation, screening, and shredding.

froth flotation
A process for separating small solid particles according to type by immersing them in a tank of water with a chemical surface-active agent and introducing air bubbles at the bottom of the tank. The agent causes one type of material to have a greater affinity for air than water and to rise to the surface with the bubbles for collection. The process is used to recover tiny particles of glass by separating them from rock and stone.

FRS
Federal Reserve System.

FS
Feasibility Study. N

FSQS
Food Safety & Quality Service.

FSR
Financial Status Report (EPA).

ft.
Feet.

ft^2
Square feet.

ft^3
Cubic feet.

FTC
Federal Trade Commission.

fuel
(1) Any material which is capable of releasing energy or power by combustion or other chemical or physical reaction. A (2) (a) Gasoline and diesel fuel for gasoline- or diesel-powered automobiles or (b) electrical energy for electrically powered automobiles. A

fuel bed
The layer of solid fuel or solid waste on a furnace grate or hearth.

fuel-burning equipment
Any furnace, boiler, apparatus, stack, and all appurtenances thereto, used in the process of burning fuel for the primary purpose of producing heat or power by indirect heat transfer. A

fuel cell
A device for converting chemical energy into electrical energy.

fuel cycle
The complete series of steps involved in supplying fuel for nuclear power reactors. It includes mining, refining, the original fabrication of fuel elements, their use in a reactor, chemical processing to recover the fissionable material remaining in the spent fuel, reenrichment of the fuel material, refabrication into new fuel elements, and management of radioactive waste.

fuel economy
(1) The average number of miles traveled by an automobile or group of automobiles, per gallon of gasoline or diesel fuel as computed in 40 CFR § 600.207 or (2) the equivalent

petroleum based fuel economy for an electrically powered automobile as determined by the Secretary of Energy. A

fuel economy data vehicle
A vehicle used for the purpose of determining fuel economy which is not a certification vehicle. A

fuel economy standard
The Corporate Average Fuel Economy Standard (CAFE) which went into effect in 1978. It was meant to enhance the national fuel conservation effort by slowing fuel consumption through a miles-per-gallon requirement for motor vehicles. N

fuel evaporative emissions
Vaporized fuel emitted into the atmosphere from the fuel system of a motor vehicle. A

fuel gas
Any gas which is generated at a petroleum refinery and which is combusted. Fuel gas also includes natural gas when the natural gas is combined and combusted in any proportion with a gas generated at a refinery. Fuel gas does not include gases generated by catalytic cracking unit, catalyst regenerators and fluid coking burners. A

fuel gas combustion device
Any equipment, such as process heaters, boilers and flares used to combust fuel gas, except facilities in which gases are combusted to produce sulfur or sulfuric acid. A

fuel manufacturer
Any person who, for sale or introduction into commerce, produces or manufactures a fuel or causes or directs the alteration of the chemical composition of, or the mixture of chemical compounds in, a bulk fuel by adding to it an additive. A

fuel oil grade
Numerical ratings ranging from 1 to 6. The lower the grade number, the thinner the oil is and the more easily it evaporates. A high number indicates a relatively thick, heavy oil. No. 1 and No. 2 fuel oils are usually used in domestic heaters, and the others are used by industry and ships. No. 5 and 6 oils are solids which must be liquified by heating. Kerosene, coal oil, and range oil are all No. 1 oil. No. 3 fuel oil is no longer used as a standard term. A

fuel system
The combination of fuel tank, fuel pump, fuel lines, and carburetor, or fuel injection components, and includes all fuel system vents and fuel evaporative emission control systems. A

fuel venting emissions
All raw fuel, exclusive of hydrocarbons in the exhaust emissions, discharged from aircraft gas turbine engines during all normal ground and flight operations. A

fugitive dust
Particulate matter composed of soil which is uncontaminated by pollutants

resulting from industrial activity. Fugitive dust may include emissions from haul roads, wind erosion of exposed soil surfaces and soil storage piles, and other activities in which soil is either removed, stored, transported, or redistributed; also, solid, airborne particulate matter emitted from any source other than through a stack. A

fugitive emissions
(1) Those emissions which could not reasonably pass through a stack, chimney, vent, or other functionally equivalent opening. (2) Any air pollutants emitted to the atmosphere other than from a stack. A

fume
Solid particles under 1 micron in diameter, formed as vapors condense or as chemical reactions take place.

fume scrubber
A wet air pollution control device used to remove and clean the fumes originating in the pickling operation. A

fume suppression system
The equipment comprising any system used to inhibit the generation of emissions from steelmaking facilities with an inert gas, flame, or steam blanket applied to the surface of molten iron or steel. A

fumigant
A pesticide that is vaporized to kill pests; often used in buildings or greenhouses. N

functional equivalent
EPA's decision-making process and its relationship to the environmental review conducted under the National Environmental Policy Act (NEPA). A review is considered functionally equivalent when it addresses the substantive components of a NEPA review. N

functional residual capacity
FRC. The volume of gas remaining in the lungs at the end of a normal expiration.

fund or trust fund
The Hazardous Substance Response Fund established by section 221 [of CERCLA] or, in the case of a hazardous waste disposal facility for which liability has been transferred under section 107(k) of the Act, the Post-closure Liability Fund established by section 232 of the Act. L

fungi
(1) (Singular, Fungus) Molds, mildews, yeasts, mushrooms, and puffballs, a group of organisms that lack chlorophyll (i.e., are not photosynthetic and which are usually non-mobile, filamentous, and multicellular). Some grow in the ground, others attach themselves to decaying trees and other plants, getting their nutrition from decomposing organic matter. Some cause disease, others stabilize sewage and break down solid wastes in composting. N Non-chlorophyll-bearing thallophyte (that is, any non-chlorophyll-bearing plant of a lower order than mosses and liverworts), as for example, rust, smut, mildew, mold, yeast, and bacteria, except those on or in living man or other animals and

those on or in processed food, beverages, or pharmaceuticals. C

fungicides
All substances or mixtures of substances intended for preventing or inhibiting the growth of, or destroying any fungi. A

furnace
(1) A combustion chamber; an enclosed structure in which heat is produced. (2) A solid fuel burning appliance that is designed to be located outside of ordinary living areas and that warms spaces other than the space where the appliance is located, by the distribution of air heated in the appliance through ducts. The appliance must be tested and listed as a furnace under accepted American or Canadian safety testing codes unless exempted from this provision by the Administrator. A manufacturer may request an exemption in writing from the Administrator by stating why the testing and listing requirement is not practicable and by demonstrating that his appliance is otherwise a furnace. A

furnace arch
A nearly horizontal structure that extends into a furnace and serves to deflect gases.

furnace charge
Any material introduced into the electric submerged arc furnace, and may consist of, but is not limited to, ores, slag, carbonaceous material, and limestone. A

furnace cycle
The time period from completion of

a furnace product tap to the completion of the next consecutive product tap. A

furnace power input
The resistive electrical power consumption of an electric submerged arc furnace as measured in kilowatts. A

furnace volume
The total internal volume of combustion chambers.

FURS
Federal Underground Injection Control Reporting System. N

fuse
To change from a solid to liquid, with heat. Also, to blend by melting together.

fusion
The union of light nuclei to form heavier ones, accompanied by the release of enormous quantities of energy.

fusion point
The temperature at which a particular complex mixture of minerals can flow under the weight of its own mass. Because most refractory materials have no definite fusion points but soften gradually over a range of temperatures, the conditions of measurement have been standardized by the American Society for Testing and Materials.

FWPCA
Federal Water Pollution Control Act, as amended (33 U.S.C. 1251 et seq.). A

G

g-eq.
Gram equivalent.

GAAP
Generally Accepted Accounting Principles. N

GAC
Granulated Activated Carbon.

gal.
Gallon (U.S.).

galvanized basis material
Zinc coated steel, galvalum, brass and other copper base strip which is processed in coil coating. A

game fish
Species like trout, salmon, bass, etc. caught for sport. They show more sensitivity to environmental changes than "rough" fish. N

gamma radiation
Gamma rays are true rays of energy in contrast to alpha and beta radiation. The properties are similar to x-rays and other electromagnetic waves. They are the most penetrating waves of radiant nuclear energy but can be blocked by dense materials such as lead. N

garbage
Waste materials that are likely to decompose or putrefy. [See food waste].

gas barrier
Any device or material used to divert the flow of gases produced in a sanitary landfill or by other land disposal techniques.

gas stream
The air, clean or polluted, that is present during a production process or combustion and is eventually vented to the atmosphere.

gas turbine model
A group of gas turbines having the same nominal air flow, combuster inlet pressure, combuster inlet temperature, firing temperature, turbine inlet temperature and turbine inlet pressure. A

gas well

Any well which produces natural gas in a ratio to the petroleum liquids produced greater than 15,000 cubic feet of gas per 1 barrel (42 gallons) of petroleum liquids. A

gasification

Conversion of a solid material, such as coal, into a gas for use as fuel. N

gasoline

Any petroleum distillate having a Reid vapor pressure of 4 pounds or greater which is produced for use as a motor fuel and is commonly called gasoline. A

gasoline blending stock or component

Any liquid compound which is blended with other liquid compounds or with lead additives to produce gasoline. A

gasoline importer

A person who imports gasoline or gasoline blending stocks or components from a foreign country into the United States (including the Commonwealth of Puerto Rico, the Virgin Islands, Guam, American Samoa, and the Northern Mariana Islands). A

gasoline terminal

A facility for the storage and dispensing of gasoline where incoming gasoline loads are received by pipeline, marine tanker or barge, and where outgoing gasoline loads are transferred by tank truck, trailers, railroad cars, or other non-marine mobile vessels. A

gauge pressure (p.s.i.g.)

Pressure measured by a gauge and indicating the pressure exceeding atmospheric. O

GCWR

Gross Combination Weight Rating.

Geiger counter

An electrical device that detects the presence of radioactivity. N

gene

A length of DNA that directs the synthesis of a protein. N

gene library

A collection of DNA fragments from cells or organisms. So far, no simple way for sorting the contents of gene libraries has been devised. However, DNA pieces can be moved into bacterial cells where sorting according to gene function becomes feasible. N

general permit

(1) An NPDES "permit" issued under [40 CFR] § 122.28 authorizing a category of discharges under the CWA within a geographical area. A (2) A permit applicable to a class or category of dischargers. N

generation rate

The quantity of solid waste that originates from a defined activity; or a defined number of solid waste producers per unit of time.

generator

(1) A device that changes mechanical energy into electrical energy. N (2) A facility whose act or process produces hazardous waste. (3) A facility or mobile source that emits

pollutants into the air releases hazardous wastes into water or soil. N

genetic engineering
A process of inserting new genetic information into existing cells in order to modify any organism for the purpose of changing one of its characteristics. N

Genetically Significant Dose
GSD. The gonadal dose which, if received by every member of the population, would be expected to produce the same total genetic effect on the population as the sum of the individual doses that are actually received. It is not a forecast of predictable adverse effects on any individual person or his/her unborn children.

GEP
Good Engineering Practice. N

germicide
Any compound that kills disease-carrying microorganisms. These must be registered as pesticides with EPA. N

glass melting furnace
A unit comprising a refractory vessel in which raw materials are charged, melted at high temperature, refined, and conditioned to produce molten glass. The unit includes foundations, superstructure and retaining walls, raw material charger systems, heat exchangers, melter cooling system, exhaust system, refractory brick work, fuel supply and electrical boosting equipment, integral control systems and instrumentation, and appendages for conditioning and distributing molten

glass to forming apparatuses. The forming apparatuses, including the float bath used in flat glass manufacturing, are not considered part of the glass melting furnace. A

glass produced
The weight of the glass pulled from the glass melting furnace. A

GLC
Ground Level Concentration.

global commons
That area (land, air, water) outside the jurisdiction of any nation. A

GLP
Good Laboratory Practice.

GOB
Grants Operations Balance of EPA's Grants Administration Division.

GOCO
Government-Owned/Contractor-Operated. N

GOGO
Government-Owned/Government-Operated. N

Good Engineering Practice Stack Height
GEP. The greater of: (1) 65 meters; 2(i) For stacks in existence on January 12, 1979 and for which the owner or operator had obtained all applicable preconstruction permits or approvals required under this Parts 51 and 52 of Title 40, $H_g = 2.5$ H; (ii) for all other stacks,
$H_g =$ H + 1.5 L, where
$H_g =$ good engineering practice

stack height, measured from the ground-level elevation at the base of the stack.

H = height of nearby structure(s) measured from the ground-level elevation at the base of the stack.

L = lesser dimension (height or projected width) of nearby structure(s); (3) The height demonstrated by a fluid model or a field study approved by the reviewing agency, which ensures that the emissions from a stack do not result in excessive concentrations of any air pollutant as a result of atmospheric downwash, wakes, or eddy effects created by the source itself, structures, or terrain obstacles. A

governing instruments
Those legal documents which establish the existence of an organization and define its powers and parameters of operation. They include such documents as the Articles of Incorporation or Association, Constitution, Charter and By-Laws. A

government contract
Any agreement or modification thereof between any contracting agency and any person for the furnishing of supplies or services or for the use of real or personal property, including lease arrangements. The term "services," as used in this definition includes, but is not limited to, the following services: utility, construction, transportation, research, insurance, and fund depository. The term "government contract" does not include (1) agreements in which the parties stand in the relationship of employer and employee, and (2) federally assisted construction contracts. A

government-sponsored enterprises
Enterprises with completely private ownership, such as Federal land banks and Federal home loans banks, established and chartered by the Federal Government to perform specialized functions. These enterprises are not included in the budget totals, but financial information on their operations is published in a separate part of the appendix to the President's budget.

gr.
Grain.

grab sample
A single sample which is collected at a time and place most representative of total discharge. A

grading and contouring
A process for minimizing water infiltration of a sanitary landfill by reshaping the site to fill depressions and to create runoff patterns with shorter slopes that discharge to lined troughs.

grain
(1) A unit of weight equal to 65 milligrams or 2/1,000 of an ounce. N
(2) Corn wheat, sorghum, rice, rye, oats, barley, and soybeans. A

grain elevator
Any plant or installation at which grain is unloaded, handled, dried, cleaned, stored, or loaded. A

grain handling operations
Bucket elevators or legs (excluding legs used to unload barges or ships), scale hoppers and surge bins (garners), turn heads, scalpers, cleaners, trippers, and the headhouse and other such structures. A

grain loading station
That portion of a grain elevator where the grain is transferred from the elevator to a truck, railcar, barge, or ship. A

grain loading
The rate at which particles are emitted from a pollution source-- measurement is made by the numbers of grains per cubic foot of gas emitted. N

grain storage elevator
Any grain elevator located at any wheat flour mill, wet corn mill, dry corn mill (human consumption), rice mill, or soybean oil extraction plant which has a permanent grain storage capacity of 35,200 m^3 (ca. 1 million bushels). A

grain terminal elevator
Any grain elevator which has a permanent storage capacity of more than 88,100 m^3 (ca. 2.5 million U.S. bushels), except those located at animal food manufacturers, pet food manufacturers, cereal manufacturers, breweries, and livestock feedlots. A

grant
An award of funds or other assistance by a written grant agreement pursuant to grant regulations, except fellowships.

grant agreement
The written agreement and admendments thereto between an agency or department and a grantee in which the terms and conditions governing the grant are stated and agreed to by both parties pursuant to grant regulations.

grant award official
The EPA official authorized to execute a grant agreement on behalf of the Government. A

grantee
(1) The party which has accepted a grant award and includes entities controlled by the grantee. The term "controlled" means the direct or indirect ownership of more than 50 percent of outstanding stock entitled to vote for the election of directors, or a directing influence over such stock; provided, however, that foreign entities not wholly owned by the grantee shall not be considered as "controlled." A (2) Any individual, agency, or entity which has been awarded wastewater treatment construction grant assistance. A

granular activated carbon treatment
GAC. A filtering system often used in small water systems and individual homes to remove organics. GAC can be highly effective in removing elevated levels of radon from water. N

grapple
A clamshell-type bucket with three or more jaws that is used in excavating. Also called star or orange peel bucket.

grate

A piece of furnace equipment used to support solid waste or solid fuel during the drying, igniting, and burning processes. Openings in its surface permit air to flow through the fuel and permit ash and unburned residue to be removed after combustion.

grate siftings

The materials that fall from the solid waste fuel bed through the grate openings. A

gravity separation

(1) The treatment of mineral particles which exploits differences between their specific gravities. The separation is usually performed by means of sluices, jigs, classifiers, spirals, hydrocyclones, or shaking tables. A (2) The separation of mixed material immersed in a liquid according to the differential specific gravities of its components. It is used in solid waste recovery to separate nonferrous metals from other heavy materials.

gravure cylinder

A printing cylinder with an intaglio image consisting of minute cells or indentations specially engraved or etched into the cylinder's surface to hold ink when continuously revolved through a fountain of ink. A

graywater

Galley, bath, and shower water. D

grease skimmer

A device for removing floating grease or scum from the surface of wastewater in a tank.

green belts

Certain areas restricted from being used for building and houses; they often serve as separating buffers between pollution sources and concentrations of population.

greenhouse effect

The warming of our atmosphere caused by build-up of carbon dioxide, which allows light from the Sun's rays to heat the Earth but prevents loss of the heat. N

grid casting facility

The facility which includes all lead melting pots and machines used for casting the grid used in battery manufacturing. A

grinder

A unit which is used to pulverize dry phosphate rock to the final product size used in the manufacture of phosphate fertilizer and does not include crushing devices used in mining. A

grinder pump

A mechanical device which shreds solids and raises the fluid to higher elevation through pressure sewers. N

gross alpha particle activity

(1) The total radioactivity due to alpha particle emission as inferred from measurements on a dry sample. A (2) Total activity due to emission of alpha particles. Used as the screening measurement for radioactivity generally due to naturally-occurring radionuclides. Activity is commonly measured in picocurries. N

gross beta particle activity
(1) The total radioactivity due to beta particle emission as inferred from measurements on a dry sample. A (2) Total activity due to emission of beta particles. Used as the screening measurement for radioactivity from man-made radionuclides since the decay products of fission are beta particle and gamma ray emitters. Activity is commonly measured in picocuries. N

gross calorific value
Heat liberated when waste is burned completely and the products of combustion are cooled to the initial temperature of the waste. Usually expressed in British thermal units per pound. A

Gross Combination Weight Rating
GCWR. The value specified by the manufacturer as the loaded weight of a combination vehicle. A

gross tonnage
100 cubic feet of permanently enclosed space is equal to one gross ton--nothing whatever to do with weight. This is usually the registered tonnage although it may vary somewhat according to the classifying authority or nationality. A

Gross Vehicle Weight
GVW. The manufacturer's gross weight rating for the individual vehicle. A

Gross Vehicle Weight Rating
GVWR. The value specified by the manufacturer as the maximum design loaded weight of a single vehicle. A

ground
A conducting connection, whether intentional or accidental, between an electrical circuit or equipment and the earth, or to some conducting body that serves in place of the earth. O

ground cover
Plants grown to keep soil from eroding. N

ground water
(1) The supply of fresh water under the earth's surface that forms a natural reservoir. N (2) Water below the land surface in the zone of saturation. A (3) Water in a saturated zone or stratum beneath the surface of land or water. A, L

groundwater contamination
The pollution of springs and wells from their sources underground. It can result from indiscriminate land disposal of potentially hazardous waste materials that are then dissolved or suspended in free liquids, usually water, and leach downward through the unsaturated profile to the zone of saturation or from improperly constructed or operated wells. Movement of the toxic materials in the saturated zone is horizontal, and the rate of flow is determined by the gradient of the aquifer and its permeability. Correction of the problem is seldom limited to one site.

groundwater infiltration
Water which enters the treatment facility as a result of the interception of natural springs, aquifers, or run-off which percolates into the ground and seeps into the

treatment facility's tailings pond or wastewater holding facility and that cannot be diverted by ditching or grouting the tailings pond or wastewater holding facility. A

groundwater monitoring
The periodic sampling and analysis of changes in concentrations of chemical constituents in groundwater.

GSA
General Services Administration.

GSD
Genetically significant dose.

guarantor
Any person, other than the owner or operator, who provides evidence of financial responsibility of an owner or operator under CERCLA (Superfund). L

guard or shield
A barrier designed to protect against employee contact with a hazard created by a moving machinery part. O

guide coat operation
The guide coat spray booth, flash-off area and bake oven(s) which are used to apply and dry or cure a surface coating between the prime coat and topcoat operation on the components of automobile and light-duty truck bodies.

guide specification
A general specification--often referred to as a design standard or design guideline--which is a model standard and is suggested or required for use in the design of all of the construction projects of an agency. A

guillotine damper
An adjustable plate, used to regulate the flow of gases, installed vertically in a breeching.

GVW
Gross Vehicle Weight.

GVWR
Gross Vehicle Weight Rating.

GWPS
Ground Water Protection Standards.

H

h.
Hour(s).

H/C
Hydrogen to carbon atomic ratio.

H_2O
Water.

H_2S
Hydrogen Sulfide.

H_2SO_4
Sulfuric Acid.

habitat
The sum of environmental conditions in a specific place that is occupied by an organism, population, or community. N

half-life
(1) The time taken by certain materials to lose half their strength. For example the half life of DDT is 15 years; of radium 1,580 years. M (2) The time required for a pollutant to lose half its affect on the environment. For example, the half-life of DDT in the environment is 15 years, of radium, 1,580 years. The time required for half of the atoms of a radioactive element to undergo decay. The time required for the elimination of one half a total dose from the body. N

halocarbon
The chemical compounds $CFCl_3$ and CF_2Cl_2 and such other halogenated compounds as the Administrator [of EPA] determines may reasonably be anticipated to contribute to reductions in the concentration of ozone in the stratosphere. B

halogen
Any of a group of 5 chemically-related nonmetallic elements that includes bromine, fluorine, chlorine, iodine, and astatine. N

halon
Bromine-containing compounds with long atmospheric lifetimes whose breakdown in the stratosphere cause depletion of ozone. Halons are used in fire-fighting. N

hammermill
A high-speed machine with hammers and cutters to crush, grind, chip, or shred solid wastes. N

hand glass melting furnace
A glass melting furnace where the molten glass is removed from the furnace by a glassworker using a blowpipe or a pontil. A

handrail
A bar or pipe supported on brackets from a wall or partition, as on a stairway or ramp, to furnish persons with a handhold in case of tripping. O

hang-up
The process of hydrocarbon molecules being absorbed, adsorbed, condensed, or by any other method removed from the sample flow prior to reaching the instrument detector. It also refers to any subsequent desorption of the molecules into the sample flow when they are assumed to be absent. A

hard water
Alkaline water containing dissolved mineral salts, that interfere with some industrial processes and prevent soap from lathering. N

hardness
A characteristic of water, imparted by salts of calcium, magnesium, and iron such as bicarbonates, carbonates, sulfates, chlorides, and nitrates, that cause curding of soap, deposition of scale in boilers, damage in some industrial processes, and sometimes objectionable taste. It may be determined by a standard laboratory procedure or computed from the amounts of calcium and magnesium as well as iron, aluminum, manganese, barium, strontium, and zinc, and is expressed as equivalent calcium carbonate.

hardpan
(1) A hardened, compacted, or cemented soil layer. (2) A very dense soil layer caused by compaction or cementation of soil particles by organic matter, silica, sesquioxides, or calcium carbonate, for example. N

harvesting
Physical measures employed directly upon farm, forest, or ranch crops within established agricultural and silvicultural lands to bring about their removal from farm, forest, or ranch land, but does not include the construction of farm, forest, or ranch roads. A

hatchback
A passenger automobile where the conventional luggage compartment, i.e., trunk, is replaced by a cargo area which is open to the passenger compartment and accessed vertically by a rear door which encompasses the rear window. A

haul time
The elapsed or cumulative time spent transporting solid waste between two specific locations.

hazard
A probability that a given pesticide [or other pollutant] will have an adverse effect on man or the environment in a given situation, the relative likelihood of danger or ill effect being dependent on a number of interrelated factors present at any given time. A

Hazard and Operability Study
HAZOP. A systematic technique

for identifying hazards or operability problems throughout an entire facility. One examines each segment of a process and lists all possible deviations for normal operating conditions and how they might occur. The consequences on the process are assessed, and the means available to detect and correct the deviations are examined. N

hazard correction

The elimination or control of a workplace hazard in accord with the requirements of applicable federal or state statutes, regulations or standards. O

Hazard Information Transmission Program

HIT. This program provides a digital transmission of the CHEMTREC emergency chemical report to first responders at the scene of a hazardous materials incident. The report advises the responder on the hazards of the materials, the level of protective clothing required, mitigating action to take in the event of a spill, leak or fire, and first aid for victims. HIT is a free public service provided by the Chemical Manufacturing Association. Reports are sent in emergency situations only to organizations that have pre-registered with HIT. Brochures and registration forms may be obtained by writing: Manager, CHEMTREC/ CHEMNET, 2501 M Street, N.W., Washington, DC 20037. N

Hazard Ranking System

HRS. The principle screening tool used by EPA to evaluate risks to public health and the environment associated with abandoned or uncontrolled hazardous waste sites. The HRS calculates a score based on the potential of hazardous substances spreading from the site through the air, surface water, or ground water and on other factors such as nearby population. This score is the primary factor in deciding if the site should be on the National Priorities List and, if so, what ranking it should have compared to other sites on the list. N

hazard warning

Words, pictures, symbols, or combination thereof presented on a label or other appropriate form to inform of the presence of various materials. N

hazardous air pollutant

(1) An air pollutant to which no ambient air quality standard is applicable and which in the judgment of the Administrator [of EPA] causes, or contributes to, air pollution which may reasonably be anticipated to result in an increase in mortality or an increase in serious irreversible, or incapacitating reversible, illness. B (2) An air pollutant which is not covered by ambient air quality standards but which, as defined in the Clean Air Act, may reasonably be expected to cause or contribute to irreversible illness or death. Such pollutants include asbestos, beryllium, mercury, benzene, coke oven emissions, radionuclides, and vinyl chloride. N

hazardous material

A material which has one or more of the following characteristics: (1) Has a flash point below 140° F, closed cup, or is subject to spontaneous heating; (2) Has a threshold limit value below 500 ppm for gases and vapors, below 500 mg/m^3 for fumes, and below 25 mppcf (million particles per cubic foot) for dusts; (3) Has a single dose oral LD$_{50}$ below 50 mg/kg; (4) Is subject to polymerization with the release of large amounts of energy; (5) Is a strong oxidizing or reducing agent; (6) Causes first degree burns to skin [from a] short time exposure, or is systemically toxic by skin contact; or (7) In the course of normal operations, may produce dusts, gases, fumes, vapors, mists, or smokes which have one or more of the above characteristics. N

hazardous substance

(1) Any material that poses a threat to human health and/or the environment. Typical hazardous substances are toxic, corrosive, ignitable, explosive, or chemically reactive. Any substance designated by EPA to be reported if a designated quantity of the substance is spilled in the waters of the United States or if otherwise emitted to the environment. (2) (A) Any substance designated pursuant to section 311(b)(2)(A) of the Federal Water Pollution Control Act, (B) Any element, compound, mixture, solution, or substance designated pursuant to section 102 of the Act, (C) Any hazardous waste having the characteristics identified under or listed pursuant to section 3001 of the Solid Waste Disposal Act (but not including any waste the regulation of which under the Solid Waste Disposal Act has been suspended by Act of Congress), (D) Any toxic pollutant listed under section 307(a) of the Federal Water

Pollution Control Act, (E) Any hazardous air pollutant listed under section 112 of the Clean Air Act, and (F) Any imminently hazardous chemical substance or mixture with respect to which the Administrator has taken action pursuant to section 7 of the Toxic Substances Control Act. The term does not include petroleum, including crude oil or any fraction thereof which is not otherwise specifically listed or designated as a hazardous substance under subparagraphs (A) through (F) of this paragraph, and the term does not include natural gas, natural gas liquids, liquefied natural gas, or synthetic gas usable for fuel (or mixtures of natural gas and such synthetic gas). [ed. Establishes the substances covered by Superfund]. L

hazardous waste

Any waste or combination of wastes which pose a substantial present or potential hazard to human health or living organisms because such wastes are nondegradable or persistent in nature or because they can be biologically magnified, or because they can be lethal, or because they may otherwise cause or tend to cause detrimental cumulative effects; also, a waste or combination of wastes of a solid, liquid, contained gaseous, or semisolid form which may cause, or contribute to, an increase in mortality or an increase in serious irreversible, or incapacitating reversible illness, taking into account the toxicity of such waste, its persistence and degradability in nature, its potential for accumulation or concentration in tissue, and other factors that may otherwise cause or contribute to adverse acute or chronic effects on the health of persons or other organisms. A [ed. Hazardous wastes will be those wastes listed by EPA or meeting characteristics specified by EPA in their criteria pursuant to the Resource Conservation Recovery Act (RCRA). Disposal treatment or storage of hazardous wastes can only take place in a site or facility issued a permit by EPA or a state].

Hazardous Waste Data Management System
HWDMS. I

hazardous waste discharge
The accidental or intentional spilling, leaking, pumping, pouring, emitting, emptying or dumping of hazardous waste into or on any land or water. A

hazardous waste generation
The act or process of producing hazardous waste. I

hazardous waste management
The systematic control of the collection, source separation, storage, transportation, processing, treatment, recovery, and disposal of hazardous wastes. I

Hazardous Waste Management facility
HWM facility. All contiguous land, and structures, other appurtenances, and improvements on the land used for treating, storing, or disposing of hazardous waste. A facility may consist of several treatment, storage, or disposal operational units (for example, one or more landfills, surface impoundments, or combination of them). A

hazardous waste management unit
A contiguous area of land on or in which hazardous waste is placed, or the largest area in which there is significant likelihood of mixing hazardous waste constituents in the same area. Examples of hazardous waste management units include a surface impoundment, a waste pile, a land treatment area, a landfill cell, an incinerator, a tank and its associated piping and underlying containment system and a container storage area. A container alone does not constitute a unit; the unit includes containers and the land or pad upon which they are placed. A

hazardous waste site post-closure plan
The plan for post-closure care prepared in accordance with the requirements of 40 CFR §265.117 through 265.120. A

hazards analysis
The procedures involved in (1) identifying potential sources of release of hazardous materials from fixed facilities or transportation accidents; (2) determining the vulnerability of a geographical area to a release of hazardous materials; and (3) comparing hazards to determine which present greater or lesser risks to a community. N

hazards identification
Providing information on which facilities have extremely hazardous substances, what those chemicals are,

and how much there is at each facility. The process also provides information on how the chemicals are stored and whether they are used at high temperature. N

HAZMAT
Hazardous Material. N

HAZOP
Hazard and Operability Study.

HC
Hydrocarbons.

HCFA
Health Care Financing Administration.

HCl
Hydrochloric acid.

HCRS
Heritage Conservation and Recreation Service.

headband
The component of hearing protective device which applies force to, and holds in place on the head, the component which is intended to acoustically seal the ear canal. A

health and safety study
Any study of any effect of a chemical substance or mixture on health or the environment or on both, including underlying data and epidemiological studies, studies of occupational exposure to a chemical substance or mixture, toxicological, clinical, and ecological studies of a chemical substance or mixture, and any test performed pursuant to this [TSCA] Act. Chemical identity is always part of a health and safety study. O

health assessment
An evaluation of available data on existing or potential risks to human health posed by a Superfund site. The Agency for Toxic Substances and Disease Registry of the U.S. Department of Health and Human Services is required to perform a health assessment at every site on the National Priorities List. N

health care facilities
Buildings or portions of buildings and mobile homes that contain, but are not limited to, hospitals, nursing homes, extended care facilities, clinics, and medical and dental offices, whether fixed or mobile. O

hearing
A hearing on the record open to the public and conducted under rules of practice. A

hearing clerk
The Hearing Clerk, A-110, United States Environmental Protection Agency, 401 M St. S.W., Washington, D.C. 20460. A

hearing officer
The individual or board of individuals designated to conduct hearings. A

hearing protective device
Any device or material, capable of being worn on the head or in the ear canal, that is sold wholly or in part on the basis of its ability to reduce the level of sound entering the ear. This includes devices of which hearing

protection may not be the primary function, but which are nonetheless sold partially as providing hearing protection to the user. This term is used interchangeably with the terms "hearing protector" and "device." A

hearth
The bottom of a furnace, on which waste materials or fuels are exposed to the flame.

heat balance
An accounting of the distribution of the heat input and output of an incinerator or boiler, usually on an hourly basis.

heat exchanger
A device that transfers heat from one fluid to another without allowing them to mix.

heat input
The total gross calorific value (where gross calorific value is measured by ASTM Method D2015 -66, D240-64, or D1826-64) of all fuels burned. O

heat island effect
The haze dome created in cities by pollutants combining with the heat trapped in the spaces between tall buildings. This haze prevents natural cooling of air, and in the absence of strong winds can hold high concentrations of pollutants in one place. N

heat release rate
The amount of heat liberated during complete combustion in unit time. It is usually expressed in British thermal units per hour per cubic foot of the internal volume of the furnace in which combustion takes place.

heat treatment
The application of heat of specified temperature and duration to change the physical properties of the metal. A

heavy duty vehicle
(1) A truck, bus, or other vehicle manufactured primarily for use on the public streets, roads, and highways (not including any vehicle operated exclusively on a rail or rails) which has a gross vehicle weight (as determined under regulations promulgated by the Administrator) in excess of six thousand pounds. Such term includes any such vehicle which has special features enabling off-street or off-highway operation and use. B (2) Any motor vehicle rated at more than 8,500 pounds GVWR or that has a vehicle curb weight of more than 6,000 pounds or that has a basic vehicle frontal area in excess of 45 square feet. A

heavy duty scaffold
A scaffold designed and constructed to carry a working load not to exceed 75 pounds per square foot. O

heavy media separation
The separation of mixed material immersed in a colloidal suspension according to its differential densities, or the float / sink technique. The colloidal medium is a water suspension of a finely ground, dense mineral, usually magnetite, ferrosilicon, or galena.

heavy metals
Metallic elements like mercury, chromium, cadmium, arsenic, and lead, with high molecular weights. They can damage living things at low concentrations and tend to accumulate in the food chain. N

HEI
Health Effects Institute. N

hemists
Organic soils (mucky peats and peaty mucks) in which plant remains show a fair amount of decomposition; between one-third and two-thirds of the fibers are still visible upon rubbing the material between the fingers. N

hemoglobin
The red respiratory protein of a red blood cell.

herbicide
All substances or mixtures of substances, except defoliants intended for use in preventing or inhibiting the growth of or killing or destroying plants and plant parts which are declared to be pests under § 162.14. Herbicides include, but are not limited to: (i) Direct contact herbicides intended to kill or destroy weeds, unwanted brush and trees, or unwanted plant parts, or to mitigate their adverse effects on desirable plants; (ii) Soil treatment herbicides intended to kill or destroy weeds, unwanted brush and trees, or unwanted plant parts, or to prevent the establishment of any or all plants; (iii) Pre-emerges herbicides intended to prevent or inhibit the germination or growth of weed seeds or seedlings; (iv) Root control

herbicides intended to prevent the growth of, or kill roots in certain sites such as sewer lines and drainage tiles; (v) Aquatic herbicides intended to prevent, inhibit, or control the growth of, or kill aquatic weeds; (vi) Algaecides, except, slimicides intended to prevent or inhibit the multiplication of, or destroy algae in ponds, swimming pools, aquaria or similar confined sites; (vii) Debarking agents intended to kill trees by treatment of bark on trunks; and (viii) Biological weed-control agents such as specific pathogenic organisms or entities prepared and utilized by man. O

herbivore
An animal that feeds on plants. N

hertz
Unit of frequency equal to one cycle per second, generally applied to nonionizing radiation.

heterotrophic organisms
(1) Humans and animals that can't make food from inorganic chemicals. M (2) Consumers such as humans and animals, and decomposers--chiefly bacteria and fungi--that are dependent on organic matter for food. N

HEW
U.S. Department of Health, Education and Welfare, now HHS or Health and Human Services.

HFID
Heated Flame Ionization Detector.

Hg
Mercury.

HHS
U.S. Department of Health and Human Services.

hi-volume sampler
A device used to measure and analyze suspended particulate pollution. N

high altitude
Any elevation over 1,219 meters (4,000 feet). A

high density polyethylene
A material used to make plastic bottles that produces toxic fumes when burned. N

High Temperature Gas-cooled Reactor
HTGR. A reactor in which the temperature is great enough to permit generation of mechanical power at good efficiency using gas as the coolant.

high terrain area
With respect to any facility, any area having an elevation of 900 feet or more above the base of the stack of such facility, and the term "low terrain area" means any area other than a high terrain area. B

High Velocity Air Filter
HVAF. An air pollution control filtration device for the removal of sticky, oily, or liquid aerosol particulate matter from exhaust gas streams. A

high-altitude conditions
A test altitude of 1,620 meters (5,315 ft.) plus or minus 100 meters (328 ft.), or equivalent observed barometric test conditions of 83.3 $\pm$ 1 kilopascals. A

high-altitude efficiency modification
The provision of increased air flow, restricted fuel flow, or other modification [in automobile engines] having the effect of compensating for the adverse effects on combustion efficiency of decreased air density at high altitudes. A

high-altitude reference point
An elevation of 1,620 meters (5,315 feet) plus or minus 100 meters (328 feet), or equivalent observed barometric test conditions of 83.3 kPa (24.2 inches Hg), plus or minus 1 kPa (0.30 inches Hg). A

high-contact industrial surface
A surface in an industrial setting which is repeatedly touched, often for relatively long periods of time. Manned machinery and control panels are examples of high-contact industrial surfaces. High-contact industrial surfaces are generally of impervious solid material. Examples of low-contact industrial surfaces include ceilings, walls, floors, roofs, roadways and sidewalks in the industrial area, utility poles, unmanned machinery, concrete pads beneath electrical equipment, curbing, exterior structural building components, indoor vaults, and pipes. A

high-contact residential/commercial surface
A surface in a residential / commercial area which is repeatedly touched, often for relatively long periods of time. Doors, wall areas below 6 feet in height, uncovered flooring, windowsills, fencing, bannisters, stairs,

automobiles, and children's play areas such as outdoor patios and sidewalks are examples of high-contact residential/ commercial surfaces. Examples of low-contact residential/ commercial surfaces include interior ceilings, interior wall areas above 6 feet in height, roofs, asphalt roadways, concrete roadways, wooden utility poles, unmanned machinery, concrete pads beneath electrical equipment, curbing, exterior structural building components (e.g., aluminum/ vinyl siding, cinder block, asphalt tiles), and pipes. A

high-hazard contents
High-hazard contents shall be classified as those which are liable to burn with extreme rapidity or from which poisonous fumes or explosions are to be feared in the event of fire. O

high-level liquid waste
The aqueous waste resulting from the operation of the first-cycle extraction system, equivalent concentrated wastes from a process not using solvent extraction, in a facility for processing irradiated reactor fuels.

high-level radioactive waste
The aqueous waste resulting from the operation of the first cycle solvent extraction system, or equivalent and the concentrated waste from subsequent extraction cycles, or equivalent, in a facility for reprocessing irradiated reactor fuels, or irradiated fuel from nuclear power reactors. E

highly toxic
A chemical falling within any of the following categories:
(a) A chemical with a median lethal

dose (LD_{50}) of 50 milligrams or less per kilogram of body weight when administered orally to albino rats weighing between 200 and 300 grams each.
(b) A chemical with a median lethal dose (LD_{50}) of 200 milligrams or less per kilogram of body weight when administered by continuous contact for 24 hours (or less if death occurs within 24 hours) with the bare skin of albino rabbits weighing between 2 and 3 kilograms each.
(c) A chemical that has a median lethal concentration (LC_{50}) in air or more than 200 parts per million but not more than 2,000 parts per million by volume of gas or vapor, or more than two milligrams per liter but not more than 20 milligrams per liter of mist, fume, or dust, when administered by continuous inhalation for one hour (or less if death occurs within 1 hour) to albino rats weighing between 200 and 300 grams each. N

highway fuel economy
The fuel economy determined by operating a vehicle (or vehicles) over the driving schedule in the Federal Highway Fuel Economy Test Procedure. A

histology
The study of the structure of cells and tissues; usually involves microscopic examination of tissue slices. N

HIT
Hazard Information Transmission Program.

holding pond
A pond or reservoir usually made of

earth built to store waste stream or polluted runoff. N

homeostasis
Maintenance of a constant internal environment in an organism. N

homogeneous waste
Solid waste composed of similar materials, e.g., newsprint, stationery, and cardboard.

hood capture efficiency
The emission from a process which are captured by hood and directed into the control device, expressed as a percent of all emissions. N

host
(1) Any plant or animal on or in which another lives for nourishment, development, or protection. A (2) In genetics, the organisms, typically a bacterium, into which a gene from another organism is transplanted. In medicine, an animal infected by or parasitized by another organism. N

hot
Slang for radioactive material. N

hot drying hearth
A surface upon which waste materials are placed to dry or to burn. Hot combustion gases first pass over the materials and then under the hearth.

hot soak loss
Fuel evaporative emissions during the 1-hour hot soak period which begins immediately after an automobile engine is turned off. A

housed lot
Totally roofed buildings which may be open or completely enclosed on the sides wherein animals or poultry are housed over solid concrete or dirt floors, slotted (partially open) floors over pits or manure collection areas in pens, stalls or cages, with or without bedding materials and mechanical ventilation. A

hp.
Horsepower.

hp.- hr.
Horsepower-hour.

HRS
Hazard Ranking System. N

HSL
Hazardous Substance List. N

HSWA
The Hazardous and Solid Waste Amendments of 1984. Public Law 98-616 that amended RCRA. N

HTGR
High temperature gas-cooled reactor.

HUD
Housing and Urban Development.

human environment
The natural and physical environment and the relationship of people with that environment. This means that economic or social effects are not intended by themselves to require preparation of an environmental impact statement. When an environ-

mental impact statement is prepared and economic or social and natural or physical environmental effects are interrelated, then the environmental impact statement will discuss all of these effects on the human environment. N

humus
The dark brown or black residue found in soil resulting from the decomposition of organic matter. Residues in well-digested sludges and activated sludge are similar to humus in appearance and behavior.

HVAF
High Velocity Air Filter.

HW
Hazardous Wastes.

HWDMS
Hazardous Waste Data Management System (OSWER). N I

HWM facility
Hazardous Waste Management facility.

hybrid
A cell or organism resulting from a cross between two unlike plant or animal cells or organisms. N

hybridoma
A hybrid cell that produces monoclonal antibodies in large quantities. N

hydraulic barkers
Wood processing equipment that has the function of removing bark from wood, using water under a pressure of 68atm (1000 psi) or greater. A

hydraulic tipper
A device that unloads a transfer trailer by raising its front end to a 70 degree angle.

hydrocarbon
Any of a vast family of compounds containing carbon and hydrogen in various combinations: found especially in fossil fuels. Some of the hydrocarbon compounds are major air pollutants: they may be carcinogenic or active participants in photochemical process.

Hydrogen Peroxide
H_2O_2. A fast-reaching liquid used as a bleaching agent; can be formed from gases during the photochemical process; gives off oxygen easily.

Hydrogen Sulfide
H_2S. The gas emitted during organic decomposition that smells like rotten eggs. It is also a byproduct of oil refining and burning and can cause illness in heavy concentrations. N

hydrogeology
The geology of ground water, with particular emphasis on the chemistry and movement of water. N

hydrology
The science dealing with the properties, distribution, and circulation of water. N

hydrolysis
A chemical process of decomposition in which the elements of water react with another substance to yield one or more entirely new substances. An example is the breakdown of

cellulose into carbohydrates and ultimately to glucose.

hydrotesting
The testing of piping or tubing by filling with water and pressurizing to test for integrity. A

hyperbaric conditions
Pressure conditions in excess of surface pressure. O

hypoxia
A deficiency of oxygen. N

Hz
Hertz.

I

IAGs
Interagency Agreements.

IAQ
Indoor Air Quality.

IARC
International Agency for Research on Cancer. N

IBP
Initial Boiling Point.

ICC
Interstate Commerce Commission.

ice fog
An atmospheric suspension of highly reflective ice crystals. A

ICRP
International Commission on Radiological Protection. K

I.D.
Inside diameter.

idle
That condition where all engines capable of providing motive power to the locomotive are set at the lowest operating throttle position; and where all auxiliary non-motive power engines are not operating. A

idle adjustments
A series of adjustments which include idle revolutions per minute, idle air/fuel ratio, and basic timing. A

idle emission test
A sampling procedure for exhaust emissions which requires operation of the engine in the idle mode only. At a minimum, the idle test must consist of the following procedures carried out on a fully warmed-up engine: A verification that the idle revolutions per minute is within manufacturer's specified limits and a measurement of the exhaust carbon monoxide and/or hydrocarbon concentrations during the period of time from 15 to 25 seconds after the engine either was used to move the car or was run at 2,000 to 2,500 r/min with no load for 2 or 3 seconds. A

IDLH
Immediately Dangerous to Life and Health.

ignitability
An Environmental Protection Agency characteristic of hazardous waste which identifies waste that presents a fire hazard because it is ignitable under routine waste disposal and storage conditions.

ignition arch
A refractory furnace arch or surface located over a fuel bed to radiate heat and to accelerate ignition.

ignition temperature
The lowest temperature of a fuel at which combustion becomes self-sustaining.

immediate container
That container which is directly in contact with the pesticide or device. A

Immediately Dangerous to Life and Health
IDLH. The maximum level to which a healthy individual can be exposed to a chemical for 30 minutes and escape without suffering irreversible health effects or impairing symptoms. Used as a "level of concern." N

imminent danger
Any conditions or practices in a place of employment which are such that a danger exists which could reasonably be expected to cause death or serious physical harm immediately or before the imminence of such danger can be eliminated. O

imminent hazard
A situation which exists when the continued use of a pesticide during the time required for cancellation proceedings would be likely to result in unreasonable adverse effects on the environment or will involve unreasonable hazard to the survival of a species declared endangered by the Secretary of the Interior under Pub. L. 91-135. A, C

impact mill
A machine that grinds material by throwing it against heavy metal projections rigidly attached to a rapidly rotating shaft.

impedance
The rate at which a substance absorbs and transmits sound. N

impermeable liner
A layer of natural and/or manufactured material of sufficient composition, density, and thickness to have a maximum permeability for water of 10^{-7} centimeters per second at the maximum anticipated hydrostatic pressure.

impervious
Resistant to penetration by fluids or gases.

implementation
Putting a plan into practice by carrying out planned activities, including compliance and enforcement activities, or ensuring such activities are carried out. A

implementation plan
The plan, or revision thereof, which

has been approved or promulgated by EPA under section 110 of the Clean Air Act and which is designed to attain and maintain a national primary or secondary ambient air quality standard in a State or portion thereof. A

import for [or manufacture for] commercial purposes
To import, produce, or manufacture with the purpose of obtaining an immediate or eventual commercial advantage for the manufacturer or importer. See "Manufacture for commercial purposes." A

import in bulk form
To import a chemical substance (other than as part of a mixture or article) in any quantity, in cans, bottles, drums, barrels, packages, tanks, bags, or other containers, if the chemical substance is intended to be removed from the container and the substance has an end use or commercial purpose separate from the container. A

importer
(1) Any person who imports any chemical substance or any chemical substance as part of a mixture or article into the customs territory of the United States, and includes: (A) The person primarily liable for the payment of any duties on the merchandise, or (B) an authorized agent acting on his behalf (as defined in 19 CFR 1.11). (2) Importer also includes, as appropriate: (A) The consignee; (B) The importer of record; (C) The actual owner if an actual owner's declaration and superseding

bond has been filed in accordance with 19 CFR 141.20; (D) The transferee, if the right to draw merchandise in a bonded warehouse has been transferred in accordance with Subpart C of 19 CFR part 144. For the purpose of this definition, the customs territory of the United States consists of the 50 states, Puerto Rico, and the District of Columbia. A

impoundment
A body of water confined by a dam, dike, floodgate, or other barrier. N

improved discharge
The volume, composition and location of an applicant's discharge following: (1) construction of planned outfall improvements, including, without limitation, outfall relocation, outfall repair, or diffuser modification; or (2) construction of planned treatment system improvements to treatment levels or discharge characteristics; or (3) implementation of a planned program to improve operation and maintenance of an existing treatment system or to eliminate or control the introduction of pollutants into the applicant's treatment works. A

impulsive noise
An acoustic event characterized by very short rise time and duration. A

impurity
(1) A chemical substance which is unintentionally present with another chemical substance or mixture. A (2) Any substance (or group of structurally similar substances if specified by the Agency) in a pesticide

product other than an active ingredient or an inert ingredient, including unreacted starting materials, side reaction products, contaminants, and degradation products. A

impurity associated with an active ingredient
(1) Any impurity present in the technical grade of active ingredient; and (2) Any impurity which forms in the pesticide product through reactions between the active ingredient and any other component of the product or packaging of the product. A

inability to provide records
The incapacity of any person to maintain, furnish or permit access to any records required by an environmental statute where such incapacity arises out of causes beyond the control and without the fault or negligence of such person. Such causes may include, but are not restricted to acts of God or the public enemy, fires, floods, epidemics, quarantine restrictions, strikes, and unusually severe weather, but in every case, the failure must be beyond the control and without the fault or negligence of said person. A

inactive waste disposal site
Any disposal site or portion of it where additional asbestos-containing waste material will not be deposited and where the surface is not disturbed by vehicular traffic. A

incidence rates
The number of injuries and illnesses, or lost workdays, per 100 fulltime workers. Rates are calculated as

$$\frac{N \times 200{,}000}{EH}$$

N = number of injuries and illnesses, or number of lost workdays.
EH = total hours worked by all employees during a month, a quarter, or fiscal year
200,000 = base for 100 fulltime equivalent workers (working 40 hours per week, 50 weeks per year. O

incineration
(1) The controlled process which combustible solid, liquid, or gaseous wastes are burned and changed into noncombustible gases. A (2) Burning of certain types of solid, liquid or gaseous materials. (3) A treatment of technology involving destruction of waste by controlled burning at high temperatures, e.g., burning sludge to remove the water and reduce the remaining residues to a safe, nonburnable ash which can be disposed of safely on land, in some waters or in underground locations. N

incineration at sea
Disposal of waste by burning at sea on specially-designed incinerator ships. N

incinerator
(1) Any furnace used in the process of burning waste for the primary purpose of reducing the volume of the waste by removing combustible matter. (2) An enclosed device using controlled flame combustion, the primary purpose of which is to thermally break down hazardous waste. Examples of incinerators are rotary kiln, fluidized bed, and liquid injection incinerators. A

incinerator collector

Any device used to remove suspended particles from the gaseous emissions produced in an incinerator during combustion.

incinerator stoker

A mechanically operable moving grate arrangement for supporting, burning, or transporting solid waste in a furnace and discharging the residue. C

inclined plate conveyor

A separating device that operates by feeding material onto an inclined steel plate belt conveyor so that heavy and resilient materials, such as glass, bounce down the conveyor and light and inelastic materials are carried upward by the motion of the belt.

incompatible waste

A hazardous waste which is unsuitable for: (1) Placement in a particular device or facility because it may cause corrosion or decay of containment materials (e.g., container inner liners or tank walls); or (2) Commingling with another waste or material under uncontrolled conditions because the commingling might produce heat or pressure, fire or explosion, violent reaction, toxic dusts, mists, fumes, or gases, or flammable fumes or gases. A

incomplete gasoline-fueled heavy-duty vehicle

Any gasoline-fueled heavy-duty vehicle which does not have the primary load-carrying device, or passenger compartment, or engine compartment or fuel system attached. A

incomplete truck

Any truck which does not have the primary load carrying device or container attached. A

incorporated into the soil

The injection of solid waste beneath the surface of the soil or the mixing of solid waste with the surface soil. A

increments of progress

Steps to achieve compliance which must be taken by an owner or operator of a designated facility, including: (1) Submittal of a final control plan for the designated facility to the appropriate air pollution control agency; (2) Awarding of contracts for emission control systems or for process modifications, or issuance of orders for the purchase of component parts to accomplish emission control or process modification; (3) Initiation of on-site construction or installation of emission control equipment or process change; (4) Completion of on-site construction or installation of emission control equipment or process change; and (5) Final compliance; increments of progress are individually enforceable. A

independent laboratory

A test facility operated independently of any product manufacturer capable of performing evaluation tests. Additionally, the laboratory shall have no financial interests in the outcome of these tests other than a fee charged for each test performed. A

independently audited
An audit performed by an independent certified public accountant in accordance with generally accepted auditing standards. A

Indian governing body
The governing body of any tribe, band, or group of Indians subject to the jurisdiction of the United States and recognized by the United States as possessing power of self-government. A [ed. Indian tribes generally have authority to impose their own pollution control requirements].

Indian lands
"Indian country" as defined in 18 U.S.C. 1151. That section defines Indian country as: (a) All land within the limits of any Indian reservation under the jurisdiction of the United States government, notwithstanding the issuance of any patent, and, including rights-of-way running through the reservation; (b) All dependent Indian communities within the borders of the United States whether within the original or subsequently acquired territory thereof, and whether within or without the limits of a State. A

Indian reservation
Any federally-recognized reservation established by treaty, agreement, Executive order, or act of Congress. A

Indian tribe
Any Indian Tribe, band, pueblo or community, including Native villages and Native groups as defined in the Alaska Native Claims Settlement Act, which is recognized by the Federal Government as eligible for services from the Bureau of Indian Affairs. A

indicator
(1) An event, entity, or condition that typically characterizes a prescribed environment or situation; indicators determine or aid in determining whether or not certain stated circumstances exist or criteria are satisfied. (2) In biology, an organism, species, or community that shows the presence of certain environmental conditions. N

indirect ammonia recovery system
Those systems which recover ammonium hydroxide as a by-product from coke oven gases and waste ammonia liquors. A

indirect costs
Those costs incurred for a common or joint purpose but benefiting more than one cost objective, and not readily identifiable to the costs objectives specifically benefited.

indirect discharge
(1) The discharge or the introduction of nondomestic pollutants from any source regulated by the pretreatment requirements of section 307 (b) or (c) of the FWPCA, into a POTW. A (2) Introduction of pollutants from a non-domestic source into a publicly owned waste treatment system. Indirect dischargers can be commercial or industrial facilities whose wastes go into the local sewers. N

indirect discharger
A nondomestic discharger intro-

ducing "pollutants" to a "publicly owned treatment works." A

indirect source
A facility, building, structure, installation, real property, road, or highway which attracts, or may attract, mobile sources of pollution. Such term includes parking lots, parking garages, and other facilities subject to any measure for management of parking supply (within the meaning of section 110(c)(2)(D)(ii)) [of the CAA], including regulation of existing off-street parking but such term does not include new or existing on-street parking. Direct emissions sources or facilities at, within, or associated with, any indirect source shall not be deemed indirect sources. B

indirect source review program
The facility-by-facility review of indirect sources of air pollution including such measures as are necessary to assure, or assist in assuring, that a new or modified indirect source will not attract mobile sources of air pollution, the emissions from which would cause or contribute to air pollution concentrations--(i) exceeding any national primary ambient air quality standard for a mobile source-related air pollutant after the primary standard attainment date, or (ii) preventing maintenance of any such standard after such date. B

individual generation site
The contiguous site at or on which one or more hazardous wastes are generated. An individual generation site, such as a large manufacturing plant, may have one or more sources of hazardous waste but is considered a single or individual generation site if the site or property is contiguous. A

individual sewage treatment systems
Privately owned alternative wastewater treatment works (including dual waterless/graywater systems) serving one or more principal residences or small commercial establishments which are neither connected into nor a part of any conventional treatment works. Normally, these are on-site systems with localized treatment and disposal of wastewater with minimal or no conveyance of untreated wastewater. Limited conveyance of treated or partially treated effluents to further treatment or disposal sites can be a function of individual systems where cost-effective. A

individual systems
Privately owned alternative wastewater treatment works (including d2ual waterless/gray water systems) serving one or more principal residences or small commercial establishments. Normally these are on-site systems with localized treatment and disposal of wastewater, but may be systems utilizing small diameter gravity, pressure or vacuum sewers conveying treated or partially treated wastewater. These systems can also include small diameter gravity sewers carrying raw wastewater to cluster systems. A

indoor air

The breathing air inside a habitable structure or conveyance. N

indoor air pollution

Chemical, physical, or biological contaminants in indoor air. N

indoor climate

Temperature, humidity, lighting, and noise levels in a habitable structure or conveyance. Indoor climate can affect indoor air pollution. N

induced draft

The negative pressure created by the action of a fan, blower, or ejector located between an incinerator and a stack.

induced-draft fan

A fan that exhausts hot gases from heat-absorbing equipment, dust collectors, or scrubbers.

industrial cost recovery

(a) The grantee's recovery from the industrial users of a treatment works of the grant amount allocable to the treatment of waste from such users under section 204(b) of the FWPCA. (b) The grantee's recovery from the commercial users of an individual system of the grant amount allocable to the treatment of waste from such users under section 201(h). A

industrial cost recovery period

That period during which the grant amount allocable to the treatment of wastes from industrial users is recovered from the industrial users of such works. A

industrial furnace

Any of the following enclosed devices that are integral components of manufacturing processes and that use controlled flame devices to accomplish recovery of materials or energy: (1) Cement kilns; (2) Lime kilns; (3) Aggregate kilns; (4) Phosphate kilns; (5) Coke ovens; (6) Blast furnaces; (7) Smelting, melting and refining furnaces (including pyrometallurgical devices such as cupolas, reverberator furnaces, sintering machine, roasters, and foundry furnaces); (8) Titanium dioxide chloride process oxidation reactors; (9) Methane reforming furnaces; (10) Pulping liquor recovery furnaces; (11) Combustion devices used in the recovery of sulfur values from spent sulfuric acid; (12) Such other devices as the Administrator may, after notice and comment, add to this list on the basis of one or more of the following factors: (i) The design and use of the device primarily to accomplish recovery of material products; (ii) The use of the device to burn or reduce raw materials to make a material product; (iii) The use of the device to burn or reduce secondary materials as effective substitutes for raw materials, in processes using raw materials as principal feedstocks; (iv) The use of the device to burn or reduce secondary materials as ingredients in an industrial process to make a material product; (v) The use of the device in common industrial practice to produce a material product; and (vi) Other factors, as appropriate. A

industrial incinerator
An incinerator designed to burn a particular industrial waste.

industrial solid waste
The solid waste generated by industrial processes and manufacturing. A

industrial source
Any source of nondomestic pollutants regulated under section 307 (b) or (c) of the Clean Water Act which discharges into a POTW. A

industrial user
(1) (a) Any nongovernmental, nonresidential user of a publicly owned treatment works which is identified in the Standard Industrial Classification Manual, 1972, Office of Management and Budget, as amended and supplemented, under one of the following divisions: Division A- Agriculture, Forestry, and Fishing; Division B-Mining; Division D-Manufacturing; Division E-Transportation, Communications, Electric, Gas, and Sanitary Services; Division I-Services. (1) In determining the amount of a user's discharge for purposes of industrial cost recovery, domestic wastes or discharges from sanitary conveniences may be excluded. (2) After applying the sanitary waste exclusion in paragraph (1) of this paragraph (b) (if the grantee chooses to do so), dischargers in the above divisions that have a volume exceeding 25,000 gpd or the weight of biochemical oxygen demand (BOD) or suspended solids (SS) equivalent to that weight found in 25,000 gpd of sanitary waste are considered

industrial users. Sanitary wastes, for purposes of this calculation of equivalency, are the wastes discharged from residential users. (b) Any nongovernmental user of a publicly owned treatment works which discharges wastewater to the treatment works which contains toxic pollutants or poisonous solids, liquids, or gases in sufficient quantity either singly or by interaction with other wastes, to contaminate the sludge of any municipal systems, or to injure or to interfere with any sewage treatment process, or which constitutes a hazard to humans or animals, creates a public nuisance, or creates any hazard in or has an adverse effect on the waters receiving any discharge from the treatment works. (c) All commercial users of an individual system constructed with grant assistance under section 201(h) of the FWPCA and this subpart. (See 40 CFR § 35.918 (a)(3).) A (2) Those industries identified in the Standard Industrial Classification Manual, Bureau of the Budget, 1967, as amended and supplemented, under the category of "Division D--Manufacturing" and such other classes of significant waste producers as, by regulation, the Administrator deems appropriate. D

industrial waste
Any solid, semisolid, or liquid waste generated by a manufacturing or processing plant the ocean dumping of which may unreasonably degrade or endanger human health, welfare, or amenities, or the marine environment, ecological systems, and economic potentialities. E

industrial waste exchange

An information clearinghouse for industrial waste that provides information on the specific wastes available and puts companies interested in using wastes as feedstock in touch with the waste generators. The waste exchange thus fosters resource recovery and conservation.

industrial waste treatment systems needs

(1) The anticipated industrial point source wasteload reductions required to attain and maintain applicable water quality standards and effluent limitations for at least a 20-year planning period (in 5-year increments). (2) Any alternative considerations for industrial sources connected to municipal systems should be reflected in the alternative considerations for such municipal waste treatment system. A

inert gas

A vapor that doesn't react with other substances under ordinary conditions. N

inert ingredients

All ingredients [in a pesticide] which are not active ingredients including, but not limited to, the following types of ingredients (except when they are pesticidal efficacy of their own): Solvents such as water; baits such as sugar, starches, and meat scraps; dust carriers such as talc and clay; fillers; wetting and spreading agents; propellents in aerosol dispensers; emulsifiers. A, C

inertia weight class

The class, which is a group of test weights, into which a vehicle is grouped based on its loaded vehicle weight in accordance with the provisions of 40 CFR Part 86. A

inertial grate stoker

A stoker with a fixed bed of plates that is carried on rollers and activated by an electrically driven mechanism; it draws the bed slowly back against a spring and then releases it so that the entire bed moves forward until stopped abruptly by another spring. The inertia of the solid waste carries it a small distance forward along the stoker surface, and then the cycle is repeated. D

inertial separator

A device that uses centrifugal force to separate waste particles. N

in existence

The owner or operator has obtained all necessary preconstruction approvals or permits required by Federal, State, or local air pollution emissions and air quality laws or regulations and either has (1) begun, or caused to begin, a continuous program of physical on-site construction of the facility or (2) entered into binding agreements or contractual obligations, which cannot be cancelled or modified without substantial loss to the owner or operator, to undertake a program of construction of the facility to be completed in a reasonable time. A

infectious waste

(1) Equipment, instruments, utensils, and fomites of a disposable nature

from the rooms of patients who are suspected to have or have been diagnosed as having a communicable disease and must, therefore, be isolated as required by public health agencies; (2) laboratory wastes, such as pathological specimens (e.g., all tissues, specimens of blood elements, excreta, and secretions obtained from patients or laboratory animals) and disposable fomites (any substance that may harbor or transmit pathogenic organisms) attendant thereto; (3) surgical operating room pathologic specimens and disposable fomites attendant thereto, and similar disposable materials from outpatient areas and emergency rooms. A

infectiousness
A characteristic of hazardous waste under consideration by the Environmental Protection Agency that would identify waste that contains contagious pathogenic organisms.

infiltration
(1) Water other than wastewater that enters a sewer system (including sewer service connections and foundation drains) from the ground through such means as defective pipes, pipe joints, connections, or manholes. Infiltration does not include, and is distinguished from inflow. A (2) The penetration of water through the ground surface into sub-surface soil or the penetration of water from the soil into sewer or other pipes through defective joints, connections, or manhole walls. (3) A land application technique where large volumes of waste water are applied to land, allowed to penetrate the surface and

percolate through the underlying soil. (See: percolation). N

infiltration air
Air that leaks into the chambers or ducts of an incinerator.

infiltration/inflow
The total quantity of water from both infiltration and inflow without distinguishing the source. A

inflow
Water other than wastewater that enters a sewerage system (including sewer service connections) from sources such as roof leaders, cellar drains, yard drains, area drains, foundation drains, drains from springs and swampy areas, manhole covers, cross connections between storm sewers and sanitary sewers, catch basins, cooling towers, storm waters, surface runoff, street wash waters, or drainage. Inflow does not include, and is distinguished from, infiltration. A

information file
In the Superfund program, a file that contains accurate, up-to-date documents on a Superfund site. The file is usually located in a public building such as a school, library, or city hall that is convenient for local residents. N

in gas/vapor service
A piece of equipment that contains process fluid that is in the gaseous state at operating conditions. A

ingredient statement
A statement which contains--(1) the

name and percentage of each active ingredient, and total percentage of all inert ingredients, in the pesticide; and (2) if the pesticide contains arsenic in any form, a statement of the percentages of total and water soluble arsenic, calculated as elementary arsenic. C

inground tank
A device meeting the definition of "tank" whereby a portion of the tank wall is situated to any degree within the ground, thereby preventing visual inspection of that external surface area of the tank that is in the ground. A

in liquid service
A piece of equipment that is not in gas/vapor service. A

in.
Inch(es).

inhalation LC$_{50}$
A concentration of a substance, expressed as milligrams per liter of air or parts per million parts of air, that is lethal to 50 percent of the test population of animals under specified test conditions. A

inherently low-polluting propulsion system
A propulsion system that does not require control devices for exhaust emissions that are external to the energy releasing activities of the propulsion system. A

in. Hg
Inches of mercury.

in. Hgv
Inches of mercury, vacuum.

in. H$_2$O
Inches of water.

initial decision
(1) In some EPA proceedings, the decision of the Administrative Law Judge supported by findings of fact and conclusions regarding all material issues of law, fact, or discretion, as well as reasons therefor. Such decision shall become the final decision and order of the Administrator without further proceedings unless an appeal therefrom is taken or the Administrator orders review thereof as provided in EPA regulations. A (2) The decision issued by the Presiding Officer based upon the record of the proceedings out of which it arises. A

initial failure rate
The percentage of vehicles rejected because of excessive emissions of a single pollutant during the first inspection cycle of an inspection/maintenance program. (If inspection is conducted for more than one pollutant, the total failure rate may be higher than the failure rates for each single pollutant). A

initiation of construction
The issuance to a construction contractor of a notice to proceed, or, if no such notice is required, the execution of a construction contract. A

injection well
A well into which fluids are injected

for purposes such as waste disposal, improving the recovery of crude oil, or solution mining. N

injection zone
UIC. A geological formation group of formations or part of a formation receiving fluids through a well. A

in-kind contribution
The value of a non-cash contribution provided by (a) the grantee, (b) other public agencies and institutions, (c) private organizations and individuals, or (d) EPA. An in-kind contribution may consist of charges for real property and equipment and value of goods and services directly benefiting and specifically identifiable to the grant program. A

inland oil barge
A non-self-propelled vessel carrying oil in bulk as cargo and certificated to operate only in the inland waters of the United States, while operating in such waters. D

inland waters of the United States
1) Those waters of the United States lying inside the baseline from which the territorial sea is measured and those waters outside such baseline which are a part of the Gulf Intracoastal Waterway. D 2) For the purposes of classifying the size of discharges, "inland waters" means those waters of the U.S. in the inland zone, waters of the Great Lakes, and specified ports and harbors on inland rivers. A

inland zone
The environment inland of the coastal zone excluding the Great Lakes and specified ports and harbors of inland rivers. The term inland zone delineates the area of Federal responsibility for response action. Precise boundaries are determined by EPA/USCG agreement and identified in Federal regional contingency plans. A

innage
Space occupied in a product container. A

inner liner
A continuous layer of material placed inside a tank or container which protects the construction materials of the tank or container from the contained waste or reagents used to treat the waste. A

innovative control technology
Any system of air pollution control that has not been adequately demonstrated in practice, but would have a substantial likelihood of achieving greater continuous emissions reduction than any control system in current practice or of achieving at least comparable reductions at lower cost in terms of energy, economics, or nonair quality environmental impacts. A

innovative technology
Developed wastewater treatment processes and techniques which have not been fully proven under the circumstances of their contemplated use and which represent a significant advancement over the state of the art in terms of significant reduction in

life cycle cost of the project when compared to an appropriate conventional technology. A

innovative wastewater processes and techniques
Innovative waste water treatment processes and techniques are developed methods which have not been fully proven under the circumstances of their contemplated use and which represent a significant advancement over the state of the art in terms of meeting the national goals of cost reduction, increased energy conservation or recovery, greater recycling and conservation of water resources (including preventing the mixing of pollutants with water), reclamation or reuse of effluents and resources (including increased productivity of arid lands), improved efficiency and/or reliability, the beneficial use of sludges or effluent constituents, better management of toxic materials or increased environmental benefits. Innovative waste water treatment processes and techniques are generally limited to new and improved applications of those alternative processes and techniques including both treatment at centralized facilities and individual and other onsite treatment. Treatment processes based on the conventional concept of treatment (by means of biological or physical/chemical unit processes) and discharge to surface waters shall not be considered innovative waste water treatment processes and techniques except where it is demonstrated that these processes and techniques, as a minimum, meet cost-reduction or energy-reduction criterion. Treatment and discharge systems include primary treatment, suspended-growth or fixed-growth biological systems for secondary or advance waste water treatment, physical/chemical treatment, disinfection, and sludge processing. The term "innovative" does not include collector sewers, interceptors, storm or sanitary sewers or the separation of them, or major sewer rehabilitation, except insofar as they meet the criteria in paragraph 6 of these guidelines and are alternatives to conventional treatment works for small communities under 40 CFR § 35.915-1(e) or part of individual systems under 40 CFR § 35.918. A

inoculum
(1) Bacteria placed in compost to start biological action. (2) A medium containing organisms which is introduced into cultures or living organisms. N

in operation
(1) Engaging in activity related to the primary design function of the source. A (2) A facility which is treating, storing, or disposing of hazardous waste. N

inorganic chemicals
Chemical substances of mineral origin, not of basically carbon structure. N

inorganic matter
Chemical substances of mineral origin, not containing carbon-to-carbon bonding. Generally structured through ionic bonding.

inorganic pesticides
Noncarbon-containing substances used as pesticides. A

inorganic refuse
Solid waste composed of matter other than plant, animal, and certain carbon compounds (e.g., metals and glass). B

in personem
An action in personem is instituted against an individual, usually through the personal service of process, and may result in the imposition of a liability directly upon the person of a defendant. A

in-process control technology
The conservation of chemicals and water throughout the production operations to reduce the amount of wastewater to be discharged. A

inprocess wastewater
Any water which, during manufacturing or processing, comes into direct contact with the plant's product or results from the production or use of any raw material, intermediate product, finished product, by-product, or waste product but which has not been discharged to a wastewater treatment process or discharged untreated as wastewater. A

insect
Any of the numerous small invertebrate animals generally having the body more or less obviously segmented, for the most part belonging to the class insecta, comprising six-legged, usually winged forms, as for example, beetles, bugs, bees, flies, and to other allied classes of arthropods whose members are wingless and usually have more than six legs, as for example, spiders, mites, ticks, centipedes, and wood lice. C

insecticide
1) A pesticide compound specifically used to kill or control the growth of insects. N All substances or mixtures of substances intended for preventing or inhibiting the establishment, reproduction, development, or growth of, destroying or repelling any member of the Class Insecta or other allied Classes in the Phylum Arthropoda declared to be pests under 40 CFR § 162.14. Insecticides include, but are not limited to: (i) Plant protection insecticides intended for use directly or indirectly against insects or allied organisms that attack or infest plants or plant parts, to prevent or mitigate their injury, debilitation, or destruction; (ii) Animal protection insecti-cides intended for use directly or indirectly against insects or allied organisms that attack or infest plants or plant parts, to prevent or mitigate their injury, debilitation, or destruction; (ii) Animal protection insecticides intended for use directly or indirectly against insects or allied organisms that attack or infest man, other mammals, birds, or certain other animals, to prevent or mitigate their injury, irritation, harassment, or debilitation; (iii) Premise and indoor insecticides intended for use directly or indirectly against insects or allied organisms to prevent or mitigate their decimation or contamination of man's stored food and animal feeds, injury to raw or manufactured goods, or weakening or

destruction of buildings and building materials; and (iv) Biological insect control agents such as specific pathogenic organisms or entities prepared and utilized by man. A

inside information
Information obtained by a Federal employee as a result of Government employment which has not been made available to the general public or would not be made available on request. A

in-site sampling systems
Nonextractive samplers or in-line samplers. A

in-situ uranium leach methods
The processes involving the purposeful introduction of suitable leaching solutions into a uranium ore body to dissolve the valuable minerals in place and the purposeful leaching of uranium ore in a static or semistatic condition either by gravity through an open pile, or by flooding a confined ore pile. It does not include the natural dissolution of uranium by ground waters, the incidental leaching of uranium by mine drainage, nor the rehabilitation of aquifers and the monitoring of these aquifers. A

inspection
Any inspection of an employer's factory, plant, establishment, construction site, or other area, workplace or environment where work is performed by an employee of an employer, and includes any inspection conducted pursuant to a complaint, any rein-

spection, followup inspection, accident investigation or other inspection. O

Inspection and Maintenance
I/M. (1) Activities to assure proper emissions-related operation of mobile sources of air pollutants, particularly automobile emissions controls. (2) Also applies to wastewater treatment plants and other anti-pollution facilities and processes. N

inspection criteria
The pass and fail numbers associated with a particular sampling plan. A

inspection/maintenance
A program to reduce emissions from in-use vehicles through identifying vehicles that need emissions control related maintenance and requiring that maintenance be performed. A

installation
An identifiable piece of process equipment. A

institution of higher education
An educational institution described in the first sentence of section 1201 of the Higher Education Act of 1965 (other than an institution of any agency of the United States) which is accredited by a nationally recognized accrediting agency or association approved by the Administrator for this purpose. For purposes of this subsection, the Administrator shall publish a list of nationally recognized accrediting agencies or associations which he determined to be reliable authority as to the quality of training offered. D

institutional solid waste
Solid wastes generated by educational, health care, correctional, and other institutional facilities. A

institutional use
Any application of a pesticide in or around any property or facility that functions to provide a service to the general public or to public or private organizations, including but not limited to: (1) Hospitals and nursing homes; (2) Schools other than preschools and day care facilities; (3) Museums and libraries; (4) Sports facilities; (5) Office buildings. A

instream use
Water use taking place within a stream channel, e.g., hydro-electric power generation, navigation, water-quality improvement, fish propagation, recreation. N

instrumentation system
The system which consists of the analytical instruments necessary to measure the level of emissions plus any required support equipment. A

insulated wall
A furnace wall on which refractory material is installed over insulation.

insulating brick
Firebrick with a low thermal conductivity and a bulk density of less than 70 pounds per cubic feet, which is suitable for insulating industrial furnaces. Also called insulating block.

insurer
A company authorized to do business as an insurance carrier under the laws of a state or the District of Columbia. O

intake
Amount of material inhaled, ingested, or absorbed dermally during a specified period of time. N

integral vista
A view perceived from within the mandatory Class I Federal area of a specific landmark or panorama located outside the boundary of the mandatory Class I Federal area. A

integrated exposure assessment
A summation over time, in all media, of the magnitude of exposure to a toxic chemical. N

Integrated Pest Management
IPM. A mixture of pesticide and non-pesticide methods to control pests. N

integrated system
A process for producing a pesticide product that: (1) Contains any active ingredient derived from a source that is not an EPA-registered product; or (2) Contains any active ingredient that was produced or acquired in a manner that does not permit its inspection by the Agency under FIFRA sec. 9(a) prior to its use in the process. A

intensive survey
The frequent sampling or measurement of parameters at representative points for a relatively short period of time to determine water quality conditions, causes, effects, or cause and

effect relationships of such conditions. A

interceptor sewer

A sewer which is designed for one or more of the following purposes: (i) To intercept wastewater from a final point in a collector sewer and convey such wastes directly to a treatment facility or another interceptor. (ii) To replace an existing wastewater treatment facility and transport the wastes to an adjoining collector sewer or interceptor sewer for conveyance to a treatment plant. (iii) To transport wastewater from one or more municipal collector sewers to another municipality or to a regional plant for treatment. (iv) To intercept an existing major discharge of raw or inadequately treated wastewater for transport directly to another interceptor or to a treatment plant. A

interconnected

Two or more electric generating units are electrically tied together by a network of power transmission lines, and other power transmission equipment. A

interference

(1) An inhibition or disruption of the POTW, its treatment processes or operations, or its sludge processes, use or disposal which is a cause of or significantly contributes to either a violation of any requirement of the POTW's NPDES permit (including an increase in the magnitude or duration of a violation) or to the prevention of sewage sludge use or disposal by the POTW in accordance with the following

statutory provisions and regulations or permits issued thereunder (or more stringent state or local regulations): Section 405 of the Clean Water Act, the Solid Waste Disposal Act (including title II more commonly referred to as the Resource Conservation and Recovery Act (RCRA) and including state regulations contained in any state sludge management plan prepared pursuantto Subtitle D of the Solid Waste Disposal Act), the Clean Air Act, and the Toxic Substances Control Act. An Industrial User significantly contributes to such a permit violation or prevention of sludge use or disposal in accordance with above-cited authorities whenever such User: (1) Discharges a daily pollutant loading in excess of that allowed by contract with the POTW or by federal, state or local law; (2) Discharges wastewater which substantially differs in nature or constituents from the User's average discharge; or (3) Knows or has reason to know that its discharge, alone or in conjunction with discharges from other sources, would result in a POTW permit violation or prevent sewage sludge use or disposal in accordance with the above-cited authorities as they apply to the POTW's selected method of sludge management. (2) The discharge of sulfides in quantities which can result in human health hazards and/or risks to human life, and an inhibition or disruption of POTW as defined in 40 CFR 403.3(i). A

interference equivalent

(1) The portion of indicated input concentration due to the presence of

an interferant. (2) Positive or negative response caused by a substance other than the one being measured. A

interflow
That portion of precipitation that infiltrates the soil and moves laterally underground until intercepted by a stream channel or until it resurfaces downslope from its point of infiltration.

intergovernmental agreement
Any written agreement between units of government under which one public agency performs duties for or in concert with another public agency using EPA assistance. This includes substate and interagency agreements. A

interim (permit) status
Period during which treatment, storage and disposal facilities coming under RCRA in 1980 are temporarily permitted to operate while awaiting denial or issuance of a permanent permit. Permits issued under these circumstances are usually called "Part A" or "Part B" permits.

interim authorization
Approval by EPA of a State hazardous waste program which has met the requirements of section 3006(c) of RCRA and applicable requirements of 40 CFR Part 271, Subpart B. A

intermediate
(1) Any chemical substance (a) which is intentionally removed from the equipment in which it is manu-

factured, and (b) which either is consumed in whole or in part in chemical reaction(s) used for the intentional manufacture of other chemical substance(s) or mixture(s), or is intentionally present for the purpose of altering the rate of such chemical reaction(s). Note: The "equipment in which it was manufactured" includes the reaction vessel in which the chemical substance was manufactured and other equipment which is strictly ancillary to the reaction vessel, and any other equipment through which the chemical substance may flow during a continuous flow process, but does not include tanks or other vessels in which the chemical substance is stored after its manufacture. A (2) Any chemical substance which is consumed in whole or in part in a chemical reaction(s) used for the intentional manufacture of other chemical substances or mixtures, or that is intentionally present for the purpose of altering the rates of such chemical reactions. A

intermediate cover
Cover material for landfills that serves the same functions as daily cover, but must resist erosion for a longer period of time, because it is applied on areas where additional disposal cells are not to be constructed for extended periods of time. A

intermediate speed
Peak torque speed if peak torque speed occurs between 60 and 75 percent of rated speed. If the peak torque speed is less than 60 percent

of rated speed, intermediate speed means 60 percent of rated speed. If the peak torque speed is greater than 75 percent of rated speed, intermediate speed means 75 percent of rated speed. A

intermediate-level liquid waste
Fluid materials, disposed as a result of Hanford [Washington nuclear engineering facility] operations, which contain from 5 x 10^{-5} microcuries per milliliter to 100 microcuries per milliliter of mixed fission products, including less than 2 microcuries per milliliter of cesium-137, strontium-90, or long-lived alpha emitters.

intermunicipal agency
(a) Under the Clean Air Act, an agency of two or more municipalities located in the same State or in different States and having substantial powers or duties pertaining to the prevention and control of air pollution. (b) Under the Resource Conservation and Recovery Act, an agency established by two or more municipalities with responsibility for planning or administration of solid waste. I (c) In all other cases, an agency of two or more municipalities having substantial powers or duties pertaining to the control of pollution. A

intermunicipal air pollution control agency
An agency of two or more municipalities located in the same State or in different States and having substantial powers or duties pertaining to the prevention and control of air pollution. A

internal compaction transfer system
A transfer method in which the reciprocating action of a hydraulically powered bulkhead contained within an enclosed trailer packs solid waste against the rear doors.

internal radiation
Radiation from a source within the body as a result of deposition of radionuclides in body tissues by ingestion, inhalation, or implantation.

internal-combustion engine
An engine in which both the heat energy and the ensuing mechanical energy are produced inside the engine proper.

international shipment
The transportation of hazardous waste into or out of the jurisdiction of the United States. A

International Trade Commission
ITC.

interstate agency
(a) Under the Clean Air Act, an agency established by two or more States, or by two or more municipalities located in different States, having substantial powers or duties pertaining to the prevention and control of air pollution. (b) Under the Federal Water Pollution Control Act, an agency of two or more States established by or pursuant to an agreement or compact approved by the Congress or any other agency of two or more States, having substantial powers or duties pertaining to the control of pollution of waters. (c)

Under the Resource Conservation and Recovery Act, an agency of two or more municipalities in different States or an agency established by two or more States, with authority to provide for the disposal of solid wastes and serving two or more municipalities located in different States. (d) In all other cases, an agency of two or more States having substantial powers or duties pertaining to the control of pollution. A, D, I

interstate air pollution control agency
An air pollution control agency established by two or more States or two or more municipalities located in different states, which have substantial powers or duties pertaining to the prevention and control of air pollution. B

interstate air quality control region
A geographic area, designated under section 107 of the Clean Air Act, that includes areas in two or more States. A

interstate carrier water supply
A source of water for drinking and sanitary use on planes, buses, trains, and ships operating in more than one state. These sources are federally regulated. N

interstate commerce
The commerce between any place in a State and any place in another State, or between places in the same State through another State, whether such commerce moves wholly by rail or partly by rail and partly by motor vehicle, express, or water. A

interstate waters
(1) Waters that flow across or form a part of State or international boundaries, e.g., the Great Lakes, the Mississippi River, or coastal waters. N

interstitial monitoring
The continuous surveillance of the space between the walls of an underground storage tank. N

in the hands of the manufacturer
Heavy-duty engines or light-duty trucks still in the possession of the manufacturer which have not had their bills of lading transferred to another person for the purpose of transporting. A

in vacuum service
Equipment that is operating at an internal pressure which is at least 5 kilopascals (kPa) below ambient pressure. A

inventory
The list of chemical substances manufactured or processed in the United States that EPA compiled and keeps current under section 8(b) of the Toxic Substances Control Act. A

inversion
An atmospheric condition caused by a layer of warm air preventing the rise of cool air trapped beneath it. his holds down pollutants that might otherwise be dispersed, and can cause an air pollution episode. N

invertebrate animal poisons and repellents
Invertebrate animal poisons and repellents include, but are not limited

to: (A) Antifouling agents intended for use on boat and ship bottoms, pier and dock pilings, and similar submerged structures to prevent attachment or damage and destruction by marine invertebrates; (B) Mollusk control agents intended to repel or destroy snails or slugs; and (C) Protozoa control agents intended to destroy disease-inducing and/or parasitic protozoa in aquatic situations. A

in vitro studies
Studies of chemical effects conducted in tissues, cells or subcellular extracts from an organism (i.e., not in the living organism). N

in vivo studies
(1) Studies of chemical effects conducted in intact living organisms. N (2) In the living body of a plant or animal. In vivo tests are those laboratory experiments carried out on whole animals or human volunteers. N

in volatile hazardous air pollutant (VHAP) service
A piece of equipment that either contains or contacts a fluid (liquid or gas) that is at least 10 percent by weight a volatile hazardous air pollutant (VHAP) as determined according to the provisions of 40 CFR § 61.245(d). A

ion change
By interchanging ions between a liquid and solid phase, this process allows the undesirable materials to be collected. The mechanisms of ion exchange is chemical, using resins that react either positively or negatively. This method can be used to remove trace metals and cyanides from industrial sources, as well as fluorides and nitrates from drinking water supplies. The contaminants can then be recovered for recycling or disposed of safely.

ion exchange
The reversible interchange of ions of like charge between an insoluble solid and the surrounding liquid phase in which there is no permanent change in the structure of the solid. The process is used in hazardous waste treatment to remove objectionable levels of metals and cyanides from certain waste streams and excessive levels of fluorides, nitrates, and manganese from drinking water.

ionization
The process by which a neutral atom or molecule acquires a positive or negative charge.

ionization chamber
A device that detects and measures the intensity of ionizing radiation. N

ionizing radiation
Radiation that can remove electrons from atoms, i.e., alpha, beta, and gamma radiation. N

IPM
Integrated Pest Management. N

IRLG
Interagency Regulatory Liaison Group.

IRPTC
International Register of Potentially Toxic Chemicals. N

irradiated food
Food that has been subject to brief radioactivity, usually by gamma rays, to kill insects, bacteria, and mold, and preserve it without refrigeration or freezing. N

irradiation
Exposure to radiation of wavelengths shorter than those of visible light (gamma, x-ray, or ultraviolet), for medical purposes, the destruction of bacteria in milk or other foodstuffs, or for inducing polymerization of monomers or vulcanization of rubber. N

irreparable harm
Significant undesirable effect occurring after the date of permit issuance which will not be reversed after cessation or modification of the discharge. A

irrigation
Technique for applying water or wastewater to land areas to supply the water and nutrient needs of plants. N

irrigation return flow
Surface water, other than navigable waters, containing pollutants which result from the controlled application of water by any person to land used primarily for crops, forage growth, or nursery operations; the ditches and other structure that collects such surface water. This term includes water used for cranberry harvesting, rice crops, and other such controlled application of water to land for purposes of farm management. A

irritant
A chemical, which is not corrosive, but which causes a reversible inflammatory effect on living tissue by chemical action at the site of contact. A chemical is a skin irritant if, when tested on the intact skin of albino rabbits by the methods of 16 CFR 1500 41 for 4 hours exposure or by other appropriate techniques, it results in an empirical score of 5 or more. A chemical is an eye irritant if so determined under the procedure listed in 16 CFR 1500.42 or other appropriate techniques. N

irritating
An irritating material, as defined by DOT, is a liquid or solid substance which, upon contact with fire or when exposed to air, gives off dangerous or intensely irritating fumes (not including poisonous materials). (See: Poison, Class A and Poison, Class B.) N

ischemia
Local lack of oxygen due to mechanical obstruction (mainly arterial narrowing) of the blood supply.

ISO standard day conditions
288 degrees Kelvin, 60 percent relative humidity and 101.3 kilopascals pressure. A

isokinetic sampling
Sampling in which the linear velocity of the gas entering the sampling nozzle is equal to that of the

undisturbed gas stream at the sample point. A

isolated
An object that is not readily accessible to persons unless special means of access are used. O

isolated source
A source of air pollutant emissions located a substantial distance from any other source of such air pollutants and that will assume legal responsibility for all violations of the applicable national standards in its designated liability area. A

isolation waste
Discarded materials originating from the diagnosis, core, or treatment of patients placed in quarantine because of known or suspected infectious diseases. (See infectious waste).

isotope
A variation of an element that has the same atomic number but a different weight because of its neutrons. Isotopes of an element may have different radioactive behavior. N

ITC
(1) Interagency Testing Committee. N (2) International Trade Commission.

IU
Industrial User.

J

J.
  Joule.

jigging
  A process for separating presized solid materials of different densities by using the periodic pulsations of a liquid (usually water) through a bed of the mixed material to float the lighter solids.

jointly-funded projects
  A project for which assistance is sought, on a combined or coordinated basis, involving two or more Federal programs or funding authorities. A

Joule
  A unit of energy or work which is equivalent to one watt per second or 0.737 foot-pounds.

judicial officer
  (1) The person designated by the Administrator under 40 CFR §22.04 (b) to serve as the Judicial Officer. (2) An attorney who is a permanent or temporary employee of the United States Environmental Protection Agency and serves as counsel on matters appealed to the Administrator of EPA. A

junk
  Unprocessed, discarded materials that are usually suitable for reuse or recycling (e.g., rags, paper, toys, metal, furniture).

K

K.
Kelvin.

K-factor
The chemical conductivity of a material, expressed as British thermal units per square foot per hour per degree Fahrenheit per foot of thickness. See thermal conductivity.

kg.
Kilogram(s).

kinetic energy
Energy possessed by a mass because of its motion; e.g., the falling water of a dam has the energy to put turbines into motion.

kinetic rate coefficient
A number that describes the rate at which a water constituent such as a biochemical oxygen demand or dissolved oxygen increases or decreases. N

kkg.
1000 kilogram(s).

km.
Kilometer(s).

knife hog
See chipper.

known to or reasonably ascertainable
All information in a person's possession or control, plus all information that a reasonable person similarly situated might be expected to know, or could obtain without unreasonable burden or cost. A

kpa.
Kilopascals.

kraft paper
A comparatively coarse paper noted for its strength and used primarily as a wrapper or packaging material. It is made from wood pulp produced by the sulfate pulping process.

kraft pulp mill
Any stationary source which produces pulp from wood by cooking (digesting) wood chips in a water solution of sodium hydroxide and sodium sulfide (white liquor) at high temperature and pressure. Regeneration of the cooking chemicals through a recovery process is also considered part of the kraft pulp mill. A

kwh.
Kilowatt hour; the provision of one kilowatt of electrical energy for one hour.

L

l.
Liter.

label
(1) The written, printed, or graphic matter on, or attached to, the pesticide or device or any of its containers or wrappers. C̲ (2) Use of a pesticide in a manner not consistent with the label is a prohibited misuse of the product subject to enforcement under FIFRA. (3) A sticker that contains fuel economy information and is affixed to new automobiles in accordance with EPA vehicle certification regulations. A̲ (4) Any written, printed, or graphic sign or symbol displayed on or affixed to containers of hazardous chemicals pursuant to OSHA requirements. A label should contain identity of the hazardous material; appropriate hazard warnings; and name and address of the chemical manufacturer, importer, or other responsible party. N̲

labeled
Equipment is "labeled" if there is attached to it a label, symbol, or other identifying mark of a nationally recognized testing laboratory which, (a) makes periodic inspections of the production of such equipment, and (b) whose labeling indicates compliance with nationally recognized standards or tests to determine safe use in a specified manner. O̲

labeling
All labels and all other written, printed, or graphic matter--(A) accompanying the pesticide or device at any time; or (B) to which reference is made on the label or in literature accompanying the pesticide or device, except to current official publications of the Environmental Protection Agency, the United States Departments of Agriculture and Interior, the Department of Health, Education and Welfare [now the Department of Health and Human Services], State experiment stations, State agricultural colleges, and other similar Federal or State institutions or agencies authorized by law to conduct research in the field of pesticides. C̲

laboratory waste
Discarded materials generated by research and analytical activities in the laboratory.

LAER
Lowest Achievable Emission Rate.

lag time
The time interval from a step change in input concentration at the instrument inlet to the first corresponding change in the instrument output. A

lagoon
(1) A shallow pond where sunlight, bacterial action, and oxygen work to purify waste water, also used for storage of wastewaters or spent nuclear fuel rods. N (2) Shallow body of water, often separated from the sea by coral reefs or sandbars. N

land application
Discharge of wastewater onto the ground for treatment or reuse. (See: irrigation.) N

land disposal
Placement in or on the land and includes, but is not limited to, placement in a landfill, surface impoundment, waste pile, injection well, land treatment facility, salt dome formation, salt bed formation, underground mine or cave, concrete vault or bunker intended for disposal purposes and placement in or on the land by means of open detonation. The term "land disposal" does not encompass ocean disposal.

land treatment facility
A facility or part of a facility at which hazardous waste is applied onto or incorporated into the soil surface; such facilities are disposal facilities if the waste will remain after closure. A

landfarming
The application of waste to land and/or incorporation into the surface soil, including the use of such waste as a fertilizer or soil conditioner. Also called landspreading.

landfill
(1) Sanitary landfills are land disposal sites for non-hazardous solid wastes at which the waste is spread in layers, compacted to the smaller practical volume, and cover material applied at the end of each operating day. (2) Secure chemical landfills are disposal sites for hazardous waste. They are selected and designed to minimize the chance of release of hazardous substances into the environment. N (3) A disposal facility or part of a facility where hazardous waste is placed in or on land and which is not a pile, a land treatment facility, a surface impoundment, an underground injection well, a salt dome formation, a salt bed formation, an underground mine, or a cave. A

landfill cell
A discrete volume of a hazardous waste landfill which uses a liner to provide isolation of wastes from adjacent cells or wastes. Examples of landfill cells are trenches and pits. A

landfill gas
The gas produced in sanitary

landfills during anaerobic digestion of the organic contents, which goes on constantly. It has a volume composition of 40 to 60 percent methane, a gas valued as a fuel and raw material in chemical syntheses and which could be recovered from municipal solid waste disposal sites.

landyard
A rope, suitable for supporting one person. One end is fastened to a safety belt or harness and the other end is secured to a substantial object or a safety line. O

Lantz process
A destructive distillation technique in which the combustible components of solid waste are converted into combustible gases, charcoal, and a variety of distillates.

large appliance product
Any organic surface-coated metal range, oven, microwave oven, refrigerator, freezer, washer, dryer, dishwasher, water heater, or trash compactor manufactured for household, commercial, or recreational use. A

latency
Time from the first exposure to a chemical until the appearance of a toxic effect. N

lateral sewer
A sewer which connects the collector sewer to the interceptor sewer. A

lavage
A washing of a hollow organ, such as the stomach, using a tube and fluids, used in animal feeding studies. N

lb.
Pound(s).

lb-ft.
Pound feet.

LC$_{50}$
Lethal Concentration. (1) The concentration of material which is lethal to one-half of the test population of aquatic animals upon continuous exposure for 96 hours or less. A (2) Median level concentration, a standard measure of toxicity. It tells how much of a substance is needed to kill half of a group of experimental organisms at a specific time of observation. (See LD$_{50}$). N

LC$_{Lo}$
Lethal concentration low. The lowest concentration of a substance in air, other than LC$_{50}$, that has been reported to have caused death in humans or animals. The reported concentrations may be entered for periods of exposure that are less than 24 hours (acute) or greater than 24 hours (subacute and chronic). N

LD$_0$
The highest concentration of a toxic substance at which none of the test organisms die. N

LD$_{50}$
Lethal Dose. (1) The dose of a chemical taken by mouth or absorbed

by the skin which is expected to cause death in 50 percent of the test animals so treated. M (2) The dose of a toxicant that will kill 50 percent of the test organisms within a designated period of time. The lower the LD_{50}, the more toxic the compound. N

LD_{Lo}
Lethal dose low. The lowest dose (other than LD_{50}) of a substance introduced by any route, other than inhalation, over any period of time in one or more divided portions and reported to have caused death in humans or animals. N

leach
To undergo the process by which materials in the soil are moved into a lower layer of soil or are dissolved and carried through soil by water. A

leachate
Any liquid, including any suspended components in the liquid, that has percolated through or drained from hazardous waste. A

leachate collection system
A system that gathers leachate and pumps it to the surface for treatment. N

leaching
The process by which nutrient chemicals or contaminants are dissolved and carried away by water, or are moved into a lower layer of soil. N

lead
A heavy metal that may be hazardous to health if breathed or swallowed. M [ed. National ambient air quality standards have been promulgated for lead].

lead additive
Any substance containing lead or lead compounds. A

lead agency
(1) The Federal agency (or State agency operating pursuant to a contract or cooperative agreement executed pursuant to section 104(d)(1) of CERCLA) that has primary responsibility for coordinating response action. A Federal lead agency is the agency that provides the OSC or RMP as specified elsewhere in this Plan. In the case of a State as lead agency, the State shall carry out the same responsibilities delineated for OSCs/RPMs in this Plan (except coordinating and directing Federal agency response actions). (2) The agency or agencies preparing or having taken primary responsibility for preparing the environmental impact statement. A

lead recipe
Raw material formulation of the following approximate weight proportions: 56 percent silica; 8 percent potassium carbonate; and 36 percent red lead. A

lead reclamation facility
The facility that remelts lead scrap and casts it into lead ingots for use in the battery manufacturing process. A

leaded gasoline
(1) Gasoline which is produced with the use of any lead additive or which contains more than 0.05 gram of lead

per gallon or more than 0.005 gram of phosphorus per gallon. A (2) Gasoline to which lead has been added to raise the octane level. N

leak-detection system
A system capable of detecting the failure of either the primary or secondary containment structure or the presence of a release of hazardous waste or accumulated liquid in the secondary containment structure. Such a system must employ operational controls (e.g., daily visual inspections for releases into the secondary containment system of aboveground tanks) or consist of an interstitial monitoring device designed to detect continuously and automatically the failure of the primary or secondary containment structure or the presence of a release of hazardous waste into the secondary containment structure. A

ledge plate
A plate that is adjacent to or overlaps the edge of a stoker.

legal defense costs
Any expenses that an insurer incurs in defending against claims of third parties brought under the terms and conditions of an insurance policy. A

legislation
[For the purpose of determining whether an EIS is required under NEPA], a bill or legislative proposal to Congress developed by or with the significant cooperation and support of a Federal agency, but does not include

requests for appropriations. The test for significant cooperation is whether the proposal is in fact predominantly that of the agency rather than another source. Drafting does not by itself constitute significant cooperation. Proposals for legislation includes requests for ratification of treaties. Only the agency which has primary responsibility for the subject matter involved will prepare a legislative environmental impact statement. A

LEL
Lower Explosive Limit. Refers to the lowest concentration of gas or vapor (percent by volume in air) that will burn or explode if an ignition source is present at ambient temperatures. The LEL is constant up to 250° F. Decrease it by 0.7 at temperatures above 250° F because explosibility increases with higher temperature. N

LEPC
Local Emergency Planning Committee. A committee appointed by the state emergency response commission, as required by SARA Title III to formulate a comprehensive emergency plan for its jurisdiction. N

lethal concentration low
LC_{LO}. The lowest concentration of a substance in air, other than LC_{50}, that has been reported to have caused death in humans or animals. The reported concentrations may be entered for periods of exposure that are less than 24 hours (acute) or greater than 24 hours (subacute and chronic). N

lethal dose
LD$_{50}$. Generally, the quantity of a substance which is fatal to 50 percent of the population on which it is tested. With large test subjects it is often given as a quantity per unit of body weight.

lethal dose low
The lowest dose (other than LD$_{50}$) of a substance introduced by any route, other than inhalation, over any period of time in one or more divided portions and reported to have caused death in humans or animals. N

Level Of Concern
LOC. The concentration in air of an extremely hazardous substance above which there may be serious immediate health effects to anyone exposed to it for short periods of time. N

LFL
Lower Flammable Limit.

liabilities
Probable future sacrifices of economic benefits arising from present obligations to transfer assets or provide services to other entities in the future as a result of past transactions or events. A

license or permit
An authorization granted by an agency of the Federal Government or a State or Local government to conduct any activity which may result in any discharge into the navigable waters of the United States, emissions of air pollutants into the atmosphere, or other polluting activity. The license or permit will establish the conditions under which the polluting activity can take place, including specific limitations on amounts of pollutants that may be released. Violations of permit conditions are usually enforceable by the Federal, State or Local government.

licensed material
Source material, special nuclear material, or byproduct material received, possessed, used, or transferred under a general or special license issued by the U.S. Energy Research and Development Administration or a State.

licensed site
The area contained within the boundary of a location under the control of persons generating or storing uranium byproduct materials under a license issued by the Commission. This includes such areas licensed by Agreement States, i.e., those States which have entered into an effective agreement under section 274(b) of the Atomic Energy at of 1954, as amended. A

licensing or permitting agency
Any agency of the Federal Government to which application is made for a license or permit. A

life cycle
The stages an organism passes through during its existence. N

lifeline

A rope, suitable for supporting one person, to which a lanyard or safety belt (or harness) is attached. O

lift

In a sanitary landfill, a compacted layer of solid waste and the top layer of cover material. N

lifting station

(See: pumping station.) N

light-duty truck

Any motor vehicle rated at 8500 pounds GVWR or less which has a vehicle curb weight of 6000 pounds or less and which has a basic vehicle frontal area of 45 square feet or less, which is: (1) Designed primarily for purposes of transportation of property or is a derivation of such a vehicle, or (2) Designed primarily for transportation of persons and has a capacity of more than 12 persons, or (3) Available with special features enabling off-street or off-highway operation and use. A

light-duty vehicle

A passenger car or passenger car derivative capable of seating 12 passengers or less. A

lignite

Coal that is classified as lignite A or B according to the American Society of Testing and Materials' (ASTM) Standard Specification for Classification of Coals by Rank D388-77.

lime (or limestone) scrubbing process

(1) Any of a number of methods using lime and a scrubber to remove sulfur dioxide from flue gases. (2) Process in which sulfur gases moving towards a smokestack are passed through a limestone and water solution to remove sulfur before it reaches the atmosphere. N

limiting factor

A condition whose absence, or excessive concentration, exerts some restraining influence upon a population through incompatibility with species requirements or tolerance. M

limiting permissible concentration of the suspended particulate and solid phases of a material

That concentration which will not cause unreasonable acute or chronic toxicity or other sublethal adverse effects based on bioassay results using appropriate sensitive marine organisms in the case of the suspended particulate phase, or appropriate sensitive benthic marine organisms in the case of the solid phase; and which will not cause accumulation of toxic materials in the human food chain. These bioassays are to be conducted in accordance with procedures approved by EPA, or, in the case of dredged material, approved by EPA and the Corps of Engineers. A

limiting permissible concentration of the liquid phase of a material

(1) That concentration of a constituent which, after allowance for initial mixing, does not exceed applicable marine water quality criteria; or, when there are not applicable marine water quality criteria, (2) That concentration of waste or dredged material in the receiving water which, after allowance

for initial mixing, will not exceed a toxicity threshold defined as 0.01 of a concentration shown to be acutely toxic to appropriate sensitive marine organisms in a bioassay carried out in accordance with approved EPA procedures. (3) When there is reasonable scientific evidence on a specific waste material to justify the use of an application factor other than 0.01 as specified in paragraph (a)(2) of this section, such alternative application factor shall be used in calculating the LPC. A

limnology
The study of the physical chemical, meteorological, and biological aspects of fresh water. N

linear accelerators
A device for accelerating charged particles. It employs alternate electrodes and gaps arranged in a straight line, so proportioned that when potentials are varied in the proper amplitude and frequency, particles passing through the waveguide receive successive increments of energy.

linearity
The maximum deviation between an actual instrument reading and the reading predicted by a straight line drawn between upper and lower calibration points. A

liner
(1) The material used on the inside of a furnace wall to insure a chamber impervious to escaping gases; the material used on the inside of a sanitary landfill to insure the basin is impervious to fluids, thereby preventing leaching of wastes to the environment. (2) A continuous layer of natural or man-made materials, beneath or on the sides of a surface impoundment, landfill, or landfill cell, which restricts the downward or lateral escape of hazardous waste, hazardous waste constituents, or leachate. A

lipid solubility
The maximum concentration of a chemical that will dissolve in fatty substances; lipid soluble substances are insoluble in water. If a substance is lipid soluble it will very selectively disperse through the environment via living tissue. N

liquefaction
Changing a solid into a liquid form. N

Liquefied Petroleum Gases
LPG and LP Gas mean and include any material which is composed predominantly of any of the following hydrocarbons, or mixtures of them, such as propane, propylene, butane (normal butane or iso-butane), and butylenes. O

liquid-mounted seal
A foam or liquid-filled primary seal mounted in contact with the liquid between the tank wall and the floating roof continuously around the circumference of the tank. A

listed
Equipment is "listed" if it is of a kind mentioned in a list which, (a) is published by a nationally recognized laboratory which makes periodic

inspection of the production of such equipment, and (b) states such equipment meets nationally recognized standards or has been tested and found safe for use in a specified manner. O

listed waste
Wastes listed as hazardous under RCRA but which have not been subjected to the Toxic Characteristics Listing Process because the dangers they present are considered self-evident. N

lithology
The description of rocks on the basis of their physical and chemical characteristics. A

litter tax
Charges levied against items appearing in litter (e.g., cigarette butts, candy wrappers, convenience food packaging) to finance their collection and disposal.

LLRW
Low-level Radioactive Waste. Wastes less hazardous than most of those generated by a nuclear reactor. Usually generated by hospitals, research laboratories, and certain industries. The Department of Energy, Nuclear Regulatory Commission, and EPA share the responsibilities for managing them. (See: high-level radioactive wastes.) N

load cell
A device external to the locomotive, of high electrical resistance, used in locomotive testing to simulate engine loading while the locomotive is station-

ary. (Electrical energy produced by the diesel generator is dissipated in the load cell resistors instead of the traction motors). A

load on top
A procedure for ballasting and cleaning unloaded tankers without discharging oil. Half of the tanks are first filled with seawater while the others are cleaned by hosing. Then oil from the cleaned tanks, along with oil which has separated out in the full tanks, is pumped into a single slop tank. The clean water in the full tanks is then discharged while the freshly-cleaned tanks are filled with seawater. Ballast is thus constantly maintained. A

load-bearing resistance of a refractory
The degree to which a refractory resists deformation when subjected to a specified compressive load at a specified temperature and time.

loaded emissions test
A sampling procedure for exhaust emissions which requires exercising the engine under stress (i.e., loading) by use of a chassis dynamometer to simulate actual driving conditions. As a minimum requirement, the loaded emission test must include running the vehicle and measuring exhaust emissions at two speeds and loads other than idle. A

loaded vehicle weight
The vehicle curb weight plus 300 pounds. A

loaded vehicle mass
Curb mass plus 80 kg (176 lb.), average driver mass. A

LOAFL
Lowest Observed Adverse Effect Level. N

loam
A soft, easily crumbled soil composed of a mixture of sand, silt, and clay.

LOC
Level of Concern. The concentration in air of an extremely hazardous substance above which there may be serious immediate health effects to anyone exposed to it for short periods of time. N

local agency
Any local government agency, other than the State agency, which is charged with the responsibility for carrying out a portion of a pollution control plan. A

Local Emergency Planning Committee
LEPC. A committee appointed by the state emergency response commission, as required by SARA Title III to formulate a comprehensive emergency plan for its jurisdiction. N

local share
The amount of the total grant eligible and allowable project costs which a public body is obligated to pay under the grant. A

locomotive
A self-propelled vehicle designed for and used on railroad tracks in the transport or rail cars, including self-propelled rail passenger vehicles. A

locomotive load cell test stand
The load cell and associated structure, equipment, trackage and locomotive being tested. A

LOE
Level Of Effort. N

long-term contract
When used in relation to solid waste supply, a contract of sufficient duration to assure the viability of a resource recovery facility (to the extent that such viability depends upon solid waste supply). I

lost workdays
The number of days (consecutive or not) after, but not including, the day of injury or illness during which the employee would have worked but could not do so; that is, could not perform all or any part of his normal assignment during all or any part of the workday or shift, because of the occupational injury or illness. O

low altitude conditions
A test altitude less than 549 meters (1,800 feet). A

low altitude
Any elevation less than or equal to 1,219 meters (4000 feet). A [ed. Used to determine high altitude areas where changes in vehicle emission control systems are allowed to improve engine performance].

low hazard contents

Those of such low combustibility that no self-propagating fire therein can occur and that consequently the only probable danger requiring the use of emergency exits will be from panic, fumes, or smoke, or fire from some external source. O

low-emission vehicle

Any motor vehicle which--(A) emits any air pollutant in amounts significantly below new motor vehicle standards applicable under section 202 [of the CAA] at the time of procurement to that type of vehicle; and (B) with respect to all other air pollutants meets the new motor vehicle standards applicable under section 202 at the time of procurement to that type of vehicle.

low-level liquid waste

Fluid materials that are contaminated by less than 5×10^{-5} microcuries per milliliter of mixed fission products.

low-level radioactive waste

LLRW. Wastes less hazardous than most of those generated by a nuclear reactor. Usually generated by hospitals, research laboratories, and certain industries. The Department of Energy, Nuclear Regulatory Commission, and EPA share the responsibilities for managing them. (See: high-level radioactive wastes.) N

low-mileage emissions target

For a particular pollutant, the value in grams per mile resulting from the division of the emission standard by the applicable engine family deterioration factor derived from the certifi-

cation process for the applicable model year. A

low-noise emission product

Any product which emits noise in amounts significantly below the levels specified in noise emission standards under regulations applicable under section 6 [of the Noise Control Act] at the time of procurement to that type of product. G

low-noise emission product determination

The Administrator's determination whether or not a product, for which a properly filed application has been received, meets the low-noise-emission product criterion. A

low-volume waste sources

Taken collectively as if from one source, wastewater from all sources except those for which specific limitations are otherwise established. Low volume waste sources would include but are not limited to wastewaters from wet scrubber air pollution control systems, ion exchange water treatment systems, water treatment evaporator blowdown, laboratory and sampling streams, boiler blowdown, floor drains, cooling tower basin cleaning wastes and recirculating house service water systems. Sanitary wastes and air conditioning wastes are not included. A

Lower Flammable Limit

LFL. For a vapor or gas, the lowest concentration (lowest percentage of the substance in air) that will produce a flash of fire when an ignition source (heat, arc, or flame) is present. At concentrations lower than the LFL, the mixture is too "lean" to burn. N

Lower Explosive Limit
LEL. (1) The lowest percent by volume of a mixture of explosive gases which will propagate a flame in air at 25° C and atmospheric pressure. A (2) Refers to the lowest concentration of gas or concentration of gas or vapor (percent by volume in air) that will burn or explode if an ignition source is present at ambient temperatures. The LEL is constant up to 250° F. Decrease it by 0.7 at temperatures above 250° F because explosibility increases with higher temperature. N

lowest achievable emission rate
The rate of emissions which reflects for any source, the more stringent rate of emissions based on the following: (A) the most stringent emission limitation which is contained in the implementation plan of any State for such class or category of source, unless the owner or operator of the proposed source demonstrates that such limitations are not achievable, or (B) the most stringent emissions limitation which is achieved in practice by such class or category of source, whichever is more stringent. This limitation, when applied to a modification, means the lowest achievable emissions rate for the new or modified emissions units within the stationary source. In no event shall the application of this term permit a proposed new or modified source to emit any pollutant in excess of the amount allowable under applicable new source standards of

performance. A, B [ed. This is the minimum level of air pollutant emissions control required to be achieved by a new or modified stationary source that seeks to locate in an area not achieving ambient air quality standards].

Lowest Dose of a Substance
TD_{Lo}. The lowest dose of a substance introduced by any route other than inhalation over any given period of time and reported to produce any toxic effect in humans or to produce tumorigenic or reproductive effects in animals or humans. N

lpm.
Liter per minute.

LTO
Landing Take Off.

LTU
Land Treatment Unit. N

lubricating oil
The fraction of crude oil which is sold for purposes of reducing friction in any industrial or mechanical device. Such term includes re-refined oil. A, I

LUST
Leaking Underground Storage Tank.

lysimeter
A device used to measure the quantity or rate of water movement through or from a block of soil or other material, such as solid waste, or used to collect percolated water for quality analysis.

M

m.
Meter(s).

m³
Cubic meter.

MABs
Monoclonal Antibodies.

machine shop
A facility performing cutting, grinding, turning, honing, milling, deburring, lapping, electrochemical machining, etching, or other similar operations. A

MADCAP
Model of Advection, Diffusion, and Chemistry for Air Pollution. N

made
When used in connection with any invention, the conception or first actual reduction to practice of such invention. A

MAER
Maximum Allowable Emission Rate. N

magnetic separation
The process by which a permanent magnet or electromagnet is used to attract materials away from mixed waste.

major disaster
Any hurricane, tornado, storm, flood, high water, wind-driven water, tidal wave, earthquake, drought, fire, or other catastrophe in any part of the United States which, in the determination of the President, is or threatens to become of sufficient severity and magnitude to warrant disaster assistance by the Federal Government to supplement the efforts and available resources of States and local governments and relief organizations in alleviating the damage, loss, hardship, or suffering caused thereby. A

major discharge
A discharge of more than 10,000 gallons of oil to the inland waters or more than 100,000 gallons of oil to the coastal waters. A

major emitting facility

Any of the following stationary sources of air pollutants which emit, or have the potential to emit, one hundred tons per year or more of any air pollutant from the following types of stationary sources: fossil-fuel fired steam electric plants of more than two hundred and fifty million British thermal units per hour heat input, coal cleaning plants (thermal dryers), kraft pulp mills, Portland Cement plants, primary zinc smelters, iron and steel mill plants, primary aluminum ore reduction plants, primary copper smelters, municipal incinerators capable of charging more than two hundred and fifty tons of refuse per day, hydrofluoric, sulfuric, and nitric acid plants, petroleum refineries, lime plants, phosphate rock processing plants, coke oven batteries, sulfur recovery plants, carbon black plants (furnace process) primary lead smelters, fuel conversion plants, sintering plants, secondary metal production facilities, chemical process plants, fossil-fuel boilers of more than two hundred and fifty million British thermal units per hour heat input, petroleum storage and transfer facilities with a capacity exceeding three hundred thousand barrels, taconite ore processing facilities, glass fiber processing plants, charcoal production facilities. Such term also includes any other source with the potential to emit two hundred and fifty tons per year or more of any air pollutant. This term shall not include new or modified facilities which are nonprofit health or education institutions which have been exempted by the State. [See major stationary source]. B

major employment facility

Any single employer location having 250 or more employees. A

major federal action

Actions with effects that may be major and which are potentially subject to federal control and responsibility. Major reinforces but does not have a meaning independent of significantly (40 CFR § 1508.27). Actions include the circumstance where the responsible officials fail to act and that failure to act is reviewable by courts or administrative tribunals under the Administrative Procedure Act or other applicable law as agency action. (a) Actions include new and continuing activities, including projects and programs entirely or partly financed, assisted, conducted, regulated, or approved by federal agencies; new or revised agency rules, regulations, plans, policies, or procedures; and legislative proposals (40 CFR §§ 1506.8, 1508.17). Actions do not include funding assistance solely in the form of general revenue sharing funds, distributed under the State and Local Fiscal Assistance Act of 1972, 31 U.S.C. 1221 et seq., with no federal agency control over the subsequent use of such funds. Actions do not include bringing judicial or administrative civil or criminal enforcement actions. (b) Federal actions tend to fall within one of the following categories: (1) Adoption of official policy, such as rules, regulations, and interpretations adopted pursuant to the Administrative Procedure Act, 5 U.S.C. 551 et seq.; treaties and international conventions or agreements; formal documents establishing an agency's policies which will result in or substantially alter agency programs. (2) Adoption of formal plans, such as official documents prepared or approved by federal agencies which guide or prescribe alternative uses of federal resources, upon which future agency actions will be based. (3) Adoption of programs, such as a group of concerted actions to implement a specific policy or plan; systematic and connected agency decisions allocating agency resources to implement a specific statutory program or executive directive. (4) Approval of specific projects, such as construction or management activities located in a defined geographic area. Projects include actions approved by permit or other regulatory decision as well as federal and federally assisted activities. A

major modification
Used to define modifications with respect to Prevention of Significant Deterioration and New Source Review under the Clean Air Act and refers to modifications to major stationary sources of emissions and provides significant pollutant increase levels below which a modification is not considered major. N (i) Any physical change in or change in the method of operation of a major stationary source that would result in a significant net emissions increase of any pollutant subject to regulation under the [Clean Air] Act. (ii) Any net emissions increase that is considered significant for volatile organic compounds shall be considered significant for ozone. (iii) A physical change or change in the method of operation shall not include:

(a) routine maintenance, repair, and replacement; (b) use of an alternative fuel or raw material by reason of an order under sections 2(a) and (b) of the Energy Supply and Environmental Coordination Act of 1974 (or any superseding legislation) or by reason of a natural gas curtailment plan pursuant to the Federal Power Act; (c) use of an alternative fuel by reason of an order or rule under section 125 of the Act; (d) use of an alternative fuel at a steam generating unit to the extent that the fuel is generated from municipal solid waste; (e) use of an alternative fuel or raw material by a stationary source which (1) the source was capable of accommodating before December 21, 1976, unless such change would be prohibited under any federally enforceable permit condition which was established after December 21, 1976, pursuant to 40 CFR 52.21 or under regulations approved pursuant to 40 CFR 51.18 or 40 CFR 51.24; or (2) the source is approved to use under any permit issued under this ruling; (f) an increase in the hours of operation or in the production rate, unless such change is prohibited under any federally enforceable permit condition which was established after December 21, 1976 pursuant to 40 CFR 52.21 or under regulations approved pursuant to 40 CFR 51.18 or 40 CFR 51.24; (g) any change in ownership at a stationary source. A

major release
A release of any quantity of hazardous substance(s), pollutant(s), or contaminant(s) that poses a substantial threat to public health or welfare

or the environment or results in significant public concern. A

major stationary source

Used to determine to applicability of Prevention of Significant Deterioration and new source regulations. In a non-attainment area, any stationary pollutant source that has a potential to emit more than 100 tons per year is considered a major stationary source. In PSD areas the cutoff level may be either 100 or 250 tons, depending upon the type of source. N (i)(a) Any stationary source of air pollutants which emits, or has the potential to emit, 100 tons per year or more of any pollutant subject to regulation under the Act; or (b) Any physical change that would occur at a stationary source not qualifying under paragraph (f)(5)(i)(a) of this section [§52.24], as a major stationary source, if the change would constitute a major stationary source by itself. (ii) A major stationary source that is major for volatile for organic compounds shall be considered major for ozone. [See major emitting facility]. A

make available for use

To distribute, sell, ship, deliver for shipment, or receive and (having so received) deliver, to any person. However, the term excludes transactions solely between persons who are pesticide producers, registrants, wholesalers, or retail sellers, acting only in those capacities. A

malfunction

Any unanticipated and unavoidable failure of air pollution control equipment or process equipment or of a process to operate in a normal or usual manner. Failures that are caused entirely or in part by poor design, poor maintenance, careless operation, or any other preventable upset condition or preventable equipment breakdown shall not be considered malfunctions. A malfunction exists only for the minimum time necessary to implement corrective measures. A

mammal poisons and repellents

All substances, or mixtures of substances, except rodenticides, intended for preventing, destroying, repelling, or mitigating mammals declared to be pests under 40 CFR §162.14. Mammal poisons and repellents include, but are not limited to: (i) Taste, odor, and irritant repellents intended to repel mammals or their adverse, undesired, or destructive activities such as attacking, foraging, chewing, gnawing, urinating, or defecating in or on specific sites or on or near specific objects, person, plants, or animals; (ii) Predacides intended to kill certain mammals that prey upon other vertebrate animals which man deems necessary to protect; (iii) Toxicants, baits, and poisons intended to kill certain mammals causing injury or destruction to crops, stored foods, or other organisms and objects which man deems necessary to protect; and (iv) Reproductive inhibitors intended to reduce or otherwise alter the reproductive capacity or potential of certain mammals. A

man-made beta particle and photon emitters

All radionuclides emitting beta

particles and/or photons listed in Maximum Permissible Body Burdens and Maximum Permissible Concentration of Radionuclides in Air or Water for Occupational Exposure, NBS Handbook 69, except the daughter products of thorium-232, uranium-235 and uranium-238. A

man-rem
The product of the average individual dose in a population times the number of individuals in the population. Syn: person-rem.

management agencies
(1) The identification of those agencies recommended for designation by the Governor pursuant to Section 208 of the FWPCA to carry out each of the provisions of the water quality management plan. The identification shall include those agencies necessary to construct, operate and maintain all treatment works identified in the plan and those agencies necessary to implement the regulatory programs. (2) Depending upon an agency's assigned responsibilities under the plan, the agency must have adequate authority and capability: (i) To carry out its assigned portions of an approved State water quality management plan(s) (including the plans developed for areawide planning areas designated pursuant to Section 208(a) (2), (3), or (4) of the Act) developed under this part; (ii) To effectively manage waste treatment works and related point and nonpoint source facilities and practices serving such area in conformance with the approved plan; (iii) Directly or by contract, to design and construct new works, and to operate and maintain new and existing works as required by any approved water quality management plan developed under this part; (iv) To accept and utilize grants or other funds from any source for waste treatment management or nonpoint source control purposes; (v) To raise revenues, including the assessment of user charges; (vi) To incur short and long term indebtedness; (vii) To assure, in implementation of an approved water quality management plan, that each participating community pays its proportionate share of related costs; (viii) To refuse to receive any wastes from a municipality or subdivision thereof, which does not comply with any provision of an approved water quality management plan applicable to such areas; and (ix) To accept for treatment industrial wastes. A

management of migration
Actions that are taken to minimize and mitigate the migration of hazardous substances or pollutants or contaminants and the effects of such migration. Management of migration actions may be appropriate where the hazardous substances or pollutants or contaminants are no longer at or near the area where they were originally located or situations where a source cannot be adequately identified or characterized. Measures may include, but are not limited to, provision of alternative water supplies, management of a plume of contamination, or treatment of a drinking water aquifer. A

management or hazardous waste management

The systematic control of collection, source separation, storage, transportation, processing, treatment, recovery, and disposal of hazardous waste. A

management system

The total equipment required for the determination of the gas volumetric flow rate in a duct or stack. The system consists of three major subsystems: (A) Analyzer--that portion of the measurement system which senses the stack gas flow rate or velocity pressure and generates a signal output that is a function of the flow rate or velocity of the gases. (B) Data presentation--that portion of the measurement system that provides a display of the output signal in terms of volumetric flow rate units, or other units which are convertible to volumetric flow rate units. (C) Sampling interface--that portion of the measurement system that performs one or more of the following operations: delineation, acquisition, transportation, and conditioning of a signal from the stack gas and protection of the analyzer from any hostile aspects of the source environment. A

manifest

The form used for identifying the quantity, composition, and the origin, routing, and destination of hazardous waste during its transportation from the point of generation to the point of disposal, treatment, or storage. I

manifest document number

The U.S. EPA twelve digit identification number assigned to the generator plus a unique five digit document number assigned to the [Hazardous Waste] Manifest by the generator for recording and reporting purposes. A

manifest system

The clerical procedure to be followed by an owner / operator of a facility that receives hazardous waste accompanied by a manifest or delivery document.

manmade air pollution

Air pollution which results directly or indirectly from human activities. B

manmade wetland

Any wetland area that has been purposely or accidentally created by some activity of man; also called artificial wetlands. N

manometer

An instrument for measuring pressure. It usually consists of a U-shaped tube containing a liquid, the surface of which in one end of the tube moves proportionally with changes in pressure on the liquid in the other end. Also, a tube type of differential pressure gauge.

manual method

A method for measuring concentrations of an ambient air pollutant in which sample collection, analysis, or measurement, or some combination thereof, is performed manually. A

manual separation

The separation of mixed waste by hand (e.g., the practice of keeping newspapers separate from garbage in the home).

manufacture for commercial purposes

(1) To import, produce, or manufacture with the purpose of obtaining an immediate or eventual commercial advantage for the manufacturer, and includes, among other things, such "manufacture" of any amount of a chemical substance or mixture: (i) For commercial distribution, including for test marketing, and (ii) For use by the manufacturer, including use for product research and development, or as an intermediate. (2) Manufacture for commercial purposes also applies to substances that are produced coincidentally during the manufacture, processing, use, or disposal of another substance or mixture, including both byproducts that are separated from that other substance or mixture and impurities that remain in that substance or mixture. Such byproducts and impurities may, or may not, in themselves have commercial value. They are nonetheless produced for the purpose of obtaining a commercial advantage since they are part of the manufacture of a chemical product for a commercial purpose. A

manufacture of semi-conductors

Those processes, beginning with the use of crystal wafers, which lead to or are associated with the manufacture of semiconductor devices. A

manufacture of electronic crystals

The growing of crystals and/or the production of crystal wafers for use in the manufacture of electronic devices. A

manufacture or import for commercial purposes

(1) For distribution in commerce, including for test marketing purposes, or (2) For use by the manufacturer, including for use as an intermediate. A

manufacture solely for export

To manufacture for a commercial purpose solely for export from the United States under the following restrictions on domestic activity: (1) Processing is limited solely to sites under the control of the manufacturer. (2) Distribution in commerce is limited to purposes of export. (3) The manufacturer may not use the substance except in small quantities solely for research and development. A

manufacturer

(1) Any person engaged in the manufacturing or assembling of new products, or the importing of new products for resale, or who acts for, and is controlled by, any such person in connection with the distribution of such products, including any establishment engaged in the mechanical or chemical transformation of materials or substances into new products including but not limited to the blending of materials such as pesticidal products, resins, or liquors. A , B, G (2) A person who imports, produces or manufactures a chemical substance. A person who extracts a component chemical substance from a previously existing chemical substance or a complex combination of substances is a manufacturer of that component chemical substance. A person who

contracts with a manufacturer to manufacture or produce a chemical substance is also a manufacturer if (1) the manufacturer manufactures or produces the substance exclusively for that person, and (2) that person specifies the identity of the substance and controls the total amount produced and the basic technology for the plant process. A

manufacturers formulation
A list of substances or component parts as described by the maker of a coating, pesticide or other product containing chemicals or other substances. N

manufacturing process
All of a series of unit operations operating at a site, resulting in the production of a product. A

manufacturing use product
1) Any pesticide product other than an end use product. A product may consist of the technical grade of active ingredient only, or may contain inert ingredients, such as stabilizers or solvents. A 2) Any pesticide product other than a product to be labeled with directions for end use. This term includes any product intended for use as a pesticide after re-formulation or re-packaging. A

Mar Ad
Maritime Administration in the U.S. Department of Commerce.

margin of safety
When setting primary standards-- by law, based entirely on health con-

siderations -- EPA first determines the concentration of a pollutant that is safe for most people. It then sets the standard at a lower concentration level. The difference in the two levels -- the margin of safety -- protects people who may be especially vulnerable to air pollution. See primary standards. N

marine environment
That territorial seas, the contiguous zone and the oceans. A

marine sanitation device
Any equipment installed on board a vessel to receive, retain, treat, or discharge sewage and any process to treat such sewage. N, A, D

mark
The descriptive name, instructions, cautions, or other information applied to chemical substances, mixtures, articles, containers, equipment, or other objects or activities described in these regulations. A

marking
The act of physically indicating the classification assignment on classified material. A

marsh
(1) Wet, soft, low-lying land that provides a habitat for many plants and animals. It can be destroyed by dredging and filling. (2) A type of wetland that does not accumulate appreciable peat deposits and is dominated by herbaceous vegetation. Marshes may be either fresh or salt-water and tidal or non-tidal. N

masking
Blocking out a sight, sound, or smell with another. N

master inventory file
EPA's comprehensive list of chemical substances which constitute the Chemical Substances Inventory compiled under section 8(b) of the Act. A

MATC
Maximum Allowable Toxicant Concentration. N

matching share
That portion of the project costs that is not derived from Federal assistance. See cost-sharing.

material
Matter of any kind or description, including, but not limited to, dredged material, solid waste, incinerator residue, garbage, sewage, sewage sludge, munitions, radiological, chemical, and biological warfare agents, radioactive materials, chemicals, biological and laboratory waste, wreck or discarded equipment, rock, sand, excavation debris, and industrial, municipal, agricultural, and other waste; but such term does not mean sewage from vessels within the meaning of [33 USC] §1322. Oil within the meaning of [33 USC] §1321 of this title shall be included only to the extent that such oil is taken on board a vessel or aircraft for the purpose of dumping. E

material balance
An accounting of the weights of materials entering or leaving a processing unit, such as an incinerator, usually on an hourly basis.

material exchange
An industrial waste exchange that also buys and sells the waste.

Material Safety Data Sheet
MSDS. A compilation of information required under the OSHA Communication Standard on the identity of hazardous chemicals, health, and physical hazards, exposure limits, and precautions. Section 311 of SARA requires facilities to submit MSDSs under certain circumstances. N

material specification
A specification that stipulates the use of certain materials to meet the necessary performance requirements. A

material storage runoff
The rainfall runoff from or through any coal, ash or other material storage pile. A

max.
Maximum.

Maximum Contaminant Level Goal
MCLG. The maximum level of a contaminant in drinking water at which no known or anticipated adverse effect on the health of persons would occur, and which allows an adequate margin of safety. Maximum contaminant level goals are non-enforceable health goals. A

maximum contaminant level
(1) The maximum permissible level of a contaminant in water which is delivered to the free flowing outlet of the ultimate user of a public water system, except in the case of turbidity

where the maximum permissible level is measured at the point of entry to the distribution system. Contaminants added to the water under circumstances controlled by the user, except those resulting from corrosion of piping and plumbing caused by water quality, are excluded from this definition. A (2) The maximum permissible level of a contaminant in water which is delivered to any user of a public water system. J MCLs are enforceable standards. N

maximum daily discharge limitation
The highest allowable "daily discharge." A

Maximum Permissible Dose Equivalent
MPDE. The greatest dose equivalent that a person or specified part of the body shall be allowed to receive in a given period of time.

maximum rated torque
The maximum torque produced by an engine as stated by the manufacturer in his sales and service literature and his application for certification under 40 CFR § 86.082-21. A

maximum rated RPM
The engine speed measured in revolutions per minute (RPM) at which peak net brake power (SAE J-245) is developed for motorcycles of a given configuration. A

maximum rated horsepower
The maximum brake horsepower output of an engine as stated by the manufacturer in his sales and service literature and his application for

certification under 40 CFR § 86.082-21. A

maximum sound level
The greatest A-weighted sound level in decibels measured at fast meter response § 201.1(l) during the designated time interval or during the event. It is abbreviated as L_{max}. A

Maximum Total Trihalomethane (THM) Potential
MTP. The maximum concentration of total trihalomethanes produced in a given water containing a disinfectant residual after 7 days at a temperature of 25° C or above. A

mbbl.
1,000 barrels (one barrel = 42 gallons).

MCAs
MABs, Monoclonal Antibodies.

MCL
Maximum Contaminant Level.

MCLG
Maximum Contaminant Level Goal. A

MDL
Method Detection Limit.

means of emission limitation
A system of continuous emission reduction (including the use of specific technology or fuels with specified pollution characteristics). B

measurement period
A continuous period of time during which noise of railroad yard operations

is assessed, the beginning and finishing times of which may be selected after completion of the measurements. A

mechanical aeration
Use of mechanical energy to inject air into water to cause a waste stream to absorb oxygen. N

mechanical collector
A device that traps particulate matter by the use of mechanical energy, rather than chemically or electrically.

mechanical composting
A method in which the compost is continuously and mechanically mixed and aerated.

mechanical energy
Energy in a form which can do work directly.

mechanical removal methods
Include the use of pumps, skimmers, booms, earthmoving equipment, and other mechanical devices. A

mechanical separation
The separation of mixed material by mechanical means (e.g., air classifier, spiral classifier). See separator.

mechanical turbulence
Random irregularities of fluid motion in air caused by buildings or mechanical, non-thermal processes. N

media
Specific environments -- air, water, soil -- which are the subject of regulatory concern and activities. N

medical treatment
Treatment administered by a physician or by registered professional personnel under the standing orders of a physician. Medical treatment does not include first aid treatment even though provided by a physician or registered professional personnel. O

medically contaminated waste
Discarded materials that contain or have come into contact with objects or substances used in patient diagnosis, care, or treatment.

medium discharge
A discharge of 1,000 to 10,000 gallons of oil to the inland waters or a discharge of 10,000 to 100,000 gallons of oil to the coastal waters. A

medium release
All releases not meeting the criteria for classification as a minor or major release. A

mega-
A prefix meaning 1 million. J

meltdown and refining
That phase of the steel production cycle when charge material is melted and undesirable elements are removed from the metal. A

meltdown and refining period
The time period commencing at the termination of the initial charging period and ending at the initiation of the tapping period, excluding any intermediate charging periods. A

membrane barrier
A thin layer of material impervious to the flow of gas or water.

meq.
Milliequivalent.

merchant
Those by-product cokemaking operations which provide more than fifty percent of the coke produced to operations, industries, or processes other than iron making blast furnaces associated with steel production. A

mercury
A heavy metal that can accumulate in the environment and is highly toxic if breathed or swallowed. (See: heavy metals.) N

metabolism
The sum of the chemical reactions occurring within a cell or a whole organism; includes the energy-releasing breakdown of molecules (catabolism) and the synthesis of new molecules (anabolism). N

metabolite
Any substance produced in or by living organisms by biological processes and derived from a pesticide. A

metal cleaning waste
Any wastewater resulting from cleaning [with or without chemical cleaning compounds] any metal process equipment including, but not limited to, boiler tube cleaning, boiler fireside cleaning, and air preheater cleaning. A

metal coil surface coating operation
The application system used to apply an organic coating to the surface of any continuous metal strip with thickness of 0.15 millimeter (mm) (0.006 in.) or more that is packaged in a roll or coil. A

metal preparation
Any and all of the metal processing steps preparatory to applying the enamel slip. Usually this includes cleaning, pickling and applying a nickel flash or chemical coating. A

metallic shoe seal
Includes but is not limited to a metal sheet held vertically against the tank wall by springs or weighted levers and is connected by braces to the floating roof. A flexible coated fabric (envelope) spans the annular space between the metal sheet and the floating roof. A

metallo-organic active ingredients
Carbon containing active ingredients containing one or more metallic atoms in the structure. A

metastasis
The transmission of a disease from one part of the body to another. N

methane
(1) A colorless, nonpoisonous, flammable gas created by anaerobic decomposition of organic compounds. N
(2) A colorless, nonpoisonous, flammable gas emitted by marshes and dumps undergoing anaerobic decomposition. N [ed. The principal component of natural gas].

methods of operation
The installation, emplacement, or introduction of materials, including those involved in construction, to achieve a process or procedure to control: Surface water pollution from non-point sources, i.e. agricultural, forest practices, mining, construction; ground or surface water pollution from well, subsurface, or surface disposal operations; activities resulting in salt water intrusion; or changes in the movement, flow, or circulation of navigable or ground waters. A

MFBI
Major Fuel Burning Installation. N

mg.
Abbreviation for milligram(s).

Mg.
Megagram = 10^6 grams.

mg/m³
Milligrams per cubic meter of air. N

mgal.
1,000 gallons.

mi.
Mile(s).

micro-
A prefix meaning 1/1,000,000; abbreviated by the Greek letter (u). J

microbes
(1) Tiny plants and animals, some that cause disease are found in sewage. N (2) Microscopic organisms such as algae, animals, viruses, bacteria, fungus, and protozoa, some of which cause diseases. (See: microorganism). N

microbial inoculation
The process in which microorganisms are introduced into organic waste materials to initiate decomposition. It is a practical approach to site restoration if the depth of contamination is fairly shallow, the extent of contamination is relatively small, and the waste materials are organic compounds.

microbial pesticide
A microorganism that is used to control a pest. They are of low toxicity to man. N

microorganism
Living organisms so small that individually they can usually only be seen through a microscope. N

MICROMORT
A One-in-a-Million Chance of Death from an Environmental Hazard. N

micron
Symbol (u); a unit of measurement equal to 1/1,000,000 of a meter. J

micron efficiency curve
A curve showing how well a collector traps micron-size dust particles.

microscale
The concentrations in air volumes associated with area dimensions ranging from several meters up to about 100 meters. A

midden
A refuse pile in which bones, broken tools, and pottery have been accumulating, layer by layer, in long inhabi-

ted places since human beings lived in caves. It is the earliest historical evidence of waste materials.

middle scale
The concentration typical of areas up to several city blocks in size with dimensions ranging from about 100 meters to 0.5 kilometer. A

midnight dumper
An idiomatic term referring to a person who disposes of hazardous or noxious wastes in a stealthy, illegal manner.

midrange
The value of oxygen or carbon dioxide concentration that is representative of the normal conditions in the stack gas of the affected facility at typical operating rates. A

military engine
Any engine manufactured solely for the Department of Defense to meet military specifications. A

mill
A preparation facility within which the metal ore is cleaned, concentrated or otherwise processed prior to shipping to the consumer, refiner, smelter or manufacturer. A mill includes all ancillary operations and structures necessary for the cleaning, concentrating or other processing of the metal ore such as ore and gangue storage areas, and loading facilities. A

milled refuse
Solid waste that has been mechanically reduced in size. C

millfeed
The ore and other material introduced into the milling process.

milli-
A prefix meaning 1/1,000; abbreviated by the letter m, such as milligram (mg). J

milligram
10^{-3} gram.

milliliter
10^{-3} liter.

millimeter
10^{-3} meter.

millirem (mrem)
10^{-3} rem.

min.
Abbreviation for minute(s).

mine
An active mining area, including all land and property placed, under or above the surface of such land, used in or resulting from the work of extracting metal ore or minerals from their natural deposits by any means or method, including secondary recovery of metal ore from refuse or other storage piles, wastes, or rock dumps and mill tailings derived from the mining, cleaning, or concentration of metal ores. A

mine dewatering
Any water that is impounded or that collects in the mine and is pumped, drained or otherwise removed from the mine through the efforts of the

mine operator. This term shall also include wet pit overflows caused solely by direct rainfall and ground water seepage. However, if a mine is also used for treatment of process generated waste water, discharges of commingled water from the mine shall be deemed discharges of process generated waste water. A

mine drainage
Any drainage, and any water pumped or siphoned, from an active mining area or a post-mining area. A

miner of asbestos
A person who produces asbestos by mining or extracting asbestos containing ore so that it may be further milled to produce bulk asbestos for distribution in commerce, and includes persons who conduct milling operations to produce bulk asbestos by processing asbestos-containing ore. Milling involves the separation of the fibers from the ore, grading and sorting the fibers, or fiberizing crude asbestos ore. To mine or to mill is to "manufacture" for commercial purposes under TSCA. A

mineral handling and storage facility
The areas in asphalt roofing plants in which minerals are unloaded from a carrier, the conveyor transfer points between the carrier and the storage silos, and the storage silos. A

minimum detectable sensitivity
The smallest amount of input concentration that can be detected as the concentration approaches zero. A

mining overburden returned to the mine site
Any material overlying an economic mineral deposit which is removed to gain access to that deposit and is then used for reclamation of a surface mine. A

mining wastes
Residues which result from the extraction of raw materials from the earth. A

minor discharge
1) A discharge to the inland waters of less than 1,000 gallons of oil or a discharge to the coastal waters of less than 10,000 gallons of oil. A 2) Any discharge which (1) has a total volume of less than 50,000 gallons on every day of the year, (2) does not affect the waters of any other State, and (3) is not identified by the Director, the Regional Administrator, or by the Administrator [of EPA] in regulations issued pursuant to section 307(a) of the [Federal Water Pollution Control] Act as a discharge which is not a minor discharge. If there is more than one discharge from a facility and the sum of the volumes of all discharges from the facility exceeds 50,000 gallons on any day of the year, then no discharge from the facility is a "minor discharge" as defined herein. A

minor release
A release of a quantity of hazardous substance(s), pollutant(s), or contaminant(s) that poses minimal threat to public health or welfare or the environment. A

minority business enterprise

A business which is (1) certified as socially and economically disadvantaged by the Small Business Administration, (2) certified as a minority business enterprise by a state or federal agency, or (3) an independent business concern which is at least 51 percent owned and controlled by minority group member(s). A minority group member is an individual who is a citizen of the United States and one of the following: (i) Black American; (ii) Hispanic American (with origins from Puerto Rico, Mexico, Cuba, South or Central America); (iii) Native American (American Indian, Eskimo, Aleut, native Hawaiian), or (iv) Asian-Pacific American (with origins from Japan, China, the Philippines, Vietnam, Korea, Samoa, Guam, the U.S. Trust Territories of the Pacific, Northern Marianas, Laos, Cambodia, Taiwan or the Indian subcontinent). A

minute volume

The minute volume of breathing; a product of tidal volume times the respiratory frequency in one minute.

misbranded

A pesticide is misbranded under FIFRA if--(A) its labeling bears any statement, design, or graphic representation relative thereto or to its ingredients which is false or misleading in any particular; (B) it is contained in a package or other container or wrapping which does not conform to the standards established by the Administrator pursuant to section 25(c)(3); (C) it is an imitation of, or is offered for sale under the name of, another pesticide; (D) its label does not bear the registration number assigned under section 7 to each establishment in which it was produced; (E) any word, statement, or other information required by or under authority of FIFRA to appear on the label or labeling is not prominently placed thereon with such conspicuousness (as compared with other words, statements, designs, or graphic matter in the labeling) and in such terms as to render it likely to be read and understood by the ordinary individual under customary conditions of purchase and use; (F) the labeling accompanying it does not contain directions for use which are necessary for effecting the purpose for which the product is intended and if complied with, together with any requirements imposed under section 3(d) of FIFRA, are adequate to protect health and the environment; (G) the label does not contain a warning or caution statement which may be necessary and if complied with, together with any requirements imposed under section 3(d) of this Act, is adequate to protect health and the environment; or (H) in the case of a pesticide not registered in accordance with section 3 of FIFRA and intended for export, the label does not contain, in words prominently placed thereon with such conspicuousness (as compared with other words, statements, designs, or graphic matter in the labeling) as to render it likely to be noted by the ordinary individual under customary conditions of purchase and use, the following: "Not Registered for Use in the United States of America." (2) A pesticide is misbranded if--(A) the label does not bear an ingredient statement on that part of the immediate container (and on the outside container or wrapper of the retail package, if there be one, through which the ingredient statement on the immediate container cannot be clearly read) which is presented or displayed under customary conditions of purchase, except that a pesticide is not misbranded under this subparagraph if: (i) the size or form of the immediate container, or the outside container or wrapper of the retail package, makes it impracticable to place the ingredient statement on the part which is presented or displayed under customary conditions of purchase: and (ii) the ingredient statement appears prominently on another part of the immediate container, or outside container or wrapper, permitted by the Administrator; (B) the labeling does not contain a statement of the use classification under which the product is registered; (C) there is not affixed to its container, and to the outside container or wrapper of the retail package, if there be one, through which the required information on the immediate container cannot be clearly read, a label bearing (i) the name and address of the producer, registrant, or person for whom produced; (ii) the name, brand, or trademark under which the pesticide is sold; (iii) the net weight or measure of the content: Provided, That the Administrator may permit reasonable variations; and (iv) when required by regulation of the Administrator to effectuate the purposes of this Act, the registration number assigned to the pesticide under this Act, and the use classification; and (D) the pesticide contains any sub-stance or substances in quantities highly toxic to man, unless the label shall bear, in addition to any other matter required by this Act (i) the skull and crossbones; (ii) the word "poison" prominently in red on a background of distinctly contrasting color; and (iii) a statement of a practical treatment (first aid or otherwise) in case of poisoning by the pesticide. A, C

mist
Liquid particles measuring 500 to 40 microns, that are found by condensation of vapor. By comparison, fog particles are smaller than 40 microns. N

mitigation
(a) Avoiding the impact altogether by not taking a certain action or parts of an action. (b) Minimizing impacts by limiting the degree or magnitude of the action and its implementation. (c) Rectifying the impact by repairing, rehabilitating, or restoring the affected environment. (d) Reducing or eliminating the impact over time by preservation and maintenance operations during the life of the action. (e) Compensating for the impact by replacing or providing substitute resources or environments. A

mixed fertilizer
A mixture of wet and / or dry straight fertilizer materials, mixed fertilizer materials, fillers and additives prepared through chemical reaction to a given formulation. A

mixed liquor
Activated sludge and water con-

taining organic matter being treated in an aeration tank. N

mixed-waste processing
A system that involves the centralized treatment of collected, mixed, municipal waste to sort out reusable or recyclable materials and/or to convert mixed fractions into new forms of marketable materials or fuels.

mixing chamber
A chamber usually placed between the primary and secondary combustion chambers and in which the products of combustion are thoroughly mixed by turbulence that is created by increased velocities of gases, checker work, or turns in the direction of the gas flow.

mixing depth
The expanse in which air rises from the earth and mixes with the air above it until it meets air equal or warmer in temperature.

mixing zone
The zone extending from the sea's surface to seabed and extending laterally to a distance of 100 meters in all directions from the discharge point(s) or to the boundary of the zone of initial dilution as calculated by a plume model, whichever is greater, unless the director determines that the more restrictive mixing zone or another definition of the mixing zone is more appropriate for a specific discharge. A

mixture
Any combination of two or more chemical substances if the combination does not occur in nature and is not, in whole or part, the result of a chemical reaction; except that such term does include (1) any combination which occurs, in whole or in part, as a result of a chemical reaction if the combination could have been manufactured for commercial purposes without a chemical reaction at the time the chemical substances comprising the combination were combined, and if all the chemical substances comprising the combination are not new chemical substances, and (2) hydrates of a chemical substance or hydrated ions formed by association of a chemical substance with water, so long as the non-hydrated form is itself not a new chemical substance. [40 CFR §720.3]. A [40 CFR §712.3 varies the definition from this point and continues: "and if all of the chemical substances comprising the combination are included in the EPA, TSCA Chemical Substance Inventory after the effective date of the premanufacture notification requirement under 40 CFR § 720, and (2) hydrates of a chemical substance or hydrated ions formed by association of a chemical substance with water. The term mixture includes alloys, inorganic glasses, ceramics, frits, and cements, including Portland Cement."] A

ml.
Milliliter(s).

ml/l
Milliliter(s) per liter.

mm.
Abbreviation for millimeter(s).

MOA
Memorandum of Agreement. D

mobile compactor
A vehicle with an enclosed body containing mechanical devices that convey solid waste into the main compartment of the body and compress it.

mobile source
A moving producer of air pollution, mainly forms of transportation -- cars, motorcycles, planes. N

model
(1) A specific combination of car-line, body style, and drivetrain configuration. A (2) A computer program designed to simulate actual conditions, e.g. air movement, used to predict environmental effects of proposed new sources of pollution.

model plant
A description of a typical but theoretical plant used for developing economic, environmental impact and energy impact analyses as support for regulations or regulatory guidelines. It is an imaginary plant, with features of existing or future plants used to estimate the cost of incorporating air pollution control technology as the first step in exploring the economic impact of a potential NSPS. N

model specific code
The designation used for labeling purposes in 40 CFR §§ 205.158 and 205.169 for identifying the motorcycle

manufacturer, class, and "advertised engine displacement," respectively. A

model type
A unique combination of car line, basic engine, and transmission class. A

model year
The manufacturer's annual production period (as determined by the Administrator) which includes January 1 of such calendar year. If a manufacturer has no annual production period, the term "model year" means the calendar year. A

modeling
(1) An investigative technique using a mathematical or physical representation of a system or theory that accounts for all or some of its known properties. Models are often used to test the effect of changes of system components on the overall performance of the system. N (2) Use of mathematical equations to simulate and predict real events and processes. N

modification
Any physical change in, or change in the method of operation of, a stationary source which increases the amount of any air pollutant emitted by such source or which results in the emission of any air pollutant not previously emitted, except that: (1) Routine maintenance, repair, and replacement shall not be considered physical changes, and (2) The following shall not be considered a change in the method of operation: (i) An increase in the production rate,

if such increase does not exceed the operating design capacity of the stationary source; (ii) An increase in hours of operation. A

modified discharge
The volume, composition and location of the discharge proposed by the applicant for which a modification under section 301(h) of the Clean Water Act is requested. A modified discharge may be a current discharge, improved discharge, or altered discharge. A

modified source
Any physical change in, or change in the method of operation of, a stationary source which increases the emission rate of any pollutant for which a national standard has been promulgated under [40 CFR] Part 50 of this chapter or which results in the emission of any such pollutant not previously emitted, except that: (1) Routine maintenance, repair, and replacement shall not be considered a physical change, and (2) The following shall not be considered a change in the method of operation: (i) An increase in the production rate, if such increase does not exceed the operating design capacity of the source; (ii) An increase in the hours of operation; (iii) Use of an alternative fuel or raw material, if prior to the effective date of a paragraph in this Part which imposes conditions on or limits modifications, the source is designed to accommodate such alternative use. A

modular combustion unit
One of a series of incinerator units

designed to operate independently and can handle small quantities of solid waste.

moisture content of solid waste
The weight loss (expressed as a percentage) when a sample of solid waste is dried to a constant weight at a temperature of 100° C to 105° C.

moisture penetration
The depth to which irrigation water or precipitation penetrates soil before the rate of downward movement becomes negligible.

mol.
Mole, or weight in grams of a compound equal to its mol. wt.

mol. wt.
Molecular weight.

molecule
The smallest part of a substance that can exist separately and still retain its chemical properties and characteristic composition; the smallest combination of atoms that will form a given chemical compound.

monitor pathlength
The depth of effluent at the installed location of the continuous monitoring system. A

monitoring
Periodic or continuous surveillance or testing to determine the level of compliance with statutory requirements and / or pollutant levels in various media or in humans, animals, and other living things. N

monitoring activity
Includes but is not limited to, the following: the collection of samples, including preservation and transport, and the collection of information concerning the quality or condition of ambient waters, including ground waters, or aquatic biota; the collection of samples, including preservation and transport, and the collection of information concerning the physical, chemical, or biological character of waste discharges to ambient waters, including ground waters; the operation and maintenance of field and laboratory support facilities including approved quality assurance practices; the processing, analysis, interpretation, and reporting of resulting data and information; and the management of such activities in terms of staffing, funding, scheduling, and coordination with other agents, including other State, interstate, Federal, local, and private entities or agencies. A

monitoring device
The total equipment, required under the monitoring of operations sections in applicable subparts, used to measure and record (if applicable) process parameters. A

monitoring well
(1) A well used to obtain water samples for water quality analysis or to measure groundwater levels. (2) A well drilled at a hazardous waste management facility or Superfund site to collect ground-water samples for the purpose of physical, chemical, or biological analysis to determine the amounts, types, and distribution of contaminants in the ground water beneath the site. N

monoclonal antibodies
MABs and MCAs. Molecules of living organisms that selectively find and attach to other molecules to which their structure conforms exactly. This could also apply to equivalent activity by chemical molecules. N

monthly average
The arithmetic average of eight individual data points from effluent sampling and analysis during any calendar month. A

MOS
Margin of Safety. N

motor controller
An electronic or electromechanical device to convert energy stored in an energy storage device into a form suitable to power the traction motor. A

motor vehicle manufacturer
As used in sections 202, 203, 206, 207, and 208 [of the Clean Air Act], any person engaged in the manufacturing or assembling of new motor vehicles or new motor vehicle engines, or importing such vehicles or engines for resale, or who acts for and is under the control of any such person in connection with the distribution of new motor vehicles or new motor vehicle engines, but shall not include any dealer with respect to new motor vehicles or new motor vehicle engines received by him in commerce. B

motor vehicle
(1) Any vehicle, machine, tractor, trailer, or semitrailer propelled or drawn by mechanical power and used

upon the highways in the transportation of passengers or property, or any combination thereof, but does not include any vehicle, locomotive, or car operated exclusively on a rail or rails. A (2) Any self-propelled vehicle designed for transporting persons or property on a street or highway. B

motorcycle
Any motor vehicle, other than a tractor, that: (i) has two or three wheels; (ii) has a curb mass less than or equal to 680 kg (1499 lb); and (iii) is capable, with an 80 kg (176 lb) driver, of achieving a maximum speed of at least 24 km/h (15 mph) over a level paved surface. N

motorcycle noise level
The A-weighted noise level of a motorcycle as measured by the acceleration test procedure. N

MOU
Memorandum of Understanding. N

movable grate
A grate with moving parts. A movable grate designed to feed solid fuel or solid waste to a furnace is called a stoker.

move laterally (in soils)
To undergo transfer through soil generally in a horizontal plane from the original site of application or use by physical, chemical, or biological means. A

movement
Hazardous waste transported to a facility in an individual vehicle. A

mpc.
1,000 pieces.

MPD
Minimum Premarket Data.

mph.
Miles per hour.

MPRSA
Marine Protection Research & Sanctuaries Act of 1972. N

MPTDS
MPTER Model with Deposition and Settling of Pollutants. N

MPTER
Multiple Point Source Model with Terrain. N

MSA
Metropolitan Statistical Area as defined by the Department of Commerce. A

MSBu.
1,000 standard bushels.

MSDS
Material Sately Data Sheet. N

MSHA
Mine Safety & Health Administration.

MSW
Municipal Solid Waste.

MTP
Maximum Total Trihalomethane (THM) Potential. A

muck soils
Earth made from decaying plant materials. N

mucociliary clearance
Removal of materials from the respiratory tract via ciliary action.

mucociliary transport
The process by which mucus is transported, by ciliary action, from the lungs.

mucus
The sticky fluid covering the airways of the respiratory system.

mulch
A layer of material (wood chips, straw, leaves) placed around plants to hold moisture, prevent weed growth, and enrich soil. N

multicyclone collector
A dust collector consisting of several cyclone collectors that operate in parallel; the volume and velocity of incinerator combustion gas can be regulated by dampers to maintain efficiency over a given load range.

multiple use
Harmonious use of land for more than one purpose; i.e., grazing of livestock, wildlife production, recreation, watershed and timber production. Not necessarily the combination of uses that will yield the highest economic return or greatest unit output. N

multiple-chamber incinerator
An incinerator that consists of two or more chambers, arranged as in-line

or retort types, interconnected by gas passage ports or ducts.

multiple-effect evaporator system
The multiple-effect evaporators and associated condenser(s) and hotwell(s) used to concentrate the spent cooking liquid that is separated from the pulp (black liquor). A

mungo
Reclaimed wool of poor quality, which is combined with other fibers to make low-quality cloth.

municipal air pollution control agency
A city, county, or other local government agency responsible for enforcing ordinances or laws relating to the prevention and control of air pollution. A

municipal collection
Refuse collection by public employees and equipment under the supervision and direction of a municipal department or office.

municipal incinerator
A privately or publicly owned incinerator primarily designed and used to burn residential and commercial solid waste within a community.

municipal sanitary landfill
The disposal site for residential and commercial solid waste generated, collected, and processed within a community.

municipal solid wastes
Garbage, refuse, sludges, wastes, and other discarded materials result-

ing from residential and non-industrial operations and activities, such as household activities, office functions, and commercial housekeeping wastes. A

municipal waste treatment system needs

(1) The municipal wastewater collection and treatment system needs by 5-year increments, over at least a 20-year period including an analysis of alternative waste treatment systems, requirements for and general availability of land for waste treatment facilities and land treatment and disposal systems, total capital funding required for construction, and a program to provide the necessary financial arrangements for the development of such systems. (2) The identification of municipal waste treatment systems needs shall take into consideration: (i) Load reductions needed to be achieved by each waste treatment system in order to attain and maintain applicable water quality standards and effluent limitations. (ii) Population or population equivalents to be served, including forecasted growth or decline of such population over at least a 20-year period following the scheduled date for installation of the needed facility. (iii) The results of preliminary and completed planning conducted under Step I and Step II grants pursuant to Title II of the [Federal Water Pollution Control] Act. A

municipality

(A) A city, town, borough, county, parish, district, association, or other public body created by or pursuant to State law, with responsibility for the planning or administration of solid waste management, or an Indian tribe or authorized Indian tribal organization or Alaska Native village or organization, and (B) includes any rural community or unincorporated town or village or any other public entity for which an application for assistance is made by a State or political subdivision thereof. I And having jurisdiction over disposal of sewage, industrial wastes, or other waste, or a designated and approved management agency under section 208 of the FWPCA. (a) This definition includes a special district created under State law such as a water district, sewer district, sanitary district, utility district, drainage district, or similar entity or an integrated waste management facility, as defined in section 201(e) of the FWPCA, which has as one of its principal responsibilities the treatment, transport, or disposal of domestic wastewater in a particular geographic area. (b) This definition excludes the following: (1) Any revenue producing entity which has as its principal responsibility an activity other than providing wastewater treatment services to the general public, such as an airport, turnpike, port facility, or other municipal utility. (2) Any special district (such as school district or a park district) which has the responsibility to provide wastewater treatment services in support of its principal activity at specific facilities, unless the special district has the responsibility under State law to provide waste water treatment services to the community surrounding the special district's facility and no other municipality, with concurrent jurisdiction to serve the community, serves or intends to serve the special district's facility or the surrounding community. A, B, J

mutagen
Any substance that causes changes in the genetic structure in subsequent generations. N

mutagenesis
The induction of heritable changes in the genetic material of either somatic or germinal cells. O

mutagenic
The property of a substance or mixture of substances to induce changes in the genetic complement of either somatic or germinal tissue in subsequent generations. A

MTD
Maximum Tolerated Dose.

MTU
Mobile Treatment Unit(s).

mv.
Millivolt(s).

MVICSA
Motor Vehicle Information and Cost Savings Act.

Mwh.
Megawatt hour(s).

MWTA
Medical Waste Tracking Act.

MYDP
Multi-Year Development Plans. N

N

N
Newton.

N_1
First stage rotor speed.

N_2
(1) Second stage rotor speed. (2) Nitrogen gas.

N_3
Third stage rotor speed.

NAAQS
National Ambient Air Quality Standard.

NACA
National Agricultural Chemicals Association. N

NAMS
National Air Monitoring Station(s). Collectively the NAMS are a subset of the SLAMS ambient air quality monitoring network. A

nano-
A prefix that divides a basic unit by one billion (10^9).

NAR
National Asbestos Registry.

NAS
National Academy of Sciences.

NASA
National Aeronautics & Space Administration.

national ambient air quality standard
A federally promulgated maximum level of an air pollutant that can exist in the ambient air without producing adverse effect to humans (primary standard) or the public welfare (secondary standard).

National and Global Scales
Measurement scales representing concentrations characterizing the nation and the globe as a whole. A

National Commission on Air Quality

A national commission created by the Clean Air Act Amendments of 1977 which studied the implementation of the CAA and made recommendations to the Congress regarding necessary changes to the CAA.

national consensus standard

Any occupational safety and health standard or modification thereof which (1) has been adopted and promulgated by a nationally recognized standards-producing organization under procedures whereby it can be determined by the Secretary [of HEW] that persons interested and affected by the scope or provisions of the standard have reached substantial agreement on its adoption, (2) was formulated in a manner which afforded an opportunity for diverse views to be considered and (3) has been designated as such a standard by the Secretary [of HEW], after consultation with other appropriate Federal agencies. H

national contingency plan

The national contingency plan published under section 311(c) of the Federal Water Pollution Control Act or revised pursuant to section 105 of CERCLA. L

national data bank

A facility or system established or to be established by the Administrator [of EPA] for the purposes of assembling, organizing, and analyzing data pertaining to water quality and the discharge of pollutants. A

National Emissions Standards for Hazardous Air Pollutants

NESHAPS. Emissions standards set by EPA for an air pollutant not covered by NAAQS that may cause an increase in deaths or in serious irreversible, or incapacitating illness. N

National Fire Protection Association

NFPA. An international membership organization which promotes/improves fire protection and prevention and establishes safeguards against loss of life and property by fire. Best known on the industrial scene for the National Fire Codes -- 16 volumes of codes, standards, recommended practices and manuals developed (and periodically updated) by NFPA technical committees. Among these is NFPA 704, the code for showing hazards of materials as they might be encountered under fire or related emergency conditions, using the familiar diamond-shaped label or placard with appropriate numbers or symbols. N

National Institute for Occupational Safety and Health

NIOSH, U.S. Public Health Service, U.S. Department of Health and Human Services (DHHS), among other activities, tests and certifies respiratory protective devices and air sampling detector tubes, recommends occupational exposure limits for various substances, and assists OSHA and MSHA in occupational safety and health investigations and research. N

National Oil and Hazardous Substances Contingency Plan
  NOHSCP/NCP. The federal regulation that guides determination of the sites to be corrected under the Superfund program and the program to prevent or control spills into surface waters or other portions of the environment. N

National Pollutant Discharge Elimination System
  NPDS. The national program for issuing, modifying, revoking and reissuing, terminating, monitoring and enforcing permits, and imposing and enforcing pretreatment requirements, under sections 307, 402, 318, and 405 of the Clean Water Act. The term includes an approved program. A

national pretreatment standard or pretreatment standard
  Any regulation containing pollutant discharge limits promulgated by the EPA in accordance with section 307 (b) and (c) of the FWPCA, which applies to Industrial Users. This term includes prohibitive discharge limits established pursuant to [40 CFR] § 403.5. A

National Primary Drinking Water Regulations
  NPDWR. D

National Priorities List
  NPL. EPA's list of the most serious uncontrolled or abandoned hazardous waste sites identified for possible long-term remedial action under Superfund. A site must be on the NPL to receive money from the Trust Fund for remedial action. The list is based primarily on the score a site receives from the Hazard Ranking System. EPA is required to update the NPL at least once a year. N

National Response Center
  NRC. (1) The federal operations center that receives notifications of all releases of oil and hazardous substances into the environment. The Center, open 24 hours a day, is operated by the U.S. Coast Guard, which evaluates all reports and notifies the appropriate agency. (2) A notification center which must be called when significant oil or chemical spills or other environment-related accidents occur. The toll-free telephone number is 1-800-424-8802. N

National Response Team
  NRT. Representatives of 13 federal agencies that, as a team, coordinate federal responses to nationally significant incidents of pollution and provide advice and technical assistance to the responding agency(ies) before and during a response action. N

national security exemption
  An exemption which may be granted under section 203(b)(1) of the CAA for the purpose of national security. A

national standard
  A primary or a secondary standard. A

National Toxicology Program
  NTP. Federal activity overseen by PHHS with resources from NIH, FDA, and the Center for Disease

Control. Its goals are to develop tests useful for public health regulations of toxic chemicals, to develop toxicological profiles of materials, to foster testing of materials, and to communicate the results for use by others. N

natural conditions
Naturally occurring phenomena that reduce visibility as measured in terms of visual range, contrast, or coloration. A

natural draft
The negative pressure created by the height of a stack or chimney and the difference in temperature between flue gases and the atmosphere.

natural gas
A natural fuel containing primarily methane and ethane that occurs in certain geologic formations. N

natural resources
Land, fish, wildlife, biota, air, water, ground water, drinking water supplies, and other such resources belonging to, managed by, held in trust by, appertaining to, or otherwise controlled by the United States (including the resources of fishery conservation zones established by the Magnuson Fishery Conservation and Management Act), any State or local government, or any foreign government (as defined by section 101(16) of CERCLA). A

natural selection
The process of survival of the fittest, by which organisms that adapt to their environment survive and those that do not disappear. N

navigable waters
(1) Traditionally, waters sufficiently deep and wide for navigation by all, or specified sizes of vessels; such waters in the United States come under federal jurisdiction and are included in certain provisions of the Clean Water Act. N (2) Includes all navigable "waters of the United States including the territorial seas," and includes, but is not limited to: (a) All waters which are presently used, or were used in the past, or may be susceptible to use as a means to transport interstate or foreign commerce, including all waters which are subject to the ebb and flow of the tide, and including adjacent wetlands; the term "wetlands" as used in this regulation shall include those areas that are inundated or saturated by surface or ground water at a frequency and duration sufficient to support, and that under normal circumstances do support, a prevalence of vegetation typically adapted for life in saturated soil conditions. Wetlands generally include swamps, marshes, bogs and similar areas; the term "adjacent" means bordering, contiguous or neighboring; (3) tributaries of navigable waters of the United States, including adjacent wetlands; (4) interstate waters, including wetlands; and (5) all other waters of the United States such as intrastate lakes, rivers, streams, mudflats, sandflats, and wetlands, the use, degradation or destruction of which affect interstate commerce including, but not limited to: (i)

intrastate lakes, rivers streams and wetlands which are utilized by interstate travelers for recreational or other purposes; and (ii) intrastate lakes, rivers, streams, and wetlands from which fish or shellfish are or could be taken and sold in interstate commerce; and (iii) intrastate lakes, rivers, streams and wetlands which are utilized for industrial purposes by industries in interstate commerce. A, D

NBAR
Nonbinding Preliminary Allocation of Responsibility. N

NCA
(1) Noise Control Act. (2) National Coal Association.

NCAQ
National Commission on Air Quality. N

NCC
National Climatic Center. N

NCHS
National Center for Health Statistics (NIH). N

NCI
National Cancer Institute, United States Department of Health and Human Services, or designee. O

NCM
Notice of Commencement of Manufacture (TSCA).

NCO
Negotiated Consent Order. N

NCP
(1) National Contingency Plan (CERCLA). N (2) Noncompliance Penalties (CAA). N

NCTR
National Center for Toxicological Research.

NDA
New Drug Application.

NDIR
Nondispersive infrared.

necessary preconstruction approvals or permits
(1) Those permits or approvals required under federal air quality control laws and regulations and those air quality control laws and regulations which are part of the applicable State Implementation Plan. [ed. Affects date a source is considered to have commenced construction in NSD areas]. A (2) Those permits or approvals required by the permitting authority as a precondition to undertaking any [regulated] activity. A, B

necrosis
Death of cells that can discolor areas on a plant or kill the entire plant. N

NEDS
National Emissions Data System. N

negative declaration
A written announcement, prepared after the environmental review, which states that EPA has decided not to

prepare an EIS and summarizes the environmental impact appraisal. A

negligible residue
Any amount of a pesticide chemical remaining in or on a raw agricultural commodity or group of raw agricultural commodities that would result in a daily intake regarded as toxicologically insignificant on the basis of scientific judgment of adequate safety data. Ordinarily this will add to the diet an amount which will be less than 1/2,000th of the amount that has been demonstrated to have no effect from feeding studies on the most sensitive animal species tested. Such toxicity studies shall usually include at least 90-day feeding studies in two species of mammals. A

NEIC
National Enforcement Investigations Center based in Denver, Colorado (EPA).

neighborhood scale
Concentrations within some extended area of the city that has relatively uniform land use with dimensions in the 0.5 to 4.0 kilometers range. A

neighboring company
Any one of those electric utility companies with one or more electric power interconnections to the principal company and which have geographically adjoining service areas. A

nematicides
All substances or mixtures of substances intended for preventing or

inhibiting the multiplication or establishment of, preventing or mitigating the adverse effects of, repelling, or destroying any members of the Class Nematoda of the Phylum Nemathelminthes declared to be pests under 40 CFR § 162.14. (i) Nematicides include but are not limited to, plant parasitic nematode control agents intended for use in or on plants, plant parts, soil, or certain infested agricultural commodities or articles. (ii) Nematicides do not include those substances or mixtures of substances subject to the provisions of the Federal Food, Drug and Cosmetic Act, as amended (21 U.S.C. 301 et seq.), such as substances or mixtures of substances intended for use in preventing reproduction of, inactivating, or destroying nematodes in living man or other animals. A

nematocide
A chemical agent which is destructive to nematodes (round worms or threadworms.) N

nematode
Invertebrate animals of the phylum nemathelminthes and class nematoda; unsegmented round worms with elongated, fusiform, or saclike bodies covered with cuticle and inhabiting soil, water, plants, or plant parts; may also be called nemas or eelworms. C

neoplasm
A new or abnormal tissue growth that is uncontrollable and progressive. A

NEPA
National Environmental Policy Act.

NEPA-associated documents

Any one or combination of: notices of intent, negative declarations, exemption certifications, environmental impact appraisals, news releases, EIS's, and environmental assessments. Associated with a Federal agency or department's compliance with NEPA. A

NESHAPS

National Emissions Standards for Hazardous Air Pollutants. N

net emissions increase

(i) The amount by which the sum of the following exceeds zero: (a) any increase in actual emissions from a particular physical change or change in the method of operation at a stationary source; and (b) any other increases and decreases in actual emissions at the source that are contemporaneous with the particular change and are otherwise creditable. (ii) An increase or decrease in actual emissions is contemporaneous with the increase from the particular change only if it occurs between: (a) the date five years before construction on the particular change commences and (b) the date that the increase from the particular change occurs. (iii) An increase or decrease in actual emissions is creditable only if the Administrator has not relied on it in issuing a permit for the source under this Ruling which permit is in effect when the increase in actual emissions from the particular change occurs. (iv) An increase or decrease in actual emissions of sulfur dioxide or particulate matter which occurs before the applicable baseline date is creditable only if it is required to be considered in calculating the amount of maximum allowable increases remaining available. (v) An increase in actual emissions is creditable only to the extent that the new level of actual emissions exceeds the old level. (vi) A decrease in actual emissions is creditable only to the extent that: (a) the old level of actual emissions or the old level of allowable emissions, whichever is lower, exceeds the new level of actual emissions; (b) it is federally enforceable at and after the time that actual construction on the particular change begins; and (c) it has approximately the same qualitative significance for public health and welfare as that attributed to the increase from the particular change. (vii) An increase that results from a physical change at a source occurs when the emissions unit on which construction occurred becomes operational and begins to emit a particular pollutant. Any replacement unit that requires shakedown becomes operational only after a reasonable shakedown period, not to exceed 180 days. A

net evaporation

The evaporation rate exceeds the precipitation rate during a one year period. A

net precipitation

The precipitation rate exceeds the evaporation rate during a one year period. A

net system capacity

The sum of the net electric generating capability (not necessarily equal to rated capacity) of all electric generating equipment owned by an electric utility company (including steam generating units, internal combustion engines, gas turbines, nuclear units, hydroelectric units, and all other electric generating equipment) plus firm contractual purchases that are interconnected to the affected facility that has the malfunctioning flue gas desulfurization system. The electric generating capability of equipment under multiple ownership is prorated based on ownership unless the proportional entitlement to electric output is otherwise established by contractual arrangement. A

net working capital
Current assets minus current liabilities. A

net worth
Total assets minus total liabilities and is equivalent to owner's equity. A

netting
A concept under the Clean Air Act by which a company can modify an existing plant without a new source review. The company must make compensatory reductions elsewhere in the plant that bring the net emissions increase below a threshold amount. N

neutralization
Any of several procedures that prevent excessively acid or alkaline wastes from being discharged in plant effluents (e.g., mixing acid and basic wastes such that the net effect is a near-neutral pH).

neutralize
To eliminate potential hazards by inactivating strong acids, caustics, and oxidizers. For example, acids can be neutralized by adding an appropriate amount of caustic substance to the spill. N

new biochemical and microbial registration review
Review of an application for registration of a biochemical or microbial pesticide product containing a biochemical or microbial active ingredient not contained in any other pesticide product that is registered under FIFRA at the time the application is made. A

new chemical substance
Any chemical substance which is not included in the chemical substance list compiled and published under section 8(b). K [ed. This determines which newly produced chemicals must undergo notification and review by EPA before production pursuant to the Toxic Substances Control Act]. A

new chemical registration review
Review of an application for registration of a pesticide product containing a chemical active ingredient which is not contained as an active ingredient in any other pesticide product that is registered under FIFRA at the time the application is made. A

new discharger
Any building, structure, facility, or installation: (a) (1) From which there is or may be a new or additional

"discharge of pollutants" at a "site" at which on October 18, 1972 it had never discharged pollutants; and (2) Which has never received a finally effective NPDES "permit" for discharges at that site; and (3) Which is not a "new source." (b) This definition includes an "indirect discharger" which commences discharging into "waters of the United States." It also includes any existing mobile point source, such as an offshore oil drilling rig, seafood processing vessel, or aggregate plant, that begins discharging at a location for which it does not have an existing permit. A

new HWM facility
A Hazardous Waste Management facility which began operation or for which construction commenced after November 19, 1980. A

new injection well
A well which begins injection after a UIC program for the State in which the well is located is approved. N

new motor vehicle engine
An engine in a new motor vehicle or a motor vehicle engine, the equitable or legal title to which has never been transferred to the ultimate purchaser. B

new motor vehicle
A motor vehicle, the equitable or legal title to which has never been transferred to an ultimate purchaser. B

new product
(1) A product, the equitable or legal title of which has never been transferred to an ultimate purchaser, or (2) A product which is imported or

offered for importation into the United States and which is manufactured after the effective date of a regulation under section 6 or section 8 [of the Noise Control Act] which would have been applicable to such product had it been manufactured in the United States. G (3) A pesticide product which is not a federally registered product. A

New Source Performance Standards
NSPS. Uniform national EPA air emission and water effluent standards which limit the amount of pollution allowed from new sources or from existing sources that have been modified. N

new source
(1) Any building, structure, facility or installation from which there is or may be the discharge [or emission] of pollutants, the construction of which is commenced after the publication of proposed regulations prescribing a standard of performance under [federal] pollution control statutes. A (2) Any stationary source, the construction or modification of which is commenced after the publication of regulations (or, if earlier, proposed regulations) prescribing a standard of performance under this section [§ 111 of the CAA] which will be applicable to such source. B (3) Any source, the construction of which is commenced after the publication of proposed regulations prescribing a standard of performance under this section [§ 306 of the FWPCA] which will be applicable to such source, if such standard is thereafter promulgated in accordance with this section. D

New Source and Environmental Questionnaire

NS/EQ. An initial document submitted by an applicant for a new source NPDES permit. This document will furnish information on the status of the proposed source that will allow determination of whether the facility is a new or existing source. In addition, the NS/EQ will also furnish information on the potential environmental impacts of the proposed source. It is the Agency's intention that in the case of sources which will probably have insignificant environmental impacts, the NS/EQ will normally provide sufficient information to fulfill the requirements for an environmental impact assessment. A

new source coal mine

(1) A coal mine (excluding coal preparation plants and coal preparation plant associated areas): (i) The construction of which is commenced after May 29, 1981 (the date of publication of the proposal of these regulations); or (ii) Which is determined by the EPA Regional Administrator to constitute a "major alteration." In making this determination, the Regional Administrator shall take into account the occurrence of one or more of the following events, in connection with the mine for which the NPDES permit is being considered, after the date of proposal of applicable new source performance standards: (A) A mine operation initiates extraction of a coal seam not previously extracted by that mine; (B) A mine operation discharges into a drainage area not previously affected by wastewater discharges from the mine; (C) A mine

operation causes extensive new surface disruption; (D) A mine operation initiates construction of a new shaft, stope, or drift; (E) A mine operation acquires additional land or mineral rights; (F) A mine operation makes significant capital investment in additional equipment or additional facilities; and (G) Such other factors as the Regional Administrator deems relevant. (2) No provision in this part shall be deemed to affect the classification as a new source, pursuant to EPA's promulgation of January 13, 1981 (46 FR 3136), of a coal mine on which construction began prior to May 29, 1981. A

new use pattern registration review

Review of an application for registration, or for amendment of a registration entailing a major change to the use pattern of an active ingredient contained in a product registered under FIFRA or pending Agency decision on a prior application at the time of application. Examples of major changes include but are not limited to, changes from non-food to food use, outdoor to indoor use, ground to aerial application, terrestrial to aquatic use, and non-residential to residential use. A

new use

When used with respect to a product containing a particular active ingredient, means: (1) Any proposed use pattern that would require the establishment of, the increase in, or the exemption from the requirement of, a tolerance or food additive regulation under section 408 or 409 of the Federal Food, Drug and Cosmetic Act; (2) Any aquatic, terrestrial, outdoor, or forestry use pattern, if no product containing the active ingredient is currently registered for that use pattern; or (3) Any additional use pattern that would result in a significant increase in the level of exposure, or a change in the route of exposure, to the active ingredient of man or other organisms. A

new vessel
Includes every description of watercraft or other artificial contrivance used, or capable of being used, as a means of transportation on the navigable waters, the construction of which is initiated after promulgation of standards and regulation under § 312 of FWPCA. D

newly certified aircraft gas turbine engine
An aircraft gas turbine engine which is originally type certified on or after the effective date of the applicable emission standard. A

NFPA
National Fire Protection Association. An international membership organization which promotes/improves fire protection and prevention and establishes safeguards against loss of life and property by fire. Best known on the industrial scene for the National Fire Codes -- 16 volumes of codes, standards, recommended practices and manuals developed (and periodically updated) by NFPA technical committees. Among these is NFPA 704, the code for showing hazards of materials as they might be encountered under fire or related emergency conditions, using the familiar diamond-shaped label or placard with appropriate numbers or symbols. N

ng.
Abbreviation for nanogram.

NHLBI
National Heart, Lung, and Blood Institute.

NHTSA
National Highway Traffic Safety Administration.

NIA
National Institute on Aging.

NIAID
National Institute of Allergy and Infectious Diseases.

NIAMDD
National Institute of Arthritis, Metabolism and Digestive Diseases.

NICHHD
National Institute of Child Health and Human Development.

NIDA
National Institute of Drug Abuse.

NIEHS
National Institute of Environmental Health Sciences, United States Department of Health and Human Services, or designee. O

NIM
National Impact Model. N

NIMBY
Not In My Backyard. N

NIOSH
National Institute for Occupational Safety and Health, U.S. Public Health Service, U.S. Department of Health and Human Services (DHHS), among other activities, tests and certifies respiratory protective devices and air sampling detector tubes, recommends occupational exposure limits for various substances, and assists OSHA and MSHA in occupational safety and health investigations and research. N

NIPDWR
National Interim Primary Drinking Water Regulations.

nitric oxide
NO_2. A gas formed by combustion under high temperature and high pressure in an internal combustion engine. It changes into nitrogen dioxide in the ambient air and contributes to photochemical smog. N

nitrification
The process whereby ammonia in wastewater is oxidized to nitrite and then to nitrate by bacterial or chemical reactions. N

Nitrilotriacetic Acid
NTA. A compound being used to replace phosphates in detergents. N

nitrite
(1) An intermediate in the process of nitrification. (2) Nitrous oxide salts used in food preservation. N

nitrogen dioxide
The result of nitric oxide combining with oxygen in the atmosphere; a major component of photochemical smog. N

nitrogen oxides
Gases formed in great part from atmospheric nitrogen and oxygen when combustion takes place under conditions of high temperature and pressure. Nitrogen oxides include nitric oxide (NO) and nitrogen dioxide (NO_2). Can be harmful themselves and are precursors of photochemical oxidant.

nitrogenous wastes
Animal or plant residues that contain large amounts of nitrogen. N

nm.
Nanometer, 10^{-9} gram.

NO
Abbreviation for nitric oxide.

no discernible adverse effect
No adverse effect observable within the limitations and sensitivity specified in the Registration Guidelines promulgated pursuant to the Federal Insecticide, Fungicide and Rodenticide Act. A

NOAA
National Oceanic and Atmospheric Administration (DOC). N

NOAEL
No Observed Adverse Effect Level; the highest dose in an experiment

which did not produce an observable adverse effect. N [See: LOAEL].

NOEC
No Observed Effect Concentration. A

NOEL
No Observed Effects Level. N

NO flowmeter
A calibrated flowmeter capable of measuring and monitoring NO flowrates with an accuracy of ± 2% of the measured flowrate. (Rotameters have been reported to operate unreliably when measuring low NO flows and are not recommended).

NOHSCP
National Oil and Hazardous Substances Contingency Plan. N

noise control system
Includes any vehicle part, component or system the primary purpose of which is to control or cause the reduction of noise emitted from a vehicle. A

noise emission test
A test conducted pursuant to the measurement methodology specified. A

Noise Reduction Rating
NRR. A single number noise reduction factor in decibels, determined by an empirically derived technique which takes into account performance variation of protectors in noise reducing effectiveness due to differing noise spectra, fit variability and the mean attenuation of test stimuli at the one-third octave band test frequencies. A

nominal concentration
The amount of an ingredient which is expected to be present in a typical sample of a pesticide product at the time the product is produced, expressed as a percentage by weight. A

nominal fuel tank capacity
The volume of the fuel tank(s), specified by the manufacturer to the nearest tenth of a U.S. gallon, which may be filled with fuel from the fuel tank filler inlet. A

nonattainment area
For any air pollutant, an area which is shown by monitored data or which is calculated by air quality modeling (or other methods determined by the Administrator to be reliable) to exceed any national ambient air quality standard for such pollutant. B

non-community water system
A public water system that is not a community water system. A

non-compliance penalty
A penalty required by section 120 of the CAA that is calculated to take away the financial advantage a source derives from not complying with air pollution requirements.

non-contact cooling water
Water which is used in a cooling system designed so as to maintain constant separation of the cooling medium from all contact with process chemicals but which may on the occasion of corrosion, cooling system

leakage or similar cooling system failures contain small amounts of process chemicals: Provided, that all reasonable measures have been taken to prevent, reduce, eliminate and control to the maximum extent feasible such contamination: And provided further, That all reasonable measures have been taken that will mitigate the effects of such contamination once it has occurred. A

noncontinental area
The State of Hawaii, the Virgin Islands, Guam, American Samoa, the Commonwealth of Puerto Rico, or the Northern Mariana Islands. A

non-continuous discharger
A plant which does not discharge pollutants during specific periods of time for reasons other than treatment plant upset, such periods being at least 24 hours in duration. A typical example of a non-continuous discharger is a plant where wastewaters are routinely stored for periods in excess of 24 hours to be treated on a batch basis. For non-continuous discharging direct discharging plants, NPDES permit authorities shall apply the mass-based annual average effluent limitations or standards and the concentration-based maximum day and maximum for monthly average effluent limitations or standards established in the regulations. POTWs may elect to establish concentration-based standards established in the regulations. POTWs may elect to establish concentration-based standards for non-continuous discharges to POTWs. They may do so by establishing

concentration-based standards for noncontinuous discharges to POTWs. They may do so by establishing concentration-based pretreatment standards equivalent to the mass-based standards. O

nondegradation clause
A legal provision stipulating that the present air quality of an area must not be lowered. The provision is meant to protect those areas whose air quality is already better than federal standards demand. A [ed. nondegradation is also a policy applied to water quality of navigable waters].

non-emission related maintenance
That maintenance which does not substantially affect emissions and which does not have a lasting effect on the deterioration of the vehicle or engine with respect to emissions once the maintenance is performed at any particular date. A

nonexcessive infiltration
The quantity of flow which is less than 120 gallons per capita per day (domestic base flow and infiltration) or the quantity of infiltration which cannot be economically and effectively eliminated from a sewer system as determined in a cost-effectiveness analysis. (See [40 CFR] §35.2005(b)(16) and 35.2120). A

nonexcessive inflow
The maximum total flow rate during storm events which does not result in chronic operational problems related to hydraulic overloading of the treat-

ment works or which does not result in a total flow of more than 275 gallons per capita per day (domestic base flow plus infiltration plus inflow). Chronic operational problems may include surcharging, backups, bypasses, and overflows. [See 40 CFR] § 35.2005(b)(16) and 35.2120). A

nonexpendable personal property
Tangible personal property having a useful life of more than 1 year and an acquisition cost of $300 or more per unit. A grantee may use its own definition of nonexpendable personal property provided that such definition would at least include all nonexpendable personal property as defined herein. A

nonferrous
Metals that contain no iron. Nonferrous waste usually includes aluminum, copper, brass, and bronze materials.

nonindustrial source
Any source of pollutants which is not an industrial source. A

non-ionizing electromagnetic radiation
(1) Radiation that does not change the structure of atoms but does heat tissue and may cause harmful biological effects. (2) Microwaves, radio waves, and low-frequency elecetromagnetic fields from high-voltage transmission lines. N

nonisolated intermediate
Any intermediate that is not intentionally removed from the equipment in which it is manufactured, including the reaction vessel in which it is manufactured, equipment which is ancillary to the reaction vessel, and any equipment through which the chemical substance passes during a continuous flow process, but not including tanks or other vessels in which the substance is stored after its manufacture. A

nonoperational storage tank
Any underground storage tank in which regulated substances will not be deposited or from which regulated substances will not be dispensed after the date of the enactment of the Hazardous and Solid Waste Amendments of 1984. I

nonperishable raw agricultural commodity
Any raw agricultural commodity not subject to rapid decay or deterioration that would render it unfit for consumption. Examples are cocoa beans, coffee beans, field-dried beans, field-dried peas, grains, and nuts. Not included are eggs, milk, meat, poultry, fresh fruits, vegetables such as onions, parsnips, potatoes, and carrots. A

nonpoint source control needs
(1) For each category of nonpoint sources of pollutants to be considered in any specified area as established in the State/EPA agreement, an identification and evaluation of all measures necessary to produce the desired level of control through application of best management practices (recognizing the application of best management practices may vary from area to area depending upon the extent of water

quality problems). (2) The evaluation shall include an assessment of nonpoint source control measures applied thus far, the period of time required to achieve the desired control, the proposed regulatory programs to achieve the controls, the management agencies needed to achieve the controls, and the costs by agency and activity, presented by 5-year increments, to achieve the desired controls, and a description of the proposed actions necessary to achieve such controls. A

nonpoint source

Causes of water pollution that are not associated with point sources, such as agricultural fertilizer runoff, sediment from construction. Examples include (i) Agriculturally related nonpoint sources of pollution including runoff from manure disposal areas, and from land used for livestock and crop production; (ii) Silviculturally related nonpoint sources of pollution; (iii) Mine-related sources of pollution including new, current and abandoned surface and underground mine runoff; (iv) Construction activity related sources of pollution; (v) Sources of pollution from disposal on land, in wells or in subsurface excavations that affect ground and surface water quality; (vi) Salt water intrusion into rivers, lakes, estuaries and groundwater resulting from reduction of fresh water flow from any cause, including irrigation, obstruction, groundwater extraction, and diversion; and (vii) Sources of pollution related to hydrologic modifications, including those caused by changes in the movement, flow, or circulation of any navigable waters or

groundwaters due to construction and operation of dams, levees, channels, or flow diversion facilities. A

nonpoint source assessment

An assessment of water quality problems caused by nonpoint sources of pollutants. (1) The assessment shall include a description of the type of problem, an identification of the waters affected (by segment or other appropriate planning area), an evaluation of the seriousness of the effects on those waters, and an identification of nonpoint sources contributing to the problem. (2) Any nonpoint sources of pollutants originating outside a segment which materially affect water quality within the segment shall be considered. (3) The results of this assessment should be reflected in the States' report required under Section 305(b) of the Federal Water Pollution Control Act. A

nonprocurement list

The portion of the *List of Parties Excluded from Federal Procurement or Nonprocurement Programs* complied, maintained and distributed by the General Services Administration (GSA) containing the names and other information about persons who have been debarred, suspended, or voluntarily excluded under Executive Order 12549 and these regulations, and those who have been determined to be ineligible. A

nonprofit organization

Any corporation, trust, foundation, or institution (a) which is entitled to exemption under section 501(c)(3) of the Internal Revenue Code, or (b) which is not organized for profit and no part of the net earnings of which inure to the benefit of any private shareholder or individual.

NONs
Notice of Noncompliance.

nonsudden accident
An unforeseen and unexpected occurrence which takes place over time and involves continuous or repeated exposure. A

nonsudden accidental occurrence
An occurrence which takes place over time and involves continuous or repeated exposure. A

nontarget organisms
Those flora and fauna (including man) that are not intended to be controlled, injured, killed or detrimentally affected in any way by a pesticide. A

nontidal
Not influenced by tides. N

Non-Transient Non-Community Water System
NTNCWS. A public water system that is not a community water system and that regularly serves at least 25 of the same persons over 6 months per year. A

non-transportation-related onshore and offshore facilities
(A) Fixed onshore and offshore oil well drilling facilities including all equipment and appurtenances related thereto used in drilling operations for exploratory or development wells, but excluding any terminal facility, unit or process integrally associated with the handling or transferring of oil in bulk to or from a vessel. (B) Mobile onshore and offshore oil well drilling platforms, barges, trucks, or other mobile facilities including all equipment and appurtenances related thereto when such mobile facilities are fixed in position for the purpose of drilling operations for exploratory or development wells, but excluding any terminal facility, unit or process integrally associated with the handling or transferring of oil in bulk to or from a vessel. (C) Fixed onshore and offshore oil production structures, platforms, derricks, and rigs including all equipment and appurtenances related thereto, as well as completed wells and the wellhead separators, oil separators, and storage facilities used in the production of oil, but excluding any terminal facility, unit or process integrally associated with the handling or transferring of oil in bulk to or from a vessel. (D) Mobile onshore and offshore oil production facilities including all equipment and appurtenances related thereto as well as completed wells and wellhead equipment, piping from wellheads to oil separators, oil separators, and storage facilities used in the production of oil when such mobile facilities are fixed in position for the purpose of oil production operations, but excluding any terminal facility, unit or process integrally associated with the handling or transferring of oil in bulk to or from a vessel. (E) Oil refining facilities including all equipment and

appurtenances related thereto as well as in-plant processing units, storage units, piping, drainage systems and waste treatment units used in the refining of oil, but excluding any terminal facility, unit or process integrally associated with the handling or transferring of oil in bulk to or from a vessel. (F) Oil storage facilities including all equipment and appurtenances related thereto as well as fixed bulk plant storage, terminal oil storage facilities, consumer storage, pumps and drainage systems used in the storage of oil, but excluding inline or breakout storage tanks needed for the continuous operation of a pipeline system and any terminal facility, unit or process integrally associated with the handling or transferring of oil in bulk to or from a vessel. (G) Industrial, commercial, agricultural or public facilities which use and store oil, but excluding any terminal facility, unit or process integrally associated with the handling or transferring of oil in bulk to or from a vessel. (H) Waste treatment facilities including in-plant pipelines, effluent discharge lines, and storage tanks, but excluding waste treatment facilities located on vessels and terminal storage tanks and appurtenances for the reception of oily ballast water or tank washings from vessels and associated systems used for off-loading vessels. (I) Loading racks, transfer hoses, loading arms and other equipment which are appurtenant to a nontransportation-related facility or terminal facility and which are used to transfer oil in bulk to or from highway vehicles or railroad cars. (J) Highway vehicles and railroad cars which are used for the transport of

oil exclusively within the confines of a nontransportation-related facility and which are not intended to transport oil in interstate or intrastate commerce. (K) Pipeline systems which are used for the transport of oil exclusively within the confines of a nontransportation-related facility or terminal facility and which are not intended to transport oil in interstate or intrastate commerce, but excluding pipeline systems used to transfer oil in bulk to or from a vessel. A

nonwetland
Any area that has sufficiently dry conditions that hydrophytic vegetation, hydric soils, and/or wetland hydrology are lacking; it includes upland as well as former wetlands that are effectively drained. N

No Observed Effect Concentration
NOEC. The highest tested concentration in an acceptable early life stage test: (i) which did not cause the occurrence of any specified adverse effect (statistically different from the control at the 95 percent level); and (ii) below which no tested concentration caused such an occurrence. A

No.
Number.

no reasonable alternatives
(1) No land-based disposal sites, discharge point(s) within internal waters, or approved ocean dumping sites within a reasonable distance of the site of the proposed discharge the use of which would not cause unwarranted economic impacts on the

discharger, or, notwithstanding the availability of such sites.

normal ambient value

That concentration of a chemical species reasonably anticipated to be present in the water column, sediments, or biota in the absence of disposal activities at the disposal site in question. A

normal operation of a spray tower

Operation utilizing formulations that present limited air quality problems from stack gases and associated need for extensive wet scrubbing; without more than 6 turnarounds in a 30 consecutive day period, thus permitting essentially complete recycle of waste water. A

notice of intent

The written announcement to Federal, State and local agencies, and to interested persons, that a draft environmental impact statement will be prepared. The notice shall briefly describe the EPA action, its location, and the issues involved. The purpose of a notice of intent is to involve other government agencies and interested persons as early as possible in the planning and evaluation of actions which may have significant environmental impacts. This notice should encourage public input in the preparation of a draft EIS and assure that environmental values will be identified and weighed from the outset, rather than accommodated by adjustments at the end of the decision-making process. A

NO₂

Abbreviation for nitrogen dioxide.

NOV

Notice of Violation. N

NOₓ

Abbreviation for nitrogen oxides or oxides of nitrogen.

NPDES

National   Pollutant   Discharge Elimination System.

NPDES application

The uniform national forms (including the NPDES application short forms, NPDES application standard forms, and any subsequent additions, revisions or modifications duly promulgated by the Administrator [of EPA] pursuant to the [Federal Water Pollution Control] Act) for application for an NPDES permit. A

NPDES permit

Any permit or equivalent document or requirements issued by the Administrator, or, where appropriate, by the Director [of a state agency], after enactment of the Federal Water Pollution Control Amendments of 1972, to regulate the discharge of pollutants pursuant to section 402 of the Act. A

NPDES reporting form

The uniform national forms (including subsequent additions, revisions, or modifications duly promulgated by the Administrator [of EPA] pursuant to the [Federal Water Pollution Control] Act) for reporting data and information pursuant to monitoring and other conditions of NPDES permits. A

NPDES State
A State or Interstate water pollution control agency with an NPDES permit program approved pursuant to section 402(b) of the [Federal Water Pollution Control] Act. A

NPDS
National Pollutant Discharge System. The national program for issuing, modifying, revoking and reissuing, terminating, monitoring and enforcing permits, and imposing and enforcing pretreatment requirements, under sections 307, 402, 318, and 405 of the Clean Water Act. The term includes an approved program. A

NPDWR
National Primary Drinking Water Regulations. D

NPL
National Priorities List.

NPRM
Notice of Proposed Rulemaking. The document issued by an agency, and published in the Federal Register, that solicits public comment on a proposed regulatory action. Under the Administrative Procedure Act, it must include, at a minimum: (a) a statement of the time, place and nature of the public rulemaking proceedings; (b) reference to the legal authority under which the rule is proposed; and (c) either the terms or substance of the regulation under development, or a description of the subject and issues involved.

NRC
(1) Nuclear Regulatory Commission. (2) National Response Center.

NRDC
Natural Resources Defense Council.

NRT
National Response Team consisting of representatives of 14 government agencies (DOD, DOI, DOT / RSPA, DOT/USCG, EPA, DOC, FEMA, DOS, USDA, DOJ, HHS, DOL, Nuclear Regulatory Commission, and DOE), is the principal organization for implementing the NCP. When the NRT is not activated for a response action, it serves as a standing committee to develop and maintain preparedness, to evaluate methods of responding to discharges or releases, to recommend needed changes in the response organization, and to recommend revisions to the NCP. The NRT may consider and make recommendations to appropriate agencies on the training, equipping, and protection of response teams; and necessary research, development, demonstration, and evaluation to improve response capabilities.

NSF
National Science Foundation.

NSPS
New Source Performance Standards under section 306 of the Clean Water Act (or section 111 of the Clean Air Act). A

NTA
Nitrilotriacetic Acid. A compound

being used to replace phosphates in detergents. N

NTIS
National Technical Information Service. Under the Department of Commerce is the central point in the United States for the public sale of government funded research and development reports and other analyses prepared by federal agencies, their contractors, or grantees.

NTNCWS
Non-Transient Non-Community Water System. A public water system that is not a community water system and that regularly serves at least 25 of the same persons over 6 months per year. A

NTP
National Toxicology Program.

nuclear energy
The force released by nuclear decay; radioactivity.

nuclear power plant
A device that converts atomic energy into usable power; heat produced by a reactor makes steam to drive electricity-generating turbines. N

nuclear winter
Prediction by some scientists that smoke and debris rising from massive fires resulting from a nuclear war could enter the atmosphere and block out sunlight for weeks or months. The scientists making this prediction project a cooling of the earth's surface, and changes in climate which could, for example, negatively effect world agricultural and weather patterns. N

nuclide
A species of atom characterized by the constitution of its nucleus. The nuclear constitution is specified by the number of protons (Z), number of neutrons (N) and energy content; or alternatively, by the atomic number (Z), mass number A = (N + Z), and atomic mass. To be regarded as a distinct nuclide, the atom must be capable of existing for a measurable time. Thus, nuclear isomers are separate nuclides, whereas promptly decaying excited nuclear states and unstable intermediates in nuclear reactions are not so considered.

nutrient(s)
(1) Any substance assimilated by living things that promotes growth. The term is generally applied to nitrogen and phosphorus in wastewater, but is also applied to other essential and trace elements. N (2) Elements or compounds essential to growth and development of living things; carbon, oxygen, nitrogen, potassium and phosphorus. N

NVACP
Neighborhoods, Voluntary Associations and Consumer Protection.

NWQSS
National Water Quality Surveillance System (EPA).

O

O.D.
Outside diameter.

O_2
Oxygen.

O_3
Ozone.

OANR
Office of Air, Noise, and Radiation at EPA.

OAQPS
Office of Air Quality Planning & Standards (EPA).

obligation of funds
Formal assignment by the Agency, through a Financial Management Officer, of a specified portion of appropriated funds to support a given project. For EPA, R&D grants funds are obligated when a GAD official signs the grant agreement or amendment.

obligations
Amounts of orders placed, contracts awarded, services rendered, or other commitments made by Federal agencies during a given period, that will require outlays during the same or some future period.

Observed Effect Concentration
OEC. The lowest tested concentration in an acceptable early life stage test: (i) Which caused the occurrence of any specified adverse effect (statistically different from the control at the 95 percent level); and (ii) above which all tested concentrations caused such an occurrence. $\underline{A}$

occupational safety and health standard
A standard which requires conditions, or the adoption or use of one or more practices, means, methods, operations, or processes, reasonably necessary or appropriate to provide safe or healthful employment and places of employment. $\underline{H}$

occurrence
An accident, including continuous or repeated exposure to conditions, which results in bodily injury or property damage which the owner or operator

neither expected nor intended to occur. A

ocean

Any portion of the high seas beyond the contiguous zone. D

ocean dumping

(1) The disposal of materials of any kind at sea, subject to regulation pursuant to the Marine Protection, Research and Sanctuaries Act. A (2) A disposition of material: Provided, That it does not mean a disposition of any effluent from any outfall structure to the extent that such disposition is regulated under the provisions of the Federal Water Pollution Control Act, as amended (33 USC 1251-1376) under the provisions of section 13 of the Rivers and Harbors Act of 1899, as amended (33 USC 407), or under the provisions of the Atomic Energy Act of 1954, as amended (42 USC 2011, et seq.), nor does it mean a routine discharge of effluent incidental to the propulsion of, or operation of motor-driven equipment on, vessels. Provided further, That it does not mean the construction of any fixed structure or artificial island nor the intentional placement of any device in ocean waters or on or in the submerged land beneath such waters, for a purpose other than disposal, when such construction or such placement is otherwise regulated by federal or state law or occurs pursuant to an authorized federal or state program. And provided further, That it does not include the deposit of oyster shells or other materials when such deposit is made for the purpose of developing, maintaining, or harvesting fisheries resources and is otherwise regulated by federal or state

law or occurs pursuant to an authorized federal or state law or occurs pursuant to an authorized federal or state program. A, E

ocean waters

(1) Those waters of the open seas lying seaward of the base line from which the territorial sea is measured, as provided for in the Convention on the Territorial Sea and the Contiguous Zone (15 UST 1606; TIAS 5639). E (2) Those coastal waters landward of the baseline of the territorial seas, and the deep waters of the territorial seas, or the waters of the contiguous zone. A

OCS

Outer Continental Shelf. N

OCSLA

Outer Continental Shelf Lands Act. N

octave band attenuation

The amount of sound reduction determined according to the measurement procedure of 40 CFR § 211.206 for one-third octave bands of noise. A

OCZM

Office of Coastal Zone Management.

odor threshold

The lowest concentration of an airborne odor that a human being can detect.

OEC

Observed Effect Concentration. A

OECD

Organization for Economic Cooperation and Development, headquartered in Paris, France.

off-budget federal entities
Organizational entities, federally owned in whole or in part, whose transactions belong in the budget under current budget accounting concepts but which have been excluded from the budget totals under provisions of law. While these transactions are not included in the budget totals, information on these entities is presented in various places in the budget documents.

off-road motorcycle
Any motorcycle that is not a street motorcycle or competition motorcycle. **A**

off-road vehicles
Forms of motorized transportation that do not require prepared surfaces and which can be used to reach remote areas. **M**

off-site facility
A hazardous waste treatment, storage or disposal area that is located at a place away from the generating site. **N**

offal
The viscera and trimmings of a slaughtered animal removed from the carcass.

office waste
Discarded materials that consist primarily of paper waste, including envelopes, ledgers, and brochures.

offsets
A condition of new source review in nonattainment areas under the Clean Air Act, whereby a company must obtain a reduction in emissions from some other source that equals or exceeds any increase in emissions from a new or modified plant. **N**

offshore facility
Any facility of any kind located in, on, or under, any of the navigable waters of the United States, and any facility of any kind which is subject to the jurisdiction of the United States and is located in, on, or under any other waters, other than a vessel or a public vessel. **D**

offshore platform gas turbines
Any stationary gas turbine located on a platform in an ocean. **A**

OGC
Office of General Counsel.

oil
Oil of any kind or in any form, including, but not limited to, petroleum, fuel oil, sludge, oil refuse, and oil mixed with wastes other than dredged spoil. **D**

oil "fingerprinting"
A method that identifies oil spills so they can be traced back to their sources. **N**

oil feedstock
The crude oil and natural gas liquids fed to the topping units. **A**

oil spill
Accidental discharge into bodies of water, can be controlled by chemical

dispersion, combustion, mechanical containment, and absorption. N

old chemical registration review
Review of an application for registration of a new product containing active ingredients and uses which are substantially similar or identical to those currently registered or for which an application is pending Agency decision. A

oligotrophic lakes
Deep clear lakes with low nutrient supplies. They contain little organic matter and have a high dissolved oxygen level. N

OMB
Office of Management and Budget, a White House staff office that controls the Federal budget.

OMSAPC
Office of Mobile Source Air Pollution Control (EPA).

on ground tank
A device meeting the definition of "tank" in 40 CFR §260.10 and that is situated in such a way that the bottom of the tank is on the same level as the adjacent surrounding surface so that the external tank bottom cannot be visually inspected. A

On-Scene Coordinator
OSC. The Federal official predesignated by EPA or USCG to coordinate and direct Federal responses and removals under the NCP; or the DOD official designated to coordinate and direct the removal actions from

releases of hazardous substances, pollutants, or contaminants from DOD vessels and facilities. When the NRC receives notification of a pollution incident, the NRC Duty Officer notifies the appropriate OSC, depending on the location of an incident. Based on this initial report and any other information that can be obtained, the OSC makes a preliminary assessment of the need for a Federal response. If an onscene response is required, the OSC will go the scene and monitor the response of the responsible party of State or local government. If the responsible party is unknown or not taking appropriate action, and the response is beyond the capability of State and local governments, the OSC may initiate Federal actions, using funding from the FWPCA Pollution Fund for oil discharges and the CERCLA Trust Fund (Superfund) for hazardous substance releases. N

on-site
The same or geographically contiguous property which may be divided by public or private right-of-way, provided the entrance and exit between the properties is at a crossroads intersection, and access is by crossing as opposed to going along, the right-of-way. Non-contiguous properties owned by the same person but connected by a right-of-way which he controls and to which the public does not have access, is also considered on-site property. A

on-site disposal
Any methods or processes to eliminate or reduce the volume or weight

of solid waste on the property of the generator.

on-site facility

A hazardous waste treatment, storage or disposal area that is located on the generating site. N

on-site incinerator

An incinerator that burns solid waste on the property used by the generator thereof.

once through cooling water

(1) Those waters discharged that are used for the purpose of heat removal and that do not come into direct contact with any raw material, intermediate or finished product. A (2) Water passed through the main cooling condensers in one or two passes for the purpose of removing waste heat. A

oncogenic

The property of a substance or a mixture of substances to produce or induce benign or malignant tumor formations in living animals. A

oncology

Study of cancer. N

one-hour period

Any 60-minute period commencing on the hour. A

one-year, 24-hour precipitation event

The maximum 24-hour precipitation event with a probable recurrence interval of once in one year as defined by the National Weather Service and Technical Paper No. 40, "Rainfall Frequency Atlas of the U.S.," May

1961, or equivalent regional or rainfall probability information developed therefrom. A

onshore

All land areas landward of the territorial seas as defined in 40 CFR 125.1(gg). A

onshore facility

Any facility (including, but not limited to, motor vehicles and rolling stock) of any kind located in, on, or under, any land or nonnavigable waters within the United States; and (b), as defined by section 311(a)(10) of the CWA, any facility (including, but not limited to, motor vehicles and rolling stock) of any kind located in, on, or under any land within the United States other than submerged land. A, L, N

onshore oil storage facility

Any facility (excluding motor vehicles and rolling stock) of any kind located in, on, or under, any land within the United States, other than submerged land. A

opacity

(1) Degree of obscuration of light. For example, a window has zero opacity; a wall is 100 percent opaque. The Ringelmann Chart of evaluating smoke density is based on opacity. (2) The fraction of a beam of light, expressed in percent, which fails to penetrate a plume of smoke. A (3) The degree to which emissions reduce the transmission of light and obscure the view of an object in the background. A (4) The fraction of a beam

of light, expressed in percent, which fails to penetrate a plume of smoke. A

opacity rating
The apparent obscuration of an observer's vision that equals the apparent obscuration of smoke of a given rating on the Ringelmann Chart.

open burning
(1) The uncontrolled burning of waste materials in the open, in outdoor ininerators, or in an open dump either intentionally or accidentally. (2) The combustion of any material without the following characteristics: (a) Control of combustion air to maintain adequate temperature for efficient combustion, (b) Containment of the combustion-reaction in an enclosed device to provide sufficient residence time and mixing for complete combustion, and (c) Control of emission of the gaseous combustion products. A

open combustion
Those basic oxygen furnace steel-making wet air cleaning systems which are designed to allow excess air to enter the air pollution control system for the purpose of combusting the carbon monoxide in furnace gases. A

open dump
Any facility or site where solid waste is disposed of which is not a sanitary landfill which meets the criteria promulgated under section 4004 of RCRA and which is not a facility for disposal of hazardous waste. A, I [ed. All open dumps will eventually be prohibited by RCRA].

open hearth furnace
(1) A long, wide, shallow reverberatory furnace used to produce steel from cast or pig iron. Now being replaced by the basic oxygen furnace. (2) A steel-making furnace in which the oxidation of a molten mixture of pig iron and steel scrap by chemicals and combustible gas takes place in a large, long, shallow pool (the hearth) that is enclosed by a brickwork ceiling. Heat is introduced by combustion products flowing between the molten mixture and the ceiling. The process uses large quantities of scrap.

open hearth furnace steelmaking
The production of steel from molten iron, steel scrap, fluxes, and various combinations thereof, in refractory lined fuel-fired furnaces equipped with regenerative chambers to recover heat from the flue and combustion gases. A

open land
Any surface or subsurface land which is not a disposal site and is not covered by a building. A

open space
A relatively undeveloped green or wooded area provided usually within an urban development to minimize feelings of congested living. M

open-pit incinerator
A burning apparatus that has an open top and a system of closely spaced nozzles that place a stream of high-velocity air over the burning zone.

operable treatment works
An operable treatment works is a

treatment works that: (a) Upon completion of construction will treat wastewater, transport wastewater to or from treatment, or transport and dispose of wastewater in a manner which will significantly improve an objectionable water quality related situation or health hazard in existence prior to construction of the treatment works, and (b) Is a component part of a complete waste treatment system which, upon completion of construction for the complete waste treatment system (or completion of construction of other treatment works in the system in accordance with a schedule approved by the Regional Administrator [of EPA]) will comply with all applicable statutory and regulatory requirements. A

operable unit
Term for each of a number of separate activities undertaken as part of a Superfund site cleanup. A typical operable unit would be removing drums and tanks from the surface of a site. N

operating humidity range
The range of ambient relative humidity over which the instrument will meet all performance specifications. A

operating temperature range
The range of ambient temperatures over which the instrument will meet all performance specifications. A

operation and maintenance
(1) Activities conducted at a site after a Superfund site action is completed to ensure that the action is effective and operating properly. (2) Actions taken after construction to assure that facilities constructed to treat waste water will be properly operated, maintained, and managed to achieve efficiency levels and prescribed effluent limitations in an optimum manner. N

operation period
(1) A minimum period of time over which a measurement system is expected to operate within certain performance specifications without unscheduled maintenance, repair, or adjustment. A (2) The period of time over which the instrument can be expected to operate unattended within specifications. A

operational test period
A minimum period of time over which the continuous monitoring system is expected to operate within certain performance specifications without unscheduled maintenance, repair, or adjustment. A

operator
The person responsible for the overall operation of a facility. M

OPM
Office of Planning and Management (EPA).

OPTS
Office of Pesticides and Toxic Substances (EPA).

oral toxicity
Adverse effects resulting from taking a substance into the body by mouth. Ordinarily used to denote effects in experimental animals. N

ORD
Office of Research and Development of the Environmental Protection Agency.

ordinance
A statute enacted by the legislative body of a local, generally a municipal, government.

organic
Referring to or derived from living organisms. In chemistry, any compound containing carbon. N

organic active ingredients
Carbon-containing active ingredients used in pesticides, excluding metallo-organic active ingredients. A

organic chemicals/compounds
Animal or plant-produced substances containing mainly carbon, hydrogen, and oxygen. N

organic coating
Any coating used in a surface coating operation, including dilution solvents, from which VOC emissions or volatile organic compound emissions occur during the application or the curing process. A

organic content
The ratio of carbon compounds, whether from living organisms or not, to the total chemical composition of a substance.

organic materials
Chemical compounds of carbon excluding carbon monoxide, carbon dioxide, carbonic acid, metallic carbides, metallic carbonates, and ammonium carbonate. A

organic pesticides
Carbon-containing substances used as pesticides, excluding metallo-organic compounds. A

organic refuse
Solid waste composed of carbon compounds and generally, but not exclusively, by-products of plant and animal life processes (e.g., paper, wood, excreta, yard trimmings).

organic solvents
Organic materials, including diluents and thinners, which are liquids at standard conditions and which are used as dissolvers, viscosity reducers, or cleaning agents. A

organism
Any living thing. N

organophosphates
Pesticide chemicals that contain phosphorus, used to control insects. They are short-lived but some can be toxic when first applied. N

organotins
Chemical compounds used in antifoulant paints to protect the hulls of boats and ships, buoys, and dock pilings from marine organisms such as barnacles. N

orientation sensitivity
The angular tolerance to which the sensor can be misaligned from its correct orientation to measure the flow rate vector before a specified error

occurs in the indicated flow rate compared to the reference flow rate. A

original equipment part

A part present in or on a vehicle at the time the vehicle is sold to the ultimate purchaser, except for components installed by a dealer which are not manufactured by the vehicle manufacturer or are not installed at the direction of the vehicle manufacturer. A

ORM

Other regulated material. DOT hazard classification of a particular hazardous material to label it in transport. ORM-A; a class of materials with an anesthetic, irritating, noxious, toxic, or other property whose leakage can cause extreme discomfort to transportation personnel. ORM-B: a class of materials (including solids wet with water) that can cause damage to a vehicle if they leak during transport. ORM-E: materials that are not in any other hazard classification but are subject to DOT regulations. A

ORP

Oxidation-Reduction Potential.

Orsat

An apparatus used to analyze flue gases volumetrically by dissolving the constituent gases selectively in various solvents.

Osborne separator

A separator that uses a pulsed, rising column of air to separate small particles of glass, metal, or other dense items from compost.

OSC

On-Scene Coordinator. The Federal official predesignated by EPA or USCG to coordinate and direct Federal responses and removals under the NCP; or the DOD official designated to coordinate and direct the removal actions from releases of hazardous substances, pollutants, or contaminants from DOD vessels and facilities. When the NRC receives notification of a pollution incident, the NRC Duty Officer notifies the appropriate OSC, depending on the location of an incident. Based on this initial report and any other information that can be obtained, the OSC makes a preliminary assessment of the need for a Federal response. If an onscene response is required, the OSC will go the scene and monitor the response of the responsible party of State or local government. If the responsible party is unknown or not taking appropriate action, and the response is beyond the capability of State and local governments, the OSC may initiate Federal actions, using funding from the FWPCA Pollution Fund for oil discharges and the CERCLA Trust Fund (Superfund) for hazardous substance releases. N

oscillating-grate stoker

A stoker whose entire grate surface oscillates to move the solid waste and residue over the grate surface.

OSHA

(1) Occupational Safety and Health Administration of the Department of Labor. (2) Occupational Safety and Health Act.

OSHRC
Occupational Safety and Health Review Commission.

OSM
Office of Surface Mining, Department of Interior.

osmosis
The tendency of a fluid to pass through a permeable membrane such as the wall of a living cell into a less concentrated solution so as to equalize the concentrations on both sides of the membrane. N

OSTP
Office of Science and Technology Policy (White House). N

OSW
Office of Solid Waste at EPA.

OTA
Office of Technology Assessment (U.S. Congress). N

other lead-emitting operation
Any lead-acid battery manufacturing plant operation from which lead emissions are collected and ducted to the atmosphere and which is not part of a grid casting, lead oxide manufacturing, lead reclamation, paste mixing, or three-process operation facility.

OTS
Office of Toxic Substances (EPA).

outage
Space left in a product container to allow for expansion during temperature changes it may undergo during ship-ment and use. Measurement of space not occupied. A

outdoor application or use
Any pesticide application or use that occurs outside enclosed manmade structures or the consequences of which extend beyond enclosed man-made structures, including, but not limited to, pulp and paper mill water treatments and industrial cooling water treatments. A

outfall
The place where an effluent is discharged into receiving waters. N

over-the-head position
The mode of use of a device with a headband, in which the headband is worn such that it passes over the user's head. This is in contrast to the behind-the-head and under-the-chin positions. A

overburden
The rock and soil cleared away before mining. N

overfire air
(1) Air forced into the top of an incinerator or boiler to fan the flames. N (2) Air under control as to quantity and direction, introduced above and beyond a fuel bed by induced or forced draft. A

overfire air fan
A fan used to provide air above a fuel bed.

overland flow
A land application technique that cleanses waste water by allowing it to

flow over a sloped surface. As the water flows over the surface, the contaminants are removed and the water is collected at the bottom of the slope for reuse. N

overload
Operation of equipment in excess of normal, full load rating, or of a conductor in excess of rated ampacity which, when it persists for a sufficient length of time, would cause damage or dangerous overheating. A fault, such as a short circuit or ground fault, is not an overload. O

overturn
The period of mixing (turnover), by top to bottom circulation, of previously stratified water masses. This phenomenon may occur in spring and/or fall; the result is a uniformity of physical and chemical properties of the water at all depths. N

OWE
Office of Water Enforcement at EPA.

OWEP
Office of Water Enforcement Permits at EPA. D

owned or controlled
Leased, operated, controlled, supervised, or in ten percent or greater part, owned. A

owned or controlled by the parent company
The parent owns or controls 50 percent or more of the other company's voting stock or other equity rights, or has the power to control the management and policies of the other company. A

owner or operator
(A)(i) In the case of a vessel, any person owning, operating, or chartering by demise, such vessel, and (ii) in the case of an onshore facility, or an offshore facility, any person owning or operating such facility, and (iii) in the case of any abandoned facility, the person who owned, operated, or otherwise controlled activities at such facility immediately prior to such abandonment. Such term does not include a person, who, without participating in the management of a vessel or facility, holds indicia of ownership primarily to protect his security interest in the vessel or facility. O (B) In the case of a hazardous substance which has been accepted for transportation by a common or contract carrier and except as provided in section 107(a) (3) or (4) of CERCLA, (i) the term "owner or operator" shall mean such common carrier or other bona fide for hire carrier acting as an independent contractor during such transportation, (ii) the shipper of such hazardous substance shall not be considered to have caused or contributed to any release during such transportation which resulted solely from circumstances or conditions beyond his control; (C) In the case of a hazardous substance which has been delivered by a common or contract carrier to a disposal or treatment facility and except as provided in section 107(a) (3) or (4) (i) the term "owner or operator" shall not include such common or contract carrier and

(ii) such common or contract carrier shall not be considered to have caused or contributed to any release at such disposal or treatment facility resulting from circumstances or conditions beyond its control. A, L

OWPE
Office of Waste Programs Enforcement. I

OWWM
Office of Water and Waste Management.

OX
Abbreviation for photochemical oxidants (ozone).

oxidant
A substance containing oxygen that reacts chemically in air to produce a new substance; primary source of photochemical smog. N

oxidation
Oxygen combining with other elements. N

oxidation control system
(1) An emission control system which reduces emissions from sulfur recovery plants by converting these emissions to sulfur dioxide. A (2) The addition of oxygen which breaks down organic waste or chemicals such as cyanides, phenols, and organic sulfur compounds in sewage by bacterial and chemical means. (3) Oxygen combining with other elements. (4) The process in chemistry whereby electrons are removed from a molecule. N

oxidation pond
(1) A holding area where organic wastes are broken down by aerobic bacteria. (2) A man-made lake or body of water in which waste is consumed by bacteria. It is used most frequently with other waste treatment processes. An oxidation pond is basically the same as a sewage lagoon. N

oxidation-reduction process
A complex of biochemical reactions in soil that influences the valence state of elements and their ions found in the soil; long periods of soil saturation during the growing season tend to elicit anaerobic conditions that shift the overall process to a reducing condition. N

oxide
A compound of two elements, one of which is oxygen.

oxides of nitrogen
The sum of the nitric oxide and nitrogen dioxide contained in a gas sample as if the nitric oxide were in the form of nitrogen dioxide. A

oxidizer
An oxidizer or oxidizing material is a substance that yields oxygen readily to stimulate the combustion (oxidation) of organic matter. A

oxidizing catalyst
A device installed in the exhaust system of the vehicle that utilizes a catalyst and, if necessary, an air pump to reduce emissions of hydrocarbons and carbon monoxide by 50 percent from that vehicle. A

oxygenated solvent

An organic solvent containing oxygen as part of the molecular structure. Alcohols and ketones are oxygenated compounds often used as paint solvents. N

oxyhemoglobin

Hemoglobin in combination with oxygen. It is the predominant form of hemoglobin present in arterial blood.

oz.

ounces.

ozonator

A device that adds ozone to water. N

ozone

O3. (1) A pungent, colorless, toxic gas that contributes to photochemical smog. _ [ed. The natural ambient air quality standard for photochemical oxidants was changed to an ozone standard]. (2) Found in two layers of the atmosphere, the stratosphere and the troposphere. In the stratosphere (the atmospheric layer beginning 7 to 10 miles above the earth's surface) ozone is a form of oxygen found naturally which provides a protective layer shielding the earth from ultraviolet radiation's harmful health effects on humans and the environment. In the troposphere (the layer extending up 7 to 10 miles from the earth's surface), ozone is a chemical oxidant and major component of photochemical smog. Ozone can seriously affect the human respiratory systems and is one of the most prevalent and widespread of all the criteria pollutants for which the Clean Air Act required EPA to set standards. Ozone in the troposphere is produced through complex chemical reactions of nitrogen oxides, which are among the primary pollutants emitted by combustion sources, hydrocarbons, released into the atmosphere through the combustion, handling and processing of petroleum products; and sunlight. N

ozone depletion

Destruction of the stratospheric ozone layer which shields the earth from ultraviolet radiation harmful to biological life. This destruction of ozone is caused by the breakdown of certain chlorine and/or bromine-containing compounds (chlorofluorocarbons or halons) which break down when they reach the stratosphere and catalytically destroy ozone molecules. N

P

PA
Preliminary Assessment.

PAAT
Public Affairs Assist Team.

package or **packaging**
The immediate container or wrapping in which any pesticide is contained for consumption, use or storage. "Package" does not include: (a) Any shipping container or wrapping used solely for the transportation of any pesticide in bulk or in quantity to manufacturers, packers or processors, or to wholesale or retail distributors thereof; or (b) Any shipping container or other wrapping used by retailers to ship or deliver any pesticide to consumers unless it is the only such container or wrapping. A

packed tower
A pollution control device that forces dirty air through a tower packed with crushed rock or wood chips while liquid is sprayed over the packing material. The pollutants in the air stream either dissolve or chemically react with the liquid. N

packer
A device lowered into a well which can be expanded to produce a watertight seal. A

PAH
Polycyclic aromatic hydrocarbons. Components in organic materials that may pose a risk of cancer. A

PAIR
Preliminary Assessment Information Rule.

pandemic
Widespread throughout an area, nation or the world. N

paper
Generally, the term for all kinds of matted or felted sheets of fiber laid down on a fine screen from a water suspension. Specifically, as one of the two subdivisions of the general term, paper refers to materials that are lighter in basis weight, thinner, and more flexible than paperboard, the other subdivision. It is used primarily for printing, writing, and wrapping.

paperboard
One of the two broad categories of paper products. It is distinguished from paper, the other category, by a heavier basis weight and greater thickness and rigidity. The category includes container board, boxboard, building board, and automobile board, and it can be manufactured from virgin pulp or a combination of recycled fibers.

paperstock
Paper waste that is recovered and reused. It is the principal ingredient in the manufacture of certain types of paperboard.

PAPR
Powered Air Purifying Respirator. N

parameter
A quantitative or characteristic element which describes physical, chemical, or biological conditions of water. A

parent company
A company that owns or controls another company. A

parent corporation
A corporation which directly owns at least 50 percent of the voting stock of the corporation which is the facility owner or operator; the latter corporation is deemed a "subsidiary" of the parent corporation. A

parking surcharge regulation
A regulation imposing or requiring the imposition of any tax, surcharge, fee, or other charge on parking spaces, or any other area used for the temporary storage of motor vehicles. B

PARS
Precision and Accuracy Reporting System. N

Parshall flume
A calibrated device developed by Parshall for measuring the flow of liquid in an open conduit. It consists essentially of a contracting length, a throat, and an expanding length. At the throat is a sill over which the flow passes at critical depth. The upper and lower heads are each measured at a definite distance from the sill. The lower head need not be measured unless the sill is submerged more than about 67 percent.

partial closure
The closure of a discrete part of a [hazardous waste] facility in accordance with the applicable closure requirements of 40 CFR Parts 264 or 265. For example, partial closure may include the closure of a trench, a unit operation, a landfill cell, or a pit, while other parts of the same facility continue in operation or will be placed in operation in the future. A

particleboard
Board products that are composed of distinct particles of wood or other lignocellulosic materials not reduced to fibers which are bonded together with an organic or inorganic binder. A

particulate asbestos material
Finely divided particles of asbestos material. A

particulate loading
(1) The introduction of particulates into ambient air. (2) The mass of

particulates per unit volume of air or water. N

particulate matter
Any material, except water in uncombined form, that is or has been airborne and exists as a liquid or a solid at standard conditions. A

particulates
Fine liquid or solid particles such as dust, smoke, mist, fumes, or smog, found in the air or emissions. N

parts per million
ppm. A volume unit of measurement; the number of parts of a given pollutant in a million parts of air.

party
Any person that participates in a hearing as complainant, respondent, or intervenor. A

PA/SI
Preliminary Assessment/Site Inspection.

pass through
The discharge of pollutants through the POTW into navigable waters in quantities or concentrations which are a cause of or significantly contribute to a violation of any requirement of the POTW's NPDES permit (including an increase in the magnitude or duration of a violation). An industrial user significantly contributes to such permit violation where it: (1) Discharges a daily pollutant loading in excess of that allowed by contract with the POTW or by federal, state, or local law; (2) Discharges wastewater which substantially

differs in nature and constituents from the user's average discharge; (3) Knows or has reason to know that its discharge, alone or in conjunction with discharges from other sources, would result in a permit violation; or (4) Knows or has reason to know that the POTW is, for any reason, violating its final effluent limitations in its permit and that such industrial user's discharge either alone or in conjunction with discharges from other sources, increases the magnitude or duration of the POTW's violations. A

passenger automobile
Any automobile which the Secretary determines is manufactured primarily for use in the transportation of no more than 10 individuals. A

passive institutional control
(1) Permanent markers placed at a disposal site, (2) public records and archives, (3) government ownership and regulations regarding land or resource use, and (4) other methods of preserving knowledge about the location, design, and contents of a disposal system. A

paste mixing facility
The facility including lead oxide storage, conveying, weighing, metering, and charging operations; paste blending, handling, and cooling operations; and plate pasting, takeoff, cooling, and drying operations. A

pasture crops
Crops such as legumes, grasses, grain stubble and stover which are consumed by animals while grazing. A

pathlength
The depth of effluent in the light beam between the receiver and the transmitter of the single-pass transmissometer, or the depth of effluent between the transceiver and reflector of a double-pass transmissometer. A

pathogen
Microorganisms that can cause disease in other organisms or in humans, animals and plants. They may be bacteria, viruses, or parasites and are found in sewage, in runoff from animal farms or rural areas populated with domestic and/or wild animals, and in water used for swimming. Fish and shellfish contaminated by pathogens, or the contaminated water itself, can cause serious illnesses. N

pathogenic
Capable of causing disease. N

pathogenic bacteria
Bacteria which may cause disease in the host organisms by their parasitic growth.

pathogenic waste
Discarded materials that contain organisms capable of causing disease. See infectious waste and isolation waste.

pathology
The study of disease. N

Pb
Lead.

PBBs
Polybrominated biphenyls. Chemical substances the compositions of which,

without regard to impurities, consist of brominated biphenyl molecules having the molecular formula $C_{12}H_xBr_y$ where $x + y = 10$ and y ranges from 1 to 10. A

PCB
Polychlorinated biphenyl. (1) Any of several organic compounds used in plastics manufacture, transformers, and capacitors that are toxic and persistent environmental pollutants and tend to accumulate in animal tissues. Further sale or new use of the compounds was barred in 1979 by TSCA. (2) Any chemical substance that is limited to the biphenyl molecule that has been chlorinated to varying degrees or any combination of substances which contains such substance.

PCB article container
(1) Any package, can, bottle, bag, barrel, drum, tank or other device used to contain PCB articles or PCB equipment, and whose surface(s) has not been in direct contact with PCBs. A

PCB article
Any manufactured article, other than a PCB container that contains PCBs and whose surface(s) has been in direct contact with PCBs. "PCB article" includes capacitors, transformers, electric motors, pumps, pipes and any other manufactured item (1) which is formed to a specific shape or design during manufacture, (2) which has end use function(s) dependent in whole or in part upon its shape or design during end use, and (3) which has either no change of chemical

composition during its end use or only those changes of composition which have no commercial purpose separate from that of the PCB article. A

PCB chemical substance
Any chemical substance which is limited to the biphenyl molecule which has been chlorinated to varying degrees. A

PCB closed manufacturing process
A manufacturing process in which PCBs are generated but from which less than 10 micrograms per cubic meter from any resolvable gas chromatographic peak are contained in any release to air; less than 100 micrograms per liter from any resolvable gas chromatographic peak are contained in any release to water; and less than 2 micrograms per gram from any resolvable gas chromatographic peak are contained in any product, or any process waste. A

PCB container
Any package, can, bottle, bag, barrel, drum, tank, or other device that contains PCBs or PCB articles and whose surface(s) has been in direct contact with PCBs. A

PCB contaminated electrical equipment
Any electrical equipment, including but not limited to transformers (including those used in railway locomotives and self-propelled cars), capacitors, circuit breakers, reclosers, voltage regulators, switches (including sectionalizers and motor starters), electromagnets, and cable, that contain 50 ppm or greater PCB, but less than 500 ppm PCB. Oil-filled electrical equipment other than circuit breakers, reclosers, and cable whose PCB concentration is unknown must be assumed to be PCB contaminated electrical equipment. A

PCB contaminated transformer
Any transformer that contains 50 ppm or greater of PCB but less than 500 ppm PCB. A

PCB controlled waste manufacturing process
A manufacturing process in which PCBs are generated but from which less 10 micrograms per cubic meter from any resolvable gas chromatographic peak are contained in any release to air; less than 100 micrograms per liter from any resolvable gas chromatographic peak are contained in any release to water; less than 2 micrograms per gram from any resolvable gas chromatographic peak are contained in any product, and the remainder of PCBs generated are incinerated in a qualified incinerator, landfilled in a landfill approved under the provisions of 761.75, or stored for such incineration or landfilling in accordance with the requirements of § 761.65(b)(1). A

PCB equipment
Any manufactured item, other than a PCB container or a PCB article container, which contains a PCB article or other PCB equipment, and includes microwave ovens, electronic equipment, and fluorescent light ballasts and fixtures. A

PCB item

Any PCB article, PCB article container, PCB container, or PCB equipment, that deliberately or unintentionally contains or has a part of it any PCB or PCBs at a concentration of 50 ppm or greater. A

PCB mixture

Any mixture which contains 0.05 percent (on a dry weight basis) or greater of a PCB chemical substance, and any mixture which contains less than 0.05 percent PCB chemical substance because of any dilution of a mixture containing more than 0.05 percent PCB chemical substance. This definition includes, but is not limited to, dielectric fluid and contaminated solvents, oils, waste oils, other chemicals, rags, soil, paints, debris, sludge, slurries, dredge spoils, and materials contaminated as a result of spills. A

PCB qualified incinerator

Means one of the following: (1) An incinerator approved under the provisions of § 761.70. Any concentration of PCBs can be destroyed in an incinerator approved under 21 §761.70. (2) A high efficiency boiler approved under the provisions of § 761.60(a)(3). Only PCBs in concentrations below 500 ppm can be destroyed in a high-efficiency boiler approved under §761.60(a)(3). (3) An incinerator approved under section 3005(c) of the Resource Conservation and Recovery Act (42 U.S.C. 6925(c)) (RCRA). Only PCBs in concentrations below 50 ppm can be destroyed in a RCRA-approved incinerator. The manufacturer seeking to qualify a process as a controlled waste process by disposing of wastes in a RCRA-approved incinerator must make a determination that the incinerator is capable of destroying less readily burned compounds than the PCB homologs to be destroyed. The manufacturer may use the same guidance used by EPA in making such determination when issuing an approval under section 3005(c) of RCRA. The manufacturer is also responsible for obtaining a reasonable assurance that the incinerator, when burning PCB wastes, will be operated under conditions which have been shown to enable the incinerator to destroy the less readily burned compounds. A

PCB transformer

Any transformer that contains 500 ppm PCB or greater. A

pCi

Picocurie. A

PCS

Permit Compliance System, a national data base under NPDES.

pct.

Percent.

PDP-CVS

Positive Displacement Pump-Constant Volume Sampler.

peak load

One hundred percent of the manufacturer's design capacity of the gas turbine at ISO standard day conditions. A

peak optical response

The wavelength of maximum sensitivity of the instrument. A

peak torque speed
The speed at which an engine develops maximum torque. A

peat
Partially decomposed organic material.

PEL
Permissible Exposure Limit. N

percent load
The fraction of the maximum available torque at a specified engine speed. A

percent removal
A percentage expression of the removal efficiency across a treatment plant for a given pollutant parameter, as determined from the 30-day average values of the raw wastewater influent pollutant concentrations to the facility and the 30-day average values of the effluent pollutant concentrations for a given time period. A

percent volatile
Percent volatile by volume is the percentage of a liquid or solid (by volume) that will evaporate at an ambient temperature of 70° F (unless some other temperature is specified). Examples: butane, gasoline, and paint thinner (mineral spirits) are 100 percent volatile; their individual evaporation rates vary, but, in time each will evaporate completely. N

perceptible leaks
Any petroleum solvent vapor or liquid leaks that are conspicuous from visual observation or that bubble after application of a soap solution, such as pools or droplets of liquid, open containers or solvent, or solvent laden waste standing open to the atmosphere. A

percolation
The movement of water downward and radially through the sub-surface soil layers, usually continuing downward to the ground water. N

performance averaging period
Thirty calendar days, one calendar month, or four consecutive weeks as specified. A

performance evaluation sample
A reference sample provided to a laboratory for the purpose of demonstrating that the laboratory can successfully analyze the sample within limits of performance specified by the Agency. The true value of the concentration of the reference material is unknown to the laboratory at the time of the analysis. A

performance specification
A specification that states the desired operation or function of a product but does not specify the materials from which the product must be constructed. A

performance standard
The EPA-set limit of emissions from an individual source within a specific source category. A source category is designated when the Environmental Protection Agency determines that sources within the category contributes significantly to air [or water] pollution. A national standard of performance applies to new sources

and is based on control achievable with the best available technology.

periodic application of cover material

The application and compaction of soil or other suitable material over disposed solid waste at the end of each operating day or at such frequencies and in such a manner as to reduce the risk of fire and to impede disease vectors' access to the waste. A

permanent storage capacity

Grain storage capacity which is inside a building, bin, or silo. A

permanently installed swimming pools, wading and therapeutic pools

Those that are constructed in the ground, on the ground, or in a building in such a manner that the pool cannot be readily disassembled for storage whether or not served by electrical circuits of any nature. O

permanently installed decorative fountains and reflection pools

Those that are constructed in the ground, on the ground, or in a building in such a manner that the pool cannot be readily disassembled for storage and are served by electrical circuits of any nature. These units are primarily constructed for their aesthetic value and not intended for swimming or wading. O

permeability

(1) The quality of the soil that enables water to move downward through the profile, measured as the number of inches per hour that water moves downward through the saturated soil. N (2) The capacity of a porous medium to conduct or transmit fluids.

permissible dose

The dose of a chemical or radiation that may be received by an individual without the expectation of significantly harmful result. N

Permissible Exposure Limit

PEL. A time-weighted average (TWA) limit or ceiling exposure limit promulgated by OSHA that legally must never be exceeded instantaneously even if the TWA exposure limit is not violated. OSHA PELs have the force of law. N

permit

An authorization, license, or equivalent control document issued by EPA or an approved state agency to implement the requirements of an environmental regulation; e.g., a permit to operate a wastewater treatment plant or to operate a facility that may generate harmful emission. N

permit-by-rule

A provision of regulations stating that a facility or activity is deemed to have a permit if it meets the requirements of the provision. A

persistence

Refers to the length of time a compound, once introduced into the environment, stays there. A compound may persist for less than a second or indefinitely. N

persistent pesticides
Pesticides that do not break down chemically and remain in the environment after a growing season. N

person
Under most environmental statutes, the term includes an individual, corporation, firm, company, joint venture, partnership, sole proprietorship, association, or any other business entity, any State or political subdivision thereof, any municipality, any interstate body and any department, agency, or instrumentality of the United States and any officer, agent, or employee thereof. A, B, D, G, H, I, J, O. Also any organized group of persons whether incorporated or not. A, C [Ed. "Person" is defined numerous times. The above is an edited definition from these].

person-rem
The product of the average individual dose in a population times the number of individuals in the population. [Syn: man-rem.]

personal property
Except as otherwise defined by State law, tangible property of any kind except real property. A

pest
(1) Any insect, rodent, nematode, fungus, weed, or (2) any other form of terrestrial or aquatic plant or animal life or virus, bacteria, or other micro-organism (except viruses, bacteria, or other micro-organisms on or in living man or other living animals) which the Administrator declares to be a pest under section 25(c)(1) [of FIFRA]. C

pest problem
(1) A pest infestation and its consequences, or (2) any condition for which the use of plant regulators, defoliants, or desiccants would be appropriate. A

pesticide
Any substance or mixture of substances intended for preventing, destroying, repelling, or mitigating any pest, or intended for use as a plant regulator, defoliant, or desiccant, other than any article that: (1) Is a new animal drug under FFDCA sec. 201(w), or (2) Is an animal drug that has been determined by regulation of the Secretary of Health and Human Services not to be a new animal drug, or (3) Is an animal feed under FFDCA sec. 201(x) that bears or contains any substances described by paragraph (s) (1) or (2) of this section. O, A, C

pesticide chemical
As defined in section 201(q) of FIFRA, means any substance which, alone, in chemical combination, or in formulation with one or more other substances, is an "economic poison" within the meaning of the Federal Insecticide, Fungicide, and Rodenticide Act (7 U.S.C. 135-135k) and which is used in the production, storage, or transportation of raw agricultural commodities. A

pesticide formulation
The substance or mixture of substances comprised of all active and inert (if any) ingredients of a pesticide product. A

pesticide incinerator

Any installation capable of the controlled combustion of pesticides, at a temperature of 1000° C (1832° F) for two seconds dwell time in the combustion zone, or lower temperatures and related dwell times that will assure complete conversion of the specific pesticide to inorganic gases and solid ash residues. A

pesticide product

A pesticide in the particular form (including composition, packaging, and labeling) in which the pesticide is, or is intended to be, distributed or sold. O, A

pesticide tolerance

The amount of pesticide residue allowed by law to remain in or on a harvested crop. By using various safety factors, EPA sets these levels well below the point where the chemicals might be harmful to consumers. N

pesticide use

A use of a pesticide (described in terms of the application site and other applicable identifying factors) that is included in the labeling of a pesticide product which is registered, or for which an application for registration is pending, and the terms and conditions (or proposed terms and conditions) of registration for the use. A

pesticide-related wastes

All pesticide-containing wastes or by-products which are produced in the manufacturing or processing of a pesticide and which are to be discarded, but which, pursuant to acceptable pesticide manufacturing or processing operations, are not ordinarily a part of or contained within an industrial waste stream discharged into a sewer or the waters of a state. A

pesticides report

Information showing the types and amounts of pesticides or devices which are being produced in the current calendar year, have been produced in the past calendar year, and which have been sold or distributed in the past calendar year. A

petrochemical operations

The production of second generation petrochemicals (i.e., alcohols, ketones, cumene, styrene, etc.) or first generation petrochemicals and isomerization products (i.e., BTX, olefins, cyclohexane, etc.) when 15 percent or more of refinery production is first generation petrochemicals and isomerization products. A

petroleum

The crude oil removed from the earth and the oils derived from tar sands, shale, and coal. A

petroleum dry cleaner

A dry cleaning facility that uses petroleum solvent in a combination of washers, dryers, filters, stills, and settling tanks. A

petroleum liquids

Petroleum, condensate, and any finished or intermediate products manufactured in a petroleum refinery but does not mean Number 2 through Number 6 fuel oils as specified in ASTM D396-78, gas turbine fuel oils Numbers 2-GT through 4-GT as specified in ASTM D-2880-78, or diesel fuel oils Numbers 2-D and 4-D as specified in ASTM D-975-78. A

petroleum refinery
Any facility engaged in producing gasoline, kerosene, distillate fuel oils, residual fuel oils, lubricants, or other products through distillation of petroleum or through redistillation, cracking, extracting or reforming of unfinished petroleum derivatives. A

pH
(1) The logarithm of the reciprocal of hydrogen ion concentration. A (2) A symbol for the degree of acidity or alkalinity.

pharmacokinetics
The dynamic behavior of chemicals inside biological systems; it includes the processes of uptake, distribution, metabolism, and excretion. N

Phase I (RCRA)
That phase of the federal hazardous waste management program commencing on the effective date of the last of the following to be initially promulgated: 40 CFR Parts 260, 261, 262, 263, 265, 270 and 271. Promulgation of Phase I refers to promulgation of the regulations necessary for Phase I to begin. A

Phase II (RCRA)
That phase of Federal hazardous waste management program commencing on the effective date of the first Subpart of 40 CFR Part 264, Subparts F through R to be initially promulgated. Promulgation of Phase II refers to

promulgation of the regulations necessary for Phase II to begin. A

phenols
Organic compounds that are by-products of petroleum refining, tanning, textile, dye, and resin manufacture. Low concentrations can cause taste and odor problems in water, higher concentrations can kill aquatic life. N

pheromone
Hormonal chemical produced by female of a species to attract a mate. N

phosphate rock plant
Any plant which produces or prepares phosphate rock product by any or all of the following processes: mining, beneficiation, crushing, screening, cleaning, drying, calcining, and grinding. A

phosphate rock feed
All material entering the process unit including, moisture and extraneous material as well as the following ore minerals: fluorapatite, hydroxyapatite, chlorapatite, and carbonate-apatite. A

phosphates
Chemical compounds containing phosphorus. N

phosphorus
An essential food element that can contribute to the eutrophication of water bodies. N

photochemical oxidants
Air pollutants formed by the action

of sunlight on oxides of nitrogen and hydrocarbons. N

photochemical process
The chemical changes brought about by the radiant energy of the sun acting upon various polluting substances. The products are known as photochemical smog. N

photochemical smog
Air pollution caused by not one pollutant but by chemical reactions of various pollutants emitted from different sources. N

photosynthesis
The manufacture by plants of carbohydrates and oxygen from carbon dioxide and water in the presence of chlorophyll, using sunlight as an energy source. N

physical and chemical treatment system
Processes generally used in large-scale waste-water treatment facilities. Physical processes may involve air-stripping or filtration. Chemical treatment includes coagulation, chlorination, or ozone addition. The term can also refer to treatment processes, treatment of toxic materials in surface waters and ground waters, oil spills, and some methods of dealing with hazardous materials on or in the ground. N

physical construction
[In the RCRA program] Excavation, movement of earth, erection of forms or structures, or similar activity to prepare a HWM facility to accept hazardous waste. N

physical hazard
A chemical for which there is scientifically valid evidence that it is a combustible liquid, a compressed gas, explosive, flammable, an organic peroxide, an oxidizer, pyrophoric, unstable (reactive) or water-reactive. N

phytoplankton
That portion of the plankton community comprised of tiny plants, e.g., algae, diatoms. N

phytotoxic
Something that harms plants. N

PIAT
Public Information Assist Team.

PIC
Products of Incomplete Combustion. N

picking belt or table
A table or belt on which solid waste is manually sorted and certain items are removed. It is normally used in composting and salvage operations.

pickup truck
A light truck which has a passenger compartment and an open cargo bed. A

picocurie
pCi. Measurement of radioactivity. A picocurie is one million millionth, or a trillionth, of a curie, and represents about 2.2 radioactive particle disintegration per minute. A

pig
A container, usually lead, used to ship or store radioactive materials. N

piggyback collection
Crew collection of refuse and paper, simultaneously, at the curb. Bundled newspapers are placed on a rack installed beneath the compactor body, and refuse is placed in the body.

PIGs
Program Implementation Guidelines. [See: regulatory interpretative memoranda for description].

PIGS
Pesticides in Groundwater Strategy. N

pile
(1) A nuclear reactor. N (2) Any non-containerized accumulation of solid, nonflowing hazardous waste that is used for treatment or storage. A

pilot program
A program that is initiated on a limited basis for the purpose of facilitating a future full scale regional program. A

PIN
Procurement Information Notice. N

pinch point
Any point other than the point of operation at which it is possible for a part of the body to be caught between the moving parts of a press or auxiliary equipment, or between moving and stationary parts of a press or auxiliary equipment, or between the material and moving part or parts of the press or auxiliary equipment. O

pitch
Pitch is the included angle between

the horizontal and the ladder, measured on the opposite side of the ladder from the climbing side. O

pitch and bark pockets
A pitch pocket is an opening extending parallel to the annual growth rings containing, or that has contained, pitch, either solid or liquid. A bark pocket is an opening between annual growth rings that contains bark. O

PL
Public Law.

plankton
Tiny plants and animals that live in water. N

planned [asbestos] renovation operations
A renovation operation, or a number of such operations, in which the amount of friable asbestos material that will be removed or stripped within a given period of time can be predicted. Individual nonscheduled operations are included if a number of such operations can be predicted to occur during a given period of time based on operating experience. A

plant blending records
Those records which document the weight fraction of organic solvents and solids used in the formulation or preparation of inks at the vinyl or urethane printing plant where they are used. A

plant community
The plant populations existing in a shared habitat or environment. N

plant regulator

1) Any substance or mixture of substances intended, through physiological action, for accelerating or retarding the rate of growth or rate of maturation, or for otherwise altering the behavior of plants or the produce thereof, but shall not include substances to the extent that they are intended as plant nutrients, trace elements, nutritional chemicals, plant inoculants, and soil amendments. Also, the term 'plant regulator' shall not be required to include any of such of those nutrient mixtures or soil amendments as are commonly known as vitamin-hormone horticultural products, intended for improvement, maintenance, survival, health, and propagation of plants, and as are not for pest destruction and are nontoxic, nonpoisonous in the undiluted packaged concentration. C 2) Include but are not limited to, substances or mixtures of substances intended to cause fruit thinning, fruit setting, stem elongation, stimulation or retardation, abscission inhibition, branch structure modification, sucker control, flower induction or inhibition, increased flowering, altered sex expression, extended flowering periods, fruit ripening stimulation, physiological disease inhibition, rooting of cuttings, or dormancy induction or release. A

plasmid

A circular piece of DNA that exists apart from the chromosome and replicates independently of it. Bacterial plasmids carry information that renders the bacteria resistant to antibiotics. Plasmids are often used in genetic engineering to carry desired genes into organisms. N

plastic body

An automobile or light-duty truck body constructed of synthetic organic material. A

plastic body component

Any component of an automobile or light-duty truck exterior surface constructed of synthetic organic material. A

plastics

Non-metallic compounds that result from a chemical reaction, and are molded or formed into rigid or pliable structural material. N

platform

A working space for persons, elevated above the surrounding floor or ground, such as a balcony or platform for the operation of machinery and equipment. O

platform ladder

A self-supporting ladder of fixed size with a platform provided at the working level. The size is determined by the distance along the front rail from the platform to the base of the ladder. O

plowing

All forms of primary tillage, including moldboard, chisel, or wide-blade, plowing, discing, harrowing, and similar physical means utilized on farm, forest or ranch land for the breaking up, cutting, turning over, or stirring of soil to prepare it for the planting of crops. The term does not include the redistribution of soil, rock, sand, or other surficial materials in a manner which changes any area of the waters of the United States to dry land. For example, the redistribution of surface materials by blading, grading, or other means to fill in wetland areas is not plowing. Rock crushing activities which result in the loss of natural drainage characteristics, the reduction of water storage and recharge capabilities, or the overburden of natural water filtration capacities do not constitute plowing. Plowing will never involve a discharge of dredged or fill material. A

plugging
The act or process of stopping the flow of water, oil, or gas into or out of a formation through a borehole or well penetrating that formation. A

plugging record
A systematic listing of permanent or temporary abandonment of water, oil, gas, test, exploration and waste injection wells, and may contain a well log, description of amounts and types of plugging material used, the method employed for plugging, a description of formations which are sealed and a graphic log of the well showing formation location, formation thickness, and location of plugging structures. A

plume
(1) A visible or measurable discharge of a contaminant from a given point of origin. Can be visible or thermal in water, or visible in the air as, for example, a plume of smoke. (2) The area of measurable and potentially harmful radiation leaking from a damaged reactor. (3) The distance from a

toxic release considered dangerous for those exposed to the leaking fumes. N

plume impaction
Concentrations measured or predicted to occur when the plume interacts with elevated terrain. A

plutonium
A radioactive metallic element similar chemically to uranium. N

PM
Particulate Matter.

PM10
Particulate Matter (nominally 10m and less). N

PM15
Particulate Matter (nominally 15m and less). N

PMN
Premanufacture Notification.

PNA
Polynuclear Aromatic Hydrocarbons. N

pneumatic ash handling
A system of pipes and cyclone separators that conveys fly ash or floor dust to a bin via an air stream.

pneumatic coal-cleaning equipment
Any facility which classifies bituminous coal by size or separates bituminous coal from refuse by application of air stream(s). A

pneumatic collection of solid waste
A mechanical system that uses a high-velocity air stream to convey

solid waste dropped from standard gravity chutes through transport pipes to a collection point.

pneumoconiosis

A condition of the lung in which there is permanent deposition of particulate matter and the tissue reaction to its presence. It may range from relatively harmless forms of iron oxide deposition to destructive forms of silicosis. N

POE

Point of Exposure. N

point of operation

That point at which cutting, shaping, or forming is accomplished upon the stock and shall include such other points as may offer a hazard to the operator in inserting or manipulating the stock in the operation of the machine. O

point source load allocations

(1) For each water quality segment, the individual load allocation for point sources of pollutants, including thermal load allocations. (Note: In those segments where water quality standards are established at levels less stringent than necessary to achieve the 1983 water quality goals specified in Section 101(a)(2) of the [Federal Water Pollution Control] Act, the Regional Administrator may request the State to provide appropriate information, such as wasteload allocation information which may be relevant in making water quality related effluent limitation determinations pursuant to Section 302 of the [Federal Water Pollution Control] Act). A [ed. Load allocations deter-

mine how much pollution each source in a stream segment can contribute without water quality standards being violated].

point source

(1) A stationary location where pollutants are discharged, usually from an industry; under the FWPCA, a point source is any discernible, confined, and discrete conveyance, including but not limited to any pipe, ditch, channel, tunnel, conduit, well, discrete fissure, container, rolling stock, concentrated animal feeding operation, vessel, or other floating craft, from which pollutants are or may be discharged. This term does not include return flows from irrigated agriculture. A, D   (2) For particulate matter, sulfur oxides, carbon monoxide, hydrocarbons, and nitrogen dioxide--(a) Any stationary source the actual emissions of which are in excess of 90.7 metric tons (100 tons) per year of the pollutant in a region containing an area whose 1970 "urban place" population, as defined by the U.S. Bureau of the Census, was equal to or greater than 1 million; (b) Any stationary source the actual emissions of which are in excess of 22.7 metric tons (25 tons) per year of the pollutant in a region containing an area whose 1970 "urban place" population, as defined by the U.S. Bureau of the Census was less than 1 million; or (c) Without regard to amount of emissions, stationary sources such as those listed in Appendix C to this part. (3) For lead, any stationary source the actual emissions of which are in excess of 4.54 metric tons (5 tons) per year of lead or lead

compounds measured as elemental lead. A

point-of-entry treatment device

A treatment device applied to the drinking water entering a house or building for the purpose of reducing contaminants in the drinking water distributed throughout the house or building. A

poison, class A

A DOT term for extremely dangerous poisons -- poisonous gases or liquids that, in very small amounts, either as gas or as vapor of the liquid, mixed with air, are dangerous to life. Examples: phosgene, cyanogen, hydrocyanic acid, nitrogen peroxide. N

poison, class B

A DOT term for liquid, solid, paste or semisolid substances--other than Class A poisons or irritating materials--that are known (or presumed on the basis of animal tests) to be so toxic to humans that they are a hazard to health during transportation. N

polarization

In electromagnetic waves, refers to the direction of the electric field vector.

pollen

(1) A fine dust produced by plants. (2) The fertilizing element of flowering plants. (3) A natural or background air pollutant. N

pollutant (NPDES and 404 of FWPCA)

(1) Generally, any substance introduced into the environment that adversely affects the usefulness of a resource. N (2) Dredged spoil, solid waste, incinerator residue, sewage, garbage, sewage sludge, munitions, chemical wastes, biological materials, radioactive materials, heat, wrecked or discarded equipment, rock, sand, cellar dirt and industrial, municipal, and agricultural waste discharged into water. It does not mean: (a) "sewage from vessels" within the meaning of section 312 of this [Clean Water] Act; or (b) water, gas, or other material which is injected into a well to facilitate production of oil or gas, or water derived in association with oil and gas production and disposed of in a well, if the well used either to facilitate production or for disposal purposes is approved by authority of the state in which the well is located, and if the state determines that such injection or disposal will not result in the degradation of ground or surface water resources. D Radioactive materials covered by the Atomic Energy Act are those encompassed in its definition of source, byproduct, or special nuclear produced isotopes. See *Train v. Colorado Public Interest Research Group, Inc.*, 426 U.S. 1 (1976). A

pollutant or contaminant (CERCLA)

Any element, substance, compound, or mixture, including disease causing agents, which after release into the environment and upon exposure, ingestion, inhalation, or assimilation into any organism, either directly from the environment or indirectly by ingesting through food chains, will or may reasonably be anticipated to cause death, disease, behavioral abnormalities, cancer, genetic mutation, physiological malfunctions (including malfunctions in reproduction), or physical deformation in such organisms or their offspring. The term does not include petroleum, including crude oil and any fraction thereof which is not otherwise specifically listed or designated as a hazardous substance under section 101(14) (A) through (F) of CERCLA, nor does it include natural gas, liquified natural gas, or synthetic gas of pipeline quality (or mixtures of natural gas and synthetic gas). The term pollutant or contaminant means any pollutant or contaminant which may present an imminent and substantial danger to public health or welfare. (as defined by section 104(a)(2) of CERCLA). A

Pollutant Standard Index
PSI. Measure of adverse health effects of air pollution levels in major cities. N

pollution
The presence of matter or energy whose nature, location or quantity produces undesired environmental effects; for purposes of the Federal Water Pollution Control Act, pollution is the man-made or man induced alteration of the chemical, physical, biological and radiological integrity of water. L, D

polyaromatic hydrocarbons
A highly reactive group of organic compounds, at least some of which are carcinogens.

Polychlorinated Biphenyls
PCBs. A mixture of compounds composed of the biphenyl molecule which has been chlorinated to varying degrees. A

polyectrolytes
Synthetic chemicals that help solids to clump during sewage treatment. N

polymer
Any of the natural or synthetic compounds of usually high molecular weight that consist of many repeated links, each link being a relatively light and simple molecule. A

polyvinyl chloride
A plastic that releases hydrochloric acid when burned. L

POM
Polycyclic Organic Matter. N

pond water surface area
When used for the purpose of calculating the volume of waste water shall mean the area within the impoundment for rainfall and the actual water surface area for evaporation. A

population
A group of interbreeding organisms of the same kind occupying a particular space. Generically, the number of humans or other living creatures in a designated area. N

population dose
The sum of radiation doses of individuals and is expressed in units of person-rem (e.g., if 1,000 people each received a radiation dose of 1 rem, their population dose would be 1,000 person-rem).

porcelain enameling
The entire process of applying a fused vitreous enamel coating to a metal basis material. Usually this includes metal preparation and coating operations. A

porosity
The ratio of the volume of pores of a material to the volume of its mass.

portable grinding
A grinding operation where the grinding machine is designed to be hand held and may be easily moved from one location to another. O

portable tank
A closed container having a liquid capacity more than 60 U.S. gallons, and not intended for fixed installation. O

portable x-ray
X-ray equipment designed to be hand-carried. O

posing an exposure risk to food or feed
Being in any location where human food or animal feed products could be exposed to PCBs released from a PCB item. A PCB item poses an exposure risk to food or feed if PCBs released in any way from the PCB item have a potential pathway to human food or animal feed. EPA considers human food or animal feed to include items regulated by the U.S. Department of Agriculture or the Food and Drug Administration as human food or animal feed; this includes direct additives. Food or feed is excluded from this definition if it is used or stored in private homes. A

positive results in short-term tests
Positive results in assays for two or more of the following types of effect: (1) The induction of DNA damage and/or repair; (2) mutagenesis in bacteria, yeast, *Neurospora* or *Drosophila melanogaster*; (3) mutagenesis in mammalian somatic cells; (4) mutagenesis in mammalian germinal cells; or (5) neoplastic transformation of mammalian cells in culture. O

positive-pressure fabric filter
A fabric filter with the fans on the upstream side of the filter bags. A

possession or control
In possession or control of the submitter, or of any subsidiary, partnership in which the submitter is a general partner, parent company, or any company or partnership which the parent company owns or controls, if the subsidiary, parent company, or other company or partnership is associated with the submitter in the research, development, test marketing, or commercial marketing of the chemical substance in question. (A parent company owns or controls another company if the parent owns or controls 50 percent or more of the other company's voting stock. A parent company owns or controls any

partnership in which it is a general partner). Information is included within this definition if it is: (1) In the submitter's own files including files maintained by employees in the course of their employment. (2) In commercially available data bases to which the submitter has purchased access. (3) Maintained in the files in the course of employment by other agents of the submitter who are associated with research, development, test marketing, or commercial marketing of the chemical substance in question. A

Post Consumer Waste
PCW. A material or product that has served its intended use and has been discarded for disposal after passing through the hands of a final user. PCW is a part of the broader category "recycled material." A

post-closure
The time period following the shutdown of a waste management or manufacturing facility. For monitoring purposes, this is often considered to be 30 years. N

post-mining area
(1) A reclamation area or (2) the underground workings of an underground coal mine after the extraction, removal, or recovery of coal from its natural deposit has ceased and prior to bond release. A

potable water
Water that is safe for drinking and cooking. N

potential combustion concentration
[From a utility boiler] the theoretical emissions (ng/J, lb/million Btu net input) that would result from combustion of a fuel in an uncleaned state (without emission control systems) and: (a) For particulate matter is: (1) 3,000 ng/J (7.0 lb/million Btu) heat input for solid fuel; and (2) 75 ng/J (0.17 lb/million Btu) heat input for liquid fuels. (b) For sulfur dioxide is determined under 60.48a(b). (c) For nitrogen oxides is: (1) 290 ng/J (0.67 lb/million Btu) heat input for gaseous fuels; (2) 310 ng/J (0.72 lb/million Btu) heat input for liquid fuels; and (3) 990 ng/J (2.30 lb/million Btu) heat input for solid fuels. A

potential electrical output capacity
Thirty-three (33) percent of the maximum design heat input capacity of the steam generating unit (e.g., a steam generating unit with a 100-MW (340 million Btu/hr) fossil-fuel heat input capacity would have a 33-MW potential electrical output capacity). For electric utility combined cycle gas turbines the potential electrical output capacity is determined on the basis of the fossil-fuel firing capacity of the steam generator exclusive of the heat input and electrical power contribution by the gas turbine. A

potential occupational carcinogen
Any substance, or combination or mixture of substances, which causes an increased incidence of benign and/or malignant neoplasms, or a substantial decrease in the latency period between exposure and onset of neoplasms in humans or in one or more experimental mammalian species as the result of any oral, respiratory

or dermal exposure, or any other exposure which results in the induction of tumors at a site other than the site of administration. This definition also includes any substance which is metabolized into one or more potential occupational carcinogens by mammals. O

potential to emit
The maximum capacity of a stationary source to emit a pollutant under its physical and operational design. Any physical or operational limitation on the capacity of the source to emit a pollutant, including air pollution control equipment, and restrictions on hours of operation or on the type or amount of material combusted, stored, or processed, shall be treated as part of its design if the limitation or the effect it would have on emissions is federally enforceable. Secondary emissions do not count in determining the potential to emit of a stationary source. A

Potentially Responsible Party
PRP. Any individual or company--including owners, operators, transporters or generators--potentially responsible for, or contributing to, the contamination problems at a Superfund site. Whenever possible, EPA requires PRPs, through administrative and legal actions, to clean up hazardous waste sites they have contaminated. N

potroom
A building unit which houses a group of electrolytic cells in which aluminum is produced. A

POTW
Publicly Owned Treatment Works.

(1) A treatment works as defined by section 212(2) of the [Clean Water] Act, which is owned by a State, municipality, or intermunicipal or interstate agency. A (2) Any device or system used in the treatment (including recycling and reclamation) of municipal sewage or industrial wastes of a liquid nature which is owned by a "state" or "municipality" (as defined by Section 502(4) of the Clean Water Act). This definition includes sewers, pipes, or other conveyances only if they convey wastewater to a POTW providing treatment. A

pound-thrust/hr
Pounds of thrust for 1 hour.

pour point
The lowest temperature at which an oil will flow or can be poured under specified conditions of test. A

powder coating
Any surface coating that is applied as a dry powder and is fused into a continuous coating film through the use of heat. A

powder or dry solid form
A state where all or part of the substance would have the potential to become fine, loose, solid particles. A

power and control tray cable
Type TC power and control tray cable is a factory assembly of two or more insulated conductors, with or without associated bare or covered grounding conductors under a nonmetallic sheath, approved for instal-

lation in cable trays, in raceways, or where supported by a messenger wire. O

power density
The intensity of electromagnetic radiation power per unit area expressed as watts/cm^2.

power fuse
(Over 600 volts, nominal). See: fuse. O

power outlet
An enclosed assembly which may include receptacles, circuit breakers, fuseholders, fused switches, buses and watt-hour meter mounting means; intended to supply and control power to mobile homes, recreational vehicles or boats, or to serve as a means for distributing power required to operate mobile or temporarily installed equipment. O

power setting
The power or thrust output of an engine in terms of kilonewtons thrust for turbojet and turbofan engines and shaft power in terms of kilowatts for turboprop engines. A

power take-off shafts
The shafts and knuckles between the tractor, or other power source, and the first gear set, pulley, sprocket, or other components on power take-off shaft driven equipment. O

Power-Limited Tray Cable
Type PLTC nonmetallic-sheathed power limited tray cable is a factory assembly of two or more insulated conductors under a nonmetallic jacket. O

ppb.
Abbreviation for parts per billion.

PPETS
Pretreatment Permitting and Enforcement Tracking System under NPDES.

ppm.
Abbreviation for parts per million by volume. A

ppm. C
Parts per million, carbon.

PPSP
Power Plant Siting Program. N

PQL
Practical Quantitation Level. The lowest level that can be reliably achieved within specified limits of precision and accuracy during routine laboratory operating conditions.

practical knowledge
The possession of pertinent facts and comprehension together with the ability to use them in dealing with specific problems and situations. A

pre-certification vehicle
An uncertified vehicle which a manufacturer employs in fleets from year to year in the ordinary course of business for product development, production method assessment, and market promotion purposes, but in a manner not involving lease or sale. A

pre-certification vehicle engine
An uncertified heavy duty engine owned by a manufacturer and used in a manner not involving lease or sale in a vehicle employed from year to

year in the ordinary course of business for product development, production method assessment and market promotion purposes. A

pre-verification exemption
A testing exemption which is applicable to products manufactured prior to product verification, and used by a manufacturer from year to year in the ordinary course of business, for product development, production method assessment, and market promotion purposes, but in a manner not involving lease or sale. A

precious metal
Gold, silver, or platinum group metals and the principal alloys of those metals. A

precipitate
A solid that separates from a solution because of some chemical or physical change. N

precipitation
Removal of solids from liquid waste so that the hazardous solid portion can be disposed of safely; removal of particles from airborne emissions. N

precipitation bath
The water, solvent, or other chemical bath into which the polymer or pre-polymer (partially reacted material) solution is extruded, and that causes physical or chemical changes to occur in the extruded solution to result in a semihardened polymeric fiber. A

precipitators
Air pollution control devices that collect particles from an emission by mechanical or electrical means. N

precision
(1) Variation about the mean of repeated measurements of the same pollutant concentration, expressed as one standard deviation about the mean. A (2) The standard deviation of replicated measurements. A

preconditioning
The operation of an automobile through one (1) EPA Urban Dynamometer Driving Schedule, described in 40 CFR Part 86. A

precontrolled vehicles
Light duty vehicles sold nationally (except in California) prior to the 1968 model-year and light-duty vehicles sold in California prior to the 1966 model year. A

precursor
(1) In photochemical terminology, a compound such as a volatile organic compound (VOC) that "precedes" an oxidant. Precursors react in sunlight to form ozone or other photochemical oxidants. N (2) A pollutant that takes part in a chemical reaction resulting in the formation of one or more new pollutants.

preferential bus/carpool lane
Any requirement for the setting aside of one or more lanes of a street or highway on a permanent or temporary basis for the exclusive use of buses or carpools, or both. B

preliminary assessment
The process of collecting and reviewing available information about

a known or suspected waste site or release. N

premises wiring system
That interior and exterior wiring, including power, lighting, control, and signal circuit wiring together with all of its associated hardware, fittings, and wiring devices, both permanently and temporarily installed, which extends from the load end of the service drop, or load end of the service lateral conductors to the outlet(s). Such wiring does not include wiring internal to appliances, fixtures, motors, controllers, motor control centers, and similar equipment. O

presence sensing device
A device designed, constructed and arranged to create a sensing field or area and to deactivate the clutch control of the press when an operator's hand or any other parts of his body is within such field or area. O

presiding officer
The official, without regard to whether he is designated as an administrative law judge or a hearing officer or examiner, who presides at the adversary adjudication. A

press
A mechanically powered machine that shears, punches, forms or assembles metal or other material by means of cutting, shaping, or combination dies attached to slides. A press consists of a stationary bed or anvil, and a slide (or slides) having a controlled reciprocating motion toward and away from the bed surface, the slide being guided in a definite path by the frame of the press. O

pressed and blown glass
Glass which is pressed, blown, or both, including textile fiberglass, noncontinuous flat glass, noncontainer glass, and other products listed in SIC 3229. It is separated into: (1) Glass of borosilicate recipe. (2) Glass of soda-lime and lead recipes. (3) Glass of opal, fluoride, and other recipes. A

pressure
A force acting on a unit area. Usually shown as pounds per square inch (p.s.i.). A

pressure release
The emission of materials resulting from system pressure being greater than set pressure of the pressure relief device. A

pressure sewers
A system of pipes in which water, wastewater, or other liquid is transported to a higher elevation by use of pumping force. N

Pressurized Water Reactor
PWR. A power reactor in which heat is transferred from the core to a heat exchanger by water kept under high pressure to achieve high temperature without boiling in the primary system. Steam is generated in a secondary circuit. Many reactors producing electric power are pressurized water reactors.

pretreatment
The reduction of the amount of pollutants, the elimination of pollutants, or the alteration of the nature of pol-

lutant properties in wastewater to a less harmful state prior to or in lieu of discharging or otherwise introducing such pollutants into a POTW. The reduction or alteration can be obtained by physical, chemical or biological processes, process changes or by other means. A

pretreatment requirements
Any substantive or procedural requirement related to pretreatment imposed on an industrial user. A

prevention
Measures taken to minimize the release of wastes to the environment. N

Prevention of Significant Deterioration
PSD. The policy incorporated in the CAA that limits increases in clean air areas to certain increments even though ambient air quality standards are being met. The policy is premised on the assumption that air quality better than ambient air quality standards is a valuable resource that should be protected, particularly around undeveloped areas of special importance such as national parks.

primary aluminum reduction plant
Any facility manufacturing aluminum by electrolytic reduction. A

primary combustion air
The air admitted to a combustion system when the fuel is first oxidized.

primary control system
An air pollution control system designed to remove gaseous and parti-

culate fluorides from exhaust gases which are captured at the cell. A

primary copper smelter
Any installation or any intermediate process engaged in the production of copper from copper sulfide ore concentrates through the use of pyrometallurgical techniques. A

primary drinking water regulation
A regulation which--(A) applies to public water systems; (B) specifies contaminants which, in the judgment of the Administrator [of EPA], may have any adverse effect on the health of persons; (C) specifies for each such contaminant either--(i) a maximum contaminant level, if, in the judgment of the Administrator [of EPA], it is economically and technologically feasible to ascertain the level of such contaminant in water in public water systems, or (ii) if, in the judgment of the Administrator [of EPA], it is not economically or technologically feasible to so ascertain the level of such contaminant, each treatment technique known to the Administrator [of EPA] which leads to a reduction in the level of such contaminant sufficient to satisfy the requirements of section 1412; and (D) contains criteria and procedures to assure a supply of drinking water which dependably complies with such maximum contaminant levels; including quality control and testing procedures to insure compliance with such levels and to insure proper operation and maintenance of the system, and requirements as to (i) the minimum quality of water which may be taken into the system and

(ii) siting for new facilities for public water systems. J

primary emission control system
The combination of equipment used for the capture and collection of primary emissions (e.g., an open hood capture system used in conjunction with a particulate matter cleaning device such as an electrostatic precipitator or a closed hood capture system used in conjunction with a particulate matter cleaning device such as a scrubber). A

primary enforcement responsibility
The primary responsibility for administration and enforcement of primary drinking water regulations and related requirements applicable to public water systems within a State. A

primary industry category
Any industry category listed in the NRDC Settlement Agreement (*Natural Resources Defense Council v. Train*, 8 ERC 2120 [D.D.C. 1976], modified 12 ERC 1833 [D.D.C. 1979]). N Also listed in Appendix A of Part 122. A

primary lead smelter
Any installation or any intermediate process engaged in the production of lead from lead sulfide ore concentrates through the use of pyrometallurgical techniques. A

primary oxygen blow
The period in the steel production cycle of a Basic Oxygen Process Furnace (BOFP) during which a high volume of oxygen-rich gas is introduced to the bath of molten iron by means of a lance inserted from the top of the vessel. This definition does not include any additional, or secondary, oxygen blows made after the primary blow. A

primary panel
The surface that is considered to be the front surface or that surface which is intended for initial viewing at the point of ultimate sale or the point of distribution for use. A

primary pollutant
A pollutant emitted directly from a polluting source.

primary recipient
Any recipient which is authorized or required to extend Federal financial assistance to another recipient for the purpose of carrying out a program for which it receives Federal financial assistance. A

primary settling tank
The first settling tank for the removal of settleable solids through which wastewater is passed in a treatment works.

primary standard attainment date
The date specified in the applicable implementation plan for the attainment of a national primary ambient air quality standard for any air pollutant. B

primary standard
A national primary ambient air quality standard promulgated pursuant to section 109 of the [Clean Air] Act. A [ed. Intended to establish a level of air quality that, with an

adequate margin of error, will protect public health].

primary treatment
The first stage in wastewater treatment where substantially all floating or settleable solids, are removed by flotation and/or sedimentation. A

primary waste treatment
First steps in wastewater treatment; screen and sedimentation tanks are sued to remove most materials that floats or settle. Primary treatment results in the removal of about 30 percent of carbonaceous biochemical oxygen demand from domestic sewage. N

primary zinc smelter
Any installation engaged in the production, or any intermediate process in the production, of zinc or zinc oxide from the zinc sulfide ore concentrates through the use of pyrometallurgical techniques. A

prime coat operation
(1) The prime coat spray booth or dip tank, flash-off area, and bake oven(s) which are used to apply and dry or cure the initial coating on components of automobile or light-duty truck bodies. A (2) The coating application station, curing oven, and quench station used to apply and dry or cure the initial coating(s) on the surface of the metal coil. A

prime movers
Include steam, gas, oil, and air engines, motors, steam and hydraulic turbines, and other equipment used as a source of power. O

principal importer
The first importer who, knowing that a new chemical substance will be imported rather than manufactured domestically, specifies the identity of the chemical substance and the total amount to be imported. Only persons who are incorporated, licensed, or doing business in the United States may be principal importers. A

principal sponsor
An individual sponsor or the joint sponsor who assumes primary responsibility for the direction of a study and for oral and written communication with EPA. A

principally traded
The market place at which the greatest volume of trades normally occur. O

priority water quality areas
For the purposes of [40 CFR] §35.2015, specific stream segments or bodies of water, as determined by the State, where municipal discharges have resulted in the impairment of a designated use or significant public health risks, and where the reduction of pollution from such discharges will substantially restore surface or groundwater uses. A

private applicator
A certified applicator who uses or supervises the use of any pesticide which is classified for restricted use for purposes of producing any agricultural commodity on property owned or rented by him or his employer or (if applied without compensation other than trading of

personal services between producers of agricultural commodities) on the property of another person. C

privately owned treatment works
Any device or system which is (a) used to treat wastes from any facility whose operator is not the operator of the treatment works and (b) not a "POTW" [publicly owned treatment work]. A, M

proceeding
Any rulemaking, adjudication, or licensing conducted by EPA under Federal environmental statutes or under regulations which implement those Acts. A

process
The preparation of a chemical substance or mixture, after its manufacture, for distribution in commerce (1) in the same form or physical state as, or in a different form or physical state from, that in which it was received by the person so preparing such substance or mixture, or (2) as part of a mixture or article containing the chemical substance or mixture. A, K

process emission
The particulate matter which is collected by a capture system. A

process for commercial purposes
The preparation of a chemical substance or mixture containing the chemical substance after manufacture of the substance, for distribution in commerce with the purpose of obtaining an immediate or eventual commercial advantage for the processor. Processing of any amount of a chemical

substance or mixture is included in this definition. If a chemical substance or mixture containing impurities is processed for commercial purpose, then the impurities also are processed for commercial purposes. A

process fugitive emissions
Particulate matter emissions from an affected facility that are not collected by a capture system. A

process gas
Any gas generated by a petroleum refinery process unit, except fuel gas and process upset gas. A

process improvement
Routine changes made for safety and occupational health requirements, for energy savings, for better utility, for ease of maintenance and operation, for correction of design deficiencies, for bottleneck removal, for changing product requirements, or for environmental control. A

process solely for export
To process for commercial purposes solely for export from the United States under the following restriction on domestic activity: Processing must be performed at sites under the control of the processor; distribution in commerce is limited to purposes of export; and the processor may not use the chemical substance except in small quantities solely for research and development. A

process unit
Equipment assembled to produce a VHAP or its derivatives as intermediates or final products, or equip-

ment assembled to use a VHAP in the production of a product. A process unit can operate independently if supplied with sufficient feed or raw materials and sufficient product storage facilities. A

process unit shutdown
A work practice or operational procedure that stops production from a process unit or part of a process unit. An unscheduled work practice or operational procedure that stops production from a process unit or part of a process unit for less than 24 hours is not a process unit shutdown. The use of spare equipment and technically feasible bypassing of equipment without stopping production are not process unit shutdowns. A

process upset gas
Any gas generated by a petroleum refinery process unit as a result of start-up, shut-down, upset or malfunction. A

process wastes
Any designated toxic pollutant, whether in wastewater or otherwise present, which is inherent to or unavoidable resulting from any manufacturing process, including that which comes into direct contact with or results from the production or use of any raw material, intermediate product, finished product, byproduct or waste product and is discharged into the navigable waters. A

process wastewater
(1) Any water which, during manufacturing or processing, comes into direct contact with or results from the production use of any raw material, intermediate product, finished product, byproduct, or waste product. A (2) The term "process wastewater" does not include contaminated non-process wastewater. A (3) Also specifically excludes noncontact cooling water, material storage yard runoff (either raw material or processed wood storage), and boiler blowdown. For the dry process hardboard, veneer, finishing, particleboard, and sawmills and planing mills subcategories, fire control water is excluded from the definition. A

process wastewater pollutants
Any pollutants present in the process wastewater. A

process weight
The total weight of all materials and solid fuels introduced into any specific process. Liquid and gaseous fuels and combustion air will not be considered as part of the process weight unless they become part of the product. For a cyclical or batch operation, the process weight per hour will be derived by dividing the total process weight by the number of hours from the beginning of any given process to the completion thereof, excluding any time during which the equipment is idle. For a continuous operation, the process weight per hour will be derived by dividing the process weight for the number of hours in a given period of time by the number of hours in that period. For fluid catalytic cracking units, process weight shall mean the total weight of material introduced as fresh feed to the cracking unit. For sulfuric acid

production units, the nitrogen in the air feed shall not be included in the calculation of process weight. A

processor
Any person who processes a chemical substance or mixture. K

procurement item
Any device, good, substance, material, product, or other item whether real or personal property which is the subject of any purchase, barter, or other exchange made to procure such an item. I

procuring agency
Any federal agency, or any state agency or agency of a political subdivision of a state which is using appropriated federal funds for such procurement, or any person contracting with any such agency with respect to work performed under such contract. A, I

produce
To manufacture, prepare, compound, propagate, or process any pesticide or device, or active ingredient used in producing a pesticide. The dilution by individuals of formulated pesticides for their own use and according to the directions on registered labels shall not of itself result in such individuals being included in the definition of "producer" for purposes of FIFRA. C

producer
The person who manufactures, prepares, compounds, propagates, or processes any pesticide or device or active ingredient used in producing a pesticide. C

product accumulator vessel
Any distillate receiver, bottoms receiver, surge control vessel, or product separator in Volatile Hazardous Air Pollutant (VHAP) service that is vented to atmosphere either directly or through a vacuum-producing system. A product accumulator vessel is in VHAP service if the liquid or the vapor in the vessel is at least 10 percent by weight VHAP. A

product change
Any change in the composition of the furnace charge that would cause the electric submerged arc furnace to become subject to a different mass standard applicable under this subpart. A

production area size
That area in which production facilities, loading facilities, and all buildings that house product processes are located. A

production verification vehicle
Any vehicle selected for testing, tested or verified pursuant to the production verification requirements of this subpart. A

production volume
(1) For a domestic manufacturer, the number of vehicle units domestically produced in a particular model year but not exported. (2) For a foreign manufacturer, the number of vehicle units of a particular model imported into the United States. A (3) The quantity of a chemical substance which is produced by a manufacturer, as measured in kilograms or pounds. N

production-weighted NO_x average

The manufacturer's production-weighted average NO_x emission level, for certification purposes, of all of its light-duty truck engine families included in the NO_x averaging program. It is calculated at the end of the model year by multiplying each family No_x emission limit by its respective production, summing those terms, and dividing the sum by the total production of the effected families. Those vehicles produced for sale in California or at high altitude shall each be averaged separately from those produced for sale in any other area. A

program

Any program, project, or activity for the provision of services, financial assistance, or other benefits to individuals (including education or training, health, welfare, housing, rehabilitation, or other services, whether provided through employees of the recipient of Federal financial assistance or provided by others through contracts or other arrangements with the recipient, and including work opportunities or other assistance to individuals), or for the provisions of facilities for furnishing services, financial assistance, or other benefits to individuals. The services, financial assistance, or other benefits provided under a program receiving Federal financial assistance shall be deemed to include (1) any services, financial assistance, or other benefits provided with the aid of Federal financial assistance or with the aid of any nonfederal funds, property, or other resources required to be expended or made available for the

program to meet matching requirements or other conditions which must be met in order to receive the Federal financial assistance, and (2) any services, financial assistance, or other benefits provided in or through a facility provided with the aid of Federal financial assistance or such non-Federal resources. A

Program of Requirements

A comprehensive document (booklet) describing program activities to be accomplished in the new special purpose facility or improvement. It includes architectural, mechanical, structural, and space requirements. A

prohibit specification

To prevent the designation of an area as a present or future disposal site. A

project costs

All costs incurred by a grantee in accomplishing the objectives of a grant project, not limited to those costs which are allowable in computing the final EPA grant amount or total Federal assistance.

project schedule

A timetable specifying the dates of key project events including public notices of proposed procurement actions, subagreement awards, issuance of notice to proceed with building, key milestones in the building schedule, completion of building, initiation of operation and certification of the project. A

properties
Characteristics by which a substance may be identified. Physical properties describe its state of matter, color, odor, and density; chemical properties describe its behavior in reaction with other materials.

proportional sampling
Sampling at a rate that produces a constant ratio of sampling rate to stack gas flow rate. A

proposal
That stage in the development of an action when an agency subject to the Act has a goal and is actively preparing to make a decision on one or more alternative means of accomplishing that goal and the effects can be meaningfully evaluated. Preparation of an environmental impact statement on a proposal should be timed so that the final statement may be completed in time for the statement to be included in any recommendation or report on the proposal. A proposal may exist in fact as well as by agency declaration that one exists. A

propose to manufacture, process, or distribute
A person has made a management decision to commit financial resources toward the manufacture, processing, or distribution of a chemical substance or mixture. A

propose to manufacture or import PBBs or Tris
A situation where a person has made a firm management decision to commit financial resources for the manufacture of PBBs and Tris. A

propose to manufacture or import
A person has made a firm management decision to commit financial resources for the manufacture or import of the specified chemical. A

protect health and the environment
Protection against any unreasonable adverse effects on the environment. C

protective clothing
At least a hat or other suitable head covering, a long sleeved shirt and long legged trousers or a coverall type garment (all of closely woven fabric covering the body, including arms and legs), shoes and socks. A

protective equipment
Clothing or any other materials or devices that shield against unintended exposure to pesticides. A

protective shield or guard
A device or guard attached to the muzzle end of the tool, which is designed to confine flying particles. O

proteins
Complex nitrogenous organic compounds of high molecular weight that contain amino acids as their basic unit and are essential for growth and repair of animal tissue. Many proteins are enzymes. N

protocol
The plan and procedures which are to be followed in conducting a test. A

protoplast
A membrane-bound cell from which the outer cell wall has been partially or completely removed. The term often

is applied to plant cells. N

proximate analysis
The analysis of a solid fuel to determine (on a percentage basis) how much moisture, volatile matter, fixed carbon, and ash the sample contains; usually the fuel's heat value is also established.

PRP
Potentially Responsible Party (CERCLA). N

PSD
Prevention of Significant Deterioration.

PSD station
Any station operated for the purpose of establishing the effect on air quality of the emissions from a proposed source for purposes of prevention of significant deterioration as required by 40 CFR 51.24(N).

PSES
Pretreatment Standards for Existing Sources, under section 307(b) of the [Federal Water Pollution Control] Act. A

PSI
Pollutant Standard Index.

psi.
Pressure in pounds of force per square inch.

psia.
Pounds per square inch absolute.

psig.
Pounds per square inch gage.

PSNS
Pretreatment Standards for New Sources, under section 307(c) of the [Federal Water Pollution Control] Act. A

PTA
Part Throttle Acceleration. A

PTD
Part Throttle Deceleration. A

PTS
Project Tracking System. N

(the) public
In the broadest sense, the people as a whole, the general populace. There are a number of identifiable "segments of the public" which may have a particular interest in a given program or decision. Interested and affected segments of the public may be affected directly by a decision, either beneficially or adversely; they may be affected indirectly; or they may have some other concern about the decision. In addition to private citizens, the public may include, among others, representatives of consumer, environmental, and minority associations; trade, industrial, agricultural, and labor organizations; public health, scientific, and professional societies; civic associations; public officials; and governmental and educational associations. A

public vessel
A vessel owned or bareboat chartered and operated by the United States, by a State or political subdivision thereof, or by a foreign nation, except when such vessel is

engaged in commerce. D

public water system

A system for the provision to the public of piped water for human consumption, if such a system has at least fifteen service connections or regularly serves at least twenty-five individuals. Such term includes (A) any collection, treatment, storage, and distribution facilities under control of the operator of such system and used primarily in connection with such system, and (B) any collection or pretreatment storage facilities not under such control which are used primarily in connection with such system. A, J

public water supplies

Water distributed from a public water system. A

publication rotogravure printing press

Any number of rotogravure printing units capable of printing simultaneously on the same continuous web or substrate and includes any associated device for continuously cutting and folding the printed web, where the following saleable paper products are printed: catalogues, including mail order premium; direct mail advertisements, including circulars, letters, pamphlets, cards, and printed envelopes; display advertisements, including general posters, outdoor advertisements, car cards, window posters, counter and floor displays, point-of-purchase, and other printed display material; magazines; miscellaneous advertisements, including brochures, pamphlets, catalogue sheets, circular folders, announcements, package inserts, book jackets, market circulars, magazine inserts, and shopping news; newspapers, magazine and comic supplements for newspapers, and preprinted newspaper inserts, including hi-fi and spectacolor rolls and sections; periodicals; and telephone and other directories, including business reference services. A

publicly owned freshwater lake

A freshwater lake that offers public access to the lake through publicly owned contiguous land so that any person has the same opportunity to enjoy non-consumptive privileges and benefits of the lake as any other person. If user fees are charged for public use and access through State or substate operated facilities, the fees must be used for maintaining the public access and recreational facilities of this lake or other publicly owned freshwater lakes in the State, or for improving the quality of these lakes. A

Publicly Owned Treatment Works

POTW. (1) A treatment works as defined by section 212(2) of the [Clean Water] Act, which is owned by a State, municipality, or intermunicipal or interstate agency. A (2) Any device or system used in the treatment (including recycling and reclamation) of municipal sewage or industrial wastes of a liquid nature which is owned by a "state" or "municipality" (as defined by Section 502(4) of the Clean Water Act). This definition includes sewers, pipes, or other conveyances only if they convey wastewater to a POTW providing treatment. A

pull-out device

A mechanism attached to the operator's hands and connected to the upper die or slide of the press, that is designed, when properly adjusted, to withdraw the operator's hands as the dies close, if the operator's hands are inadvertently within the point of operation. O

pulling tension

The longitudinal force exerted on a cable during installation. O

pulmonary edema

An accumulation of an excessive amount of fluid in the lungs.

pulmonary emphysema

An anatomic change in the lungs characterized by a breakdown of the walls of the alveoli, which can become enlarged, lose their resilience, and disintegrate. The disease is accompanied by increasingly severe shortness of breath.

pulmonary function

The performance of the respiratory system in supplying oxygen to, and removing carbon dioxide from, the body (via the circulating blood). This requires that air move into and out of the alveoli at an adequate rate (ventilation), that blood circulate through pulmonary capillaries adjacent to alveoli at an adequate rate (perfusion), and that oxygen pass freely from alveoli to blood as carbon dioxide passes in the opposite direction (diffusion). Pulmonary function tests are used to try to identify and locate abnormalities in performance capability.

pulp

Fiber material produced by chemical or mechanical means from such raw materials as virgin wood pulp, secondary fibers, and rags, and used in the manufacture of paper and paperboard.

pulping system

The equipment used to convert fibrous raw materials into a homogeneous mixture suspended in water, which can be further processed into paper products.

pulverization

The crushing or grinding of all material into small pieces. N

pumping station

Mechanical devices installed in sewer or water systems or other liquid-carrying pipelines that move the liquids to a higher level. N

purge

The coating material expelled from the spray system when clearing it. A

push pit

A waste storage system in which a hydraulically powered bulkhead that traverses the length of the pit periodically pushes the stored waste into the hopper of a compactor. It is sometimes used in stationary compactor transfer systems.

push stick

A narrow strip of wood or other soft material with a notch cut into one end and which is used to push short pieces of material through saws. O

putlog
A scaffold member upon which the platform rests. <u>O</u>

putrescible
A substance that can rot quickly enough to cause odors and attract flies.

putrescible waste
Any solid waste subject to putrefaction and capable of attracting or providing food for birds and vectors.

PWR
Pressurized Water Reactor. A power reactor in which heat is transferred from the core to a heat exchanger by water kept under high pressure to achieve high temperature without boiling in the primary system. Steam is generated in a secondary circuit. Many reactors producing electric power are pressurized water reactors.

PWS
Public Water System. <u>D</u>

PWSS
Public Water Supply System. <u>D</u>

pyrolysis
The chemical decomposition of organic matter through the application of heat in an oxygen-deficient atmosphere. The products are water, carbon monoxide, hydrogen, and an inorganic residue. The gases may be collected and stored or used, and the residue may be further processed into such useful materials as carbon and sand or used as landfill.

pyrolytic gas and oil
Gas or liquid products that possess usable heating value that is recovered from the heating of organic material (such as that found in solid waste), usually in an essentially oxygen-free atmosphere. <u>A</u>

pyrometer
An instrument for measuring or recording temperatures.

pyrophoric
A chemical transformation or change. The interaction of two or more substances to form new substances. <u>N</u>

Q

QA
Quality Assurance.

QAPP
Quality Assurance Program (or Project). N

QC
Quality Control.

QCW
Quality Criteria for Water.

QNCR
Quarterly Non-Compliance Action Plan. D

qualified person
A person who by reason of experience or training is familiar with the operation to be performed and the hazards involved. O

quality assurance program plan
A formal document which describes an orderly assembly of management policies, objectives, principles, organizational responsibilities, and procedures by which an agency or laboratory specifies how it intends to:

(a) produce data of documented quality, and (b) provide for the preparation of quality assurance project plans and standard operating procedures. A

quality assurance project plan
An organization's written procedures which delineate how it produces quality data for a specific project or measurement method. A

quality assurance/quality control
A system of procedures, checks, audits, and corrective actions to ensure that all EPA research design and performance, environmental monitoring and sampling, and other technical and reporting activities are of the highest achievable quality. N

quality factor
Q. The linear-energy-transfer-dependent factor by which absorbed doses are multiplied to obtain (for radiation protection purposes) a quantity that expresses--on a common scale for all ionizing radiations--the effectiveness of the absorbed dose.

quantum
The smallest indivisible quantity of radiant energy; a photon.

quarry method
A variation of the sanitary land-filling area method in which the waste is spread and compacted in a depression; cover material is usually obtained elsewhere. B

quarter
A 3-month period; the first quarter concludes on the last day of the last full month during the 180 days following initial startup. A

quench station
That portion of the metal coil surface coating operation where the coated metal coil is cooled, usually by a water spray, after baking or curing. A

quench tank
A water-filled tank used to cool incinerator residues, or hot materials during industrial processes. N

R

R.
Rankine.

°R
Degree Rankine.

RA
(1) Remedial Action. N (2) Regional Administrator of a federal agency such as EPA or OSHA. (3) Resource Application. (4) Risk Assessment. N

RAATS
RCRA Administrative Action Tracking System. N

RAC
Response Action Coordinator. N

raceway
A channel designed expressly for holding wires, cables, or busbars, with additional functions as permitted in this subpart. Raceways may be of metal or insulating material, and the term includes rigid metal conduit, rigid nonmetallic conduit, intermediate metal conduit, liquidtight flexible metal conduit, flexible metallic tubing, flexible metal conduit, electrical metallic tubing, underfloor raceways, cellular concrete floor raceways, cellular metal floor raceways, surface raceways, wireways, and busways. O

rack dryer
Any equipment used to reduce the moisture content of grain in which the grain flows from the top to the bottom in a cascading flow around rows of baffles (racks). A

RACM
Reasonably Available Control Measures. N

RACT
Reasonably Available Control Technology. N

RAD
Radiation Absorbed Dose. (1) The special unit of absorbed dose of ionizing radiation. A dose of one rad equals the absorption of 100 ergs of radiation energy per gram of absorbing material. [See absorbed dose]. (2) One RAD of absorbed dose is equal to .01 joules per kilogram. N

R&D
Research and Development.

radiant energy
Energy that travels outward in all directions from its sources. O

radiation
Any form of energy propagated as rays, waves, or streams of energetic particles. The term is frequently used in relation to the emission of rays from the nucleus of an atom. N

Radiation Absorbed Dose
RAD. (1) The special unit of absorbed dose of ionizing radiation. A dose of one rad equals the absorption of 100 ergs of radiation energy per gram of absorbing material. [Compare: absorbed dose]. (2) One RAD of absorbed dose is equal to .01 joules per kilogram. N

radiation standards
Regulations that govern exposure to permissible concentrations of and transportation of radioactive materials. N

radical
A group of atoms that takes part in a chemical reaction as a unit and is normally incapable of existence except as part of a compound. So-called free radicals are formed as intermediate products in some reactions of organic compounds and play an important role in the reactions.

radioactive
Substances that emit rays either naturally or as a result of scientific manipulation. N

radioactive decay
Disintegration of the nucleus of an unstable nuclide by spontaneous emission of charged particles and/or photons.

radioactive materials
As included within the definition of "pollutant" in section 502 of the [Federal Water Pollution Control] Act covers only radioactive materials which are not encompassed in the definitions of source, byproduct, or special nuclear materials as defined by the Atomic Energy Act of 1954, as amended, and regulated pursuant to the latter Act. Examples of radioactive materials not covered by the Atomic Energy Act and, therefore, included within the term "pollutant" are radium and accelerator produced isotopes. A

radioactive waste
Any waste which contains radioactive material in concentrations which exceed those listed in 10 CFR Part 20, Appendix B, Table II, Column 2, or exceed the "Criteria for Identifying and Applying Characteristics of Hazardous Waste and for Listing Hazardous Waste" in 40 CFR Part 261, whichever is applicable. A

radiobiology
The study of the principles, mechanisms, and effects of radiation on living things. N

radioecology
The study of the effects of radiation on plants and animals in natural communities. N

radioisotopes
Radioactive forms of chemical compounds; such as cobalt-60, used in the treatment of diseases. N

radionuclide
Any nuclide that emits radiation. (A nuclide is a species of atom characterized by the constitution of its nucleus and hence by the number of protons, the number of neutrons, and the energy content). A

radius of vulnerable zone
The maximum distance from the point of release of a hazardous substance in which the airborne concentration could reach the level of concern under specified weather conditions. N

radon
A colorless naturally occurring, radioactive, inert gaseous element formed by radioactive decay of radium atoms in soil or rocks. N

radon decay products
A term used to refer collectively to the immediate products of the radon decay chain. These include Po-218, Pb-214, Bi-214, and Po-214, which have an average combined half-life of about 30 minutes. N

rail car
A non-self-propelled vehicle designed for and used on railroad tracks. A

rail ladder
A fixed ladder consisting of side rails joined at regular intervals by rungs or cleats and fastened in full length or in sections to a building, structure, or equipment. O

railcar loading station
That portion of a metallic mineral processing plant where metallic minerals or metallic mineral concentrates are loaded by a conveying system into railcars. A

railcar unloading station
That portion of a metallic mineral processing plant where metallic ore is unloaded from a railcar into a hopper, screen, or crusher. A

railroad
All the roads in use by any common carrier operating a railroad, whether owned or operated under a contract, agreement, or lease. A

ramp method
A variation of the sanitary landfilling area method in which a cover material is obtained by excavating in front of the working face. A variation of this method is called the progressive slope sanitary landfilling method. C

random incident field
A sound field in which the angle of arrival of sound at a given point in space is random in time. A

RAP
Remedial Action Plan.

rasp
A machine that grinds waste into a manageable material and helps prevent odor. N

rated incinerator capacity
The number of tons of solid waste that can be processed in an incinerator per 24-hour period when specified criteria prevail.

rated power
The maximum power/thrust available for takeoff at standard day conditions as approved for the engine by the Federal Aviation Administration. A

rated pressure ratio
rPR. The ratio between the combustor inlet pressure and the engine inlet pressure achieved by an engine operating at rated output. A

rating
The rating of a jack is the maximum working load for which it is designed to lift safely that load throughout its specified amount of travel. Note: To raise the rated load of a jack, the point of application of the load, the applied force, and the length of level arm should be those designated by the manufacturer for the particular jack considered. O

raw ink
All purchased ink. A

raw sewage
Untreated wastewater. N

RCRA
The Resource Conservation and Recovery Act of 1976 (P.L. 94-580, as amended). A

RCRIS
RCRA Information System. I

RD
Remedial Design. An engineering phase that follows the record of decision when technical drawings and specifications are developed for the subsequent remedial action at a site on the National Priorities List. N

RD/RA
Remedial Design/Remedial Action. L

RDF
Refuse Derived Fuel.

rDNA
Recombinant DNA. The new DNA that is formed by combining pieces of DNA from different organisms or cells. N

RE
Reportable Event. N

re-refined oil
Used oil from which the physical and chemical contaminants acquired through previous use have been removed through a refining process. A, I

re-refining
The refining of petroleum products after they have been used in order to return them to their original uses (e.g., the re-refining of waste oil into lubricating oil).

reactivity
An Environmental Protection Agency characteristic of hazardous waste which identifies waste that under

routine management, presents a hazard because of instability or extreme reactivity (e.g., the tendency to create vigorous reactions with air or water, tendency to explode, to exhibit thermal instability with regard to shock, ready reaction to generate toxic gases).

readily accessible
Capable of being reached quickly for operation, renewal, or inspections, without requiring those to whom ready access is requisite to climb over or remove obstacles or to resort to portable ladders, chairs, etc. O

real property
Except as otherwise defined by State law, land or any interest therein including land improvements, structures, fixtures and appurtenances thereto, but excluding movable machinery and equipment. A

real-ear protection at threshold
The mean value in decibels of the occluded threshold of audibility (hearing protector in place) minus the open threshold of audibility (ears open and uncovered) for all listeners on all trials under otherwise identical test conditions. A

REAP
Regional Enforcement Activities Plan. N

reasonable further progress
Annual incremental reductions in emissions of the applicable air pollutant (including substantial reductions in the early years following approval or promulgation of plan provisions under this part and section 110(a)(2)(I) [of the CAA] and regular reductions thereafter) which are sufficient in the judgment of the Administrator, to provide for attainment of the applicable national ambient air quality standard by the date required in section 172(a) [of the CAA]. B

reasonably available control technology
(1) The level of air pollutant emissions control required to be imposed on all existing sources in non-attainment areas, pursuant to §172 of CAA. (2) Devices, systems, process modifications, or other apparatus or techniques, the application of which will permit attainment of the emission limitations set forth in Appendix B, 40 CFR Part 51, provided that Appendix B is not intended, and shall not be construed, to require or encourage State agencies to adopt such emission limitations without due consideration of (1) the necessity of imposing such emission limitations in order to attain and maintain a national standard, (2) the social and economic impact of such emission limitations, and (3) alternative means of providing for attainment and maintenance of such national standard. A

rebricking
Cold replacement of damaged or worn refractory parts of the glass melting furnace. Rebricking includes replacement of the refractories comprising the bottom, sidewalls, or roof of the melting vessel; replacement of refractory work in the heat exchanger;

replacement of refractory portions of the glass conditioning and distribution system. A

rebuttable presumption against registration
An EPA regulatory policy which provides that the existence of certain types of scientific data indicating a pesticide causes harm to humans or the environment will justify the EPA refusing to register the pesticide unless the registrant provides more persuasive evidence to the contrary.

receiving property
Any residential or commercial property that receives the sound from railroad facility operations, but that is not owned or operated by a railroad; except that occupied residences located on property owned or controlled by the railroad are included in the definition of "receiving property." For purposes of this definition, railroad crew sleeping quarters located on property owned or controlled by the railroad are not considered as residences. If, subsequent to the publication date of these regulations, the use of any property that is currently not applicable to this regulation changes, and it is newly classified as either residential or commercial, it is not receiving property until four years have elapsed from the date of the actual change in use. A

receiving property measurement location
A location on receiving property that is on or beyond the railroad facility boundary and that meets receiving property measurement location criteria. A

receiving waters
Any body of water where untreated wastes are dumped. N

receptacle
A contact device installed at the outlet for the connection of a single attachment plug. A single receptacle is a single contact device with no other contact device on the same yoke. A multiple receptacle is a single device containing two or more receptacles. O

recharge
The process by which water is added to a zone of saturation, usually by percolation from the soil surface, e.g., the recharge of an aquifer. N

recharge area
A land area in which water reaches to the zone of saturation from surface infiltration, e.g., an area where rainwater soaks through the earth to reach an aquifer. N

recharge zone
The area through which water is added to an aquifer.

recipient
Any State, or any political subdivision or instrumentality thereof, any public or private agency, institution, organization, or other entity, or any individual, in any State to which or whom Federal financial assistance is extended, directly or through another recipient, for any program, or who otherwise participates in carrying out such program, including any successor, assignee, or transferee thereof, but such term does not include any

ultimate beneficiary under such program. A

reciprocating-grate stoker
A stoker with a bed of bars or plates arranged so that alternate pieces, or rows of pieces, reciprocate slowly in a horizontal sliding mode and act to push the solid waste along the stoker surface. F

recirculated cooling water
Water which is passed through the main cooling condensers for the purpose of removing waste heat from the generating unit, passed through a cooling device for the purpose of removing such heat from the water and then passed again, except for blow-down, through the main cooling condensers. A

reclaimed
Describes a material is processed to recover a usable product, or if it is regenerated. Examples are recovery of lead values from spent batteries and regeneration of spent solvents. A

reclamation
The restoration of land, water, or waste materials to usefulness through such methods as sanitary landfilling, wastewater treatment, and materials recovery.

reclamation area
The surface area of a coal mine which has been returned to required contour and on which revegetation (specifically, seeding or planting) work has commenced. A

reclamation bond release
The time at which the appropriate regulatory authority returns a reclamation or performance bond based upon its determination that reclamation work (including, in the case of underground mines, mine sealing and abandonment procedures) has been satisfactorily completed. A

recombinant bacteria
A type of microorganism whose genetic makeup has been altered by deliberate introduction of new genetic elements. The offspring of these altered bacteria also contain these new genetic elements. N

recombinant DNA
rDNA. The new DNA that is formed by combining pieces of DNA from different organisms or cells. N

recommencing discharger
A source which recommences discharge after terminating operations. A

recommended decision
The recommended findings and conclusions of the Presiding Officer in an expedited hearing. A

Recommended Exposure Limit
REL. The highest allowable airborne concentration established by OSHA that is not expected to injure a worker. Expressed as a ceiling limit or as a time-weighted average (TWA), usually for 10-hour work shifts. N

Recommended Maximum Contaminant Level
RMCL. The maximum level of a con-

taminant in drinking water at which no known or anticipated adverse affect on human health would occur, and which includes an adequate margin of safety. Recommended levels are nonenforceable health goals. (See: maximum contaminant level.) <u>N</u>

reconfigured emission-data vehicle

An emission-data vehicle obtained by modifying a previously used emission-data vehicle to represent another emission-data vehicle. <u>A</u>

reconstructed source

An existing facility in which components are replaced to such an extent that the fixed capital cost of the new components exceed 50 percent of the capital cost that would be required to construct a comparable entirely new facility. New source performance standards may be applied to sources which are reconstructed after the proposal of the standard if it is technologically and economically feasible to meet the standard. <u>N</u>

reconstruction

Will be presumed to have taken place where the fixed capital cost of the new components exceed 50 percent of the fixed capital cost of a comparable entirely new facility or source. However, any final decision as to whether reconstruction has occurred shall be made in accordance with the provisions of 40 CFR 60.15(f)(1)-(3). A reconstructed source will be treated as a new source except that use of an alternative fuel or raw material by reason of an order in effect under Sections 2(a) and (b) of the Energy Supply and Environmental Coordina-

tion Act of 1974 (or any superseding legislation), by reason of a natural gas curtailment plan in effect pursuant to the Federal Power Act, or by reason of an order or rule under Section 125 of the [Clean Air] Act, shall not be considered reconstruction. In determining best available control technology for a reconstructed source, the provisions of 40 CFR 60.15(f)(4) shall be taken into account in assessing whether a standard of performance under 40 CFR Part 60 is applicable to such source. <u>A</u>

Record of Decision

ROD. A public document that explains which cleanup alternative(s) will be used at a National Priorities List site. The record of decision is based on information and technical analysis generated during the remedial investigation/feasibility study and consideration of public comments and community concerns. <u>N</u>

recordable occupational injuries or illnesses

Any occupational injuries or illnesses which result in: (1) Fatalities, regardless of the time between the injury and death, or the length of the illness; or (2) Lost workday cases other than fatalities, that result in lost workdays; or (3) Nonfatal cases without lost workdays which result in transfer to another job or termination of employment, or require medical treatment (other than first aid) or involve: loss of consciousness or restriction of work or motion. This category also includes any diagnosed occupational illnesses which are reported to the employer but are not classified as fatalities or lost workday cases. O

recoverable
The capability and likelihood of being recovered from solid waste for a commercial or industrial use. I

recoverable resources
Materials that still have useful physical, chemical, or biological properties after serving their original purpose and can, therefore, be reused or recycled for the same or other purposes. A

recovered material
Waste material and byproducts which have been recovered or diverted from solid waste, but such term does not include those materials and byproducts generated from, and commonly reused within, an original manufacturing process (P.L. 94-580, 90 Stat. 2800, 42 U.S.C. 6903, as amended by P.L. 96-482). A, I

recovered resources
Material or energy recovered from solid waste. I

recovered solvent
The solvent captured from liquid and gaseous process streams that is concentrated in a control device and that may be purified for reuse. A

recovery
The process of obtaining materials or energy resources from solid waste. A

recurrent expenditures
Those expenditures necessary for normal operations of the entity in the daily conduct of operations which would not be classed as unusual or extraordinary and would be expected to recur on a periodic basis. Recurrent expenditures would not include items such as procurement of real property, extraordinary equipment purchases, nor one time management studies. A

recycled material
A material that is used in place of a primary, raw or virgin material in manufacturing a product and consists of materials derived from post consumer waste, industrial scrap, material derived from agricultural wastes and other items, all of which can be used in the manufacture of new products. A

recycled oil
Any used oil which is reused, following its original use, for any purpose (including the purpose for which the oil was originally used). Such term includes oil which is re-refined, reclaimed, burned or reprocessed. I

recycling
Converting solid waste into new products by using the resources contained in discarded materials. N

red border
An EPA document that is undergoing final review before being submitted for final management decision. N

red tide
A proliferation of ocean plankton that may kill large numbers of fish.

This natural phenomenon may be stimulated by the addition of nutrients. N

reducing agent
In a reduction reaction (which always occurs simultaneously with an oxidation reaction) the reducing agent is the chemical or substance which (1) combines with oxygen or 92) loses electrons to the reaction. See "oxidation." N

reduction
The process in which the oxidants (e.g., chromium-6) contained in waste streams are converted to less noxious materials, most commonly with the addition of sulfur dioxide.

reduction control system
An emission control system which reduces emissions from sulfur recovery plants by converting these emissions to hydrogen sulfide. A

reentry
The action of entering an area or site at, in, or on which a pesticide has been applied. A

reentry time
The period of time immediately following the application of a pesticide to a field when unprotected workers should not enter. A

reference day conditions
The reference ambient conditions to which the gaseous emissions (HC, CO, CO_2, and smoke) are to be corrected. The reference day conditions are as follows: Temperature = 15° C, specific humidity = 0.00629 kg H_2O/kg of dry air, and pressure = 101325 Pa. A

referring agency
The federal agency which has referred any matter to the Council (on Environmental Quality) after a determination that the matter is unsatisfactory from the standpoint of public health or welfare or environmental quality. A

refiner
Any person who owns, leases, operates, controls, or supervises a refinery. A

refinery
A plant at which gasoline is produced. A

refinery process unit
Any segment of the petroleum refinery in which a specific processing operation is conducted. A

refractory erosion
The erosion of refractory surfaces by the washing action of moving liquids, such as molten slags or metals, or the action of moving gases.

refractory expansion joint
An open joint left open so that refractories can expand thermally or permanently; also, small spaces or gaps built into a refractory structure to permit sections of masonry to expand and contract freely and to prevent the distortion or buckling of furnace structures under excessive expansion stresses. These joints are built in such a way that the masonry can move but that little or no air or gas can leak through.

refractory material

Nonmetallic substances used to line furnaces because they can endure high temperatures and resist abrasion, spalling, and slagging.

refractory wall

A wall made of heat-resistant material.

refuse

A term generally used for all solid waste materials. [See solid waste].

Refuse Act

Section 13 of the River and Harbor Act of March 3, 1899. A

Refuse Act permit

Any permit issued under the Refuse Act. A [ed. Refuse Act permits were succeeded by NPDES permits].

refuse chute

A pipe, duct, or trough through which solid waste is conveyed pneumatically or by gravity to a central storage area.

refuse reclamation

Conversion of solid waste into useful products, e.g., composting organic wastes to make a soil conditioner. N

Refuse-Derived Fuel

RDF. The combustible, or organic, portion of municipal waste that has been separated out and processed for use as fuel.

regeneration

Manipulation of individual cells or masses of cells to cause them to develop into whole plants. N

regenerative cycle gas turbine

Any stationary gas turbine that recovers thermal energy from the exhaust gases and utilizes the thermal energy to preheat air prior to entering the combustor. A

region

(1) An air quality control region designated by the Secretary of Health, Education, and Welfare or the Administrator; (2) Any area designated by a State agency as an air quality control region and approved by the Administrator; or (3) Any area of a State not designated as an air quality control region under paragraph (m) (1) or (2) of this section. A

Regional Administrator

(1) One of the ten Regional Administrators of the U.S. Environmental Protection Agency. A (2) The Administrator of any Regional Office of EPA or any officer or employee thereof to whom his authority is duly delegated. Where the Regional Administrator has authorized the Regional Judicial Officer to act, the term "Regional Administrator" shall include the Regional Judicial Officer. In a case where the complainant is the Assistant Administrator for Enforcement or his delegate, the term "Regional Administrator" as used in these rules shall mean the Administrator. A

regional hearing clerk

An individual duly authorized by the Regional Administrator to serve as hearing clerk for a given region. Correspondence may be addressed to the Regional Hearing Clerk, United States Environmental Protection

Agency (address of Regional Office--see Appendix). In a case where the complainant is the Assistant Administrator for Enforcement or his delegate, the term "regional Hearing Clerk" as used in these rules shall mean the Hearing Clerk. A

regional judicial officer
A person designated by the Regional Administrator under 40 CFR § 22.04(b) to serve as a Regional Judicial Officer. A

regional limitation
The requirement that a source which is located in an air quality control region in which a national primary ambient air quality standard for an air pollutant is being exceeded in that region, may not emit such pollutant in amounts which exceed any emission limitation (and may not violate any other requirement) which applies to such source, under the applicable implementation plan for such pollutant. A

regional office
One of the ten EPA regional offices. A

Regional Response Team
RRT. Is composed of representatives of Federal agencies and a representative from each State in the Federal region. During a response to a major hazardous materials incident involving transportation or a fixed facility, the On-Scene Coordinator (OSC), may request that the RRT be convened to provide advice or recommendations in specific issues requiring resolution. Under the NCP, RRTs may be convened by the chairman when a hazardous materials discharge or release exceeds the response capability available to the OSC in the place where it occurs; crosses regional boundaries; or may pose a substantial threat to the public health, welfare, or environment; or the regionally significant amounts of property. Regional contingency plans specify detailed criteria for activation of RRTs. RRTs may review plans developed in compliance with Title III, if local emergency planning committee so requests. N

regional scale
Usually a rural area of reasonable homogeneous geography extending from tens to hundreds of kilometers. A

registrant
A person who has registered any pesticide pursuant to the provisions of FIFRA.

registration
Formal listing with EPA of a new pesticide before it can be sold or distributed in intra- or inter-state commerce. The product must be registered under the Federal Insecticide, Fungicide, and Rodenticide Act. EPA is responsible for registration (pre-market licensing) of pesticides on the basis of data demonstrating that they will not cause unreasonable adverse effects on human health or the environment when used according to approved label directions. N

registration standards
Published reviews of all the data available on pesticide active ingredients. N

regulated chemical
Any chemical substance or mixture for which export notice is required. A

regulated pest
A specific organism considered by a State or Federal agency to be a pest requiring regulatory restrictions, regulations, or control procedures in order to protect the host, man and/or his environment. A

regulated substance
(A) Any substance defined in section 101(14) of the Comprehensive Environmental Response, Compensation, and Liability Act of 1980 (but not including any substance regulated as a hazardous waste under subtitle C), and (B) petroleum, including crude oil or any fraction thereof which is liquid at standard conditions of temperature and pressure (60 degrees Fahrenheit and 14.7 pounds per square inch absolute). [ed. Could include other substances regulated by TSCA & FIFRA].

Regulatory Interpretative Memoranda
RIMs. In 1980, EPA adopted a formal procedure for issuing binding interpretations of the hazardous waste regulations. These interpretations were called Regulatory Interpretative Memoranda (RIMs), and EPA also considered issuing Program Implementation Guidelines (PIGs) and Technical Amendment Regulations (TARs), 45 Fed. Reg. 55386 (August 19, 1980). The RIM program could have been very helpful, especially in applying the complex hazardous waste program to specific factual situations. However, EPA has largely abandoned this approach, preferring instead to explain

and interpret its regulations by issuing regulatory amendments. Only a few RIMs have been issued by the agency. EPA has relied on technical guidance documents.

Reid Vapor Pressure
RVP. The absolute vapor pressure of volatile crude oil and volatile non-viscous petroleum liquids, except liquified petroleum gases, as determined by ASTM D323-72. A

reimbursement period
A period that begins when the data from the last non-duplicative test to be completed under a test rule are submitted to EPA and ends after an amount of time equal to that which had been required to develop data or after five years, whichever is later. A

reinforced wheels
"Reinforced" as applied to grinding wheels shall define a class of organic wheels which contain strengthening fabric or filament. The term "reinforced" does not cover wheels using such mechanical additions as steel rings, steel cup backs or wire or tape winding. O

REL
Recommended Exposure Limit.

related coatings
All non-ink purchased liquids and liquid-solid mixtures containing VOC solvent, usually referred to as extenders or varnishes, that are used at publication rotogravure printing presses. A

release

Any spilling, leaking, pumping, pouring, emitting, emptying, discharging, injecting, escaping, leaching, dumping, or disposing into the environment, but excludes (A) any release which results in exposure to persons solely within a workplace, with respect to a claim which such persons may assert against the employer of such persons, (B) emissions from the engine exhaust of a motor vehicle, rolling stock, aircraft, vessel, or pipeline pumping station engine, (C) release of source, byproduct, or special nuclear material from a nuclear incident, as those terms are defined in the Atomic Energy Act of 1954, if such release is subject to requirements with respect to financial protection established by the Nuclear Regulatory Commission under section 170 of such Act, or, for the purposes of section 104 of this title or any other response action, any release of source byproduct, or special nuclear material from any processing site designated under section 102(a)(1) or 302(a) of the Uranium Mill Tailings Radiation Control Act of 1978, and (D) the normal application of fertilizer. [ed. Establishes scope of Superfund]. L

relief valve

Each pressure relief device including pressure relief valves, rupture disks and other pressure relief systems used to protect process components from over pressure conditions. "Relief valve" does not include polymerization shortstop systems, refrigerated water systems or control valves or other devices used to control flow to an incinerator or other air pollution control device. A

rem

Roentgen Equivalent Man. A measurement of radiation by biological effect on human tissue. N

REM

Roentgen Equivalent Man.

Remedial Action

RA. The actual construction or implementation phase that follows the remedial design of the selected cleanup alternative at a site on the National Priorities List. N

Remedial Design

RD. A phase of remedial action that follows the remedial investigation/feasibility study and includes development of engineering drawings and specifications for a site cleanup. N

remedial investigation

A process undertaken by the lead agency (or responsible party if the responsible party will be developing a cleanup proposal) which emphasizes data collection and site characterization. The remedial investigation is generally performed concurrently and in an interdependent fashion with the feasibility study. However, in certain situations, the lead agency may require potentially responsible parties to conclude initial phases of the remedial investigation prior to initiation of the feasibility study. A remedial investigation is undertaken to determine the nature and extent of the problem presented by the release. This includes sampling and monitoring, as necessary, and includes the gathering of sufficient information to determine the necessity for and proposed extent of remedial action. Part of the remedial investigation involves assessing whether the threat can be mitigated or minimized by controlling the source of the contamination at or near the area where the hazardous substances or pollutants were originally located (source control remedial actions) or whether additional actions will be necessary because the hazardous substances or pollutants or contaminants have migrated from the area of their original location (management of migration). A

Remedial Investigation/Feasibility Study

RI/FS. Two distinct, but related studies, usually performed at the same time. The RI/FS is intended to: (1) gather the data necessary to determine the type and extent of contamination at a Superfund site; (2) identify and screen cleanup alternatives for remedial action; and (3) analyze in detail the technology and costs of the alternatives. N

Remedial Project Manager

RPM. The Federal official designated by EPA (or the USCG for vessels) to coordinate, monitor, or direct remedial or other response activities; or the Federal official DOD designates to coordinate and direct Federal remedial or other response actions resulting from releases of hazardous substances, pollutants, or contaminants from DOD facilities or vessels. A

remedial response

A long-term action that stops or substantially reduces a release or threat of a release of hazardous substances that is serious but not an immediate threat to public health. N

remedy or remedial action

Those actions consistent with permanent remedy taken instead of, or in addition to, removal action in the event of a release or threatened release of a hazardous substance into the environment, to prevent or minimize the release of hazardous substances so that they do not migrate to cause substantial danger to present or future public health or welfare or the environment. The term includes, but is not limited to, such actions at the location of the release as storage, confinement, perimeter protection using dikes, trenches or ditches, clay cover, neutralization, cleanup of released hazardous substances or contaminated materials, recycling or reuse, diversion, destruction, segregation of reactive wastes, dredging or excavations, repair or replacement of leaking containers, collection of leachate and runoff, on-site treatment or incineration, provision of alternative water supplies, and any monitoring reasonably required to assure that such actions protect the public health and welfare and the environment. The term includes the costs of permanent relocation of residents and businesses and community facilities where the President determines that, alone or in combination with other measures, such relocation is more cost-effective than and environmentally preferable to the transportation, storage, treatment, destruction, or secured disposition off-site of such hazardous substances, or may otherwise be necessary to protect the public health or welfare. The term does not include off-site transport of hazardous substances or contaminated materials unless the President determines that such actions: are more cost-effective than other remedial actions; will create new capacity to manage in compliance with Subtitle C of the Solid Waste Disposal Act, hazardous substances in addition to those located at the affected facility; or are necessary to protect public health or welfare or the environment from a present or potential risk which may be created by further exposure to the continued presence of such substances or materials (as defined by section 101(24) of CERCLA). A, L

remote-control circuit
Any electric circuit that controls any other circuit through a relay or an equivalent device. O

removal action
Short-term immediate actions taken to address releases of hazardous substances that require expedited response. (See: cleanup). N

remove or removal
(1) Refers to removal of oil or hazardous substances from the water and shorelines or the taking of such other actions as may be necessary to minimize or mitigate damage to the public health or welfare, including, but not limited to, fish, shellfish, wildlife, and public and private property, shorelines, and beaches. D (2) The cleanup or removal of released hazardous substances from the environ-

ment, such actions as may be necessary taken in the event of the threat of release of hazardous substances into the environment, such actions as may be necessary to monitor, assess, and evaluate the release or threat of release of hazardous substances, the disposal of removed material, or the taking of such other actions as may be necessary to prevent, minimize, or mitigate damage to the public health or welfare or to the environment, which may otherwise result from a release or threat of release. The term includes, in addition, without being limited to, security fencing or other measures to limit access, provision of alternative water supplies, temporary evacuation and housing of threatened individuals not otherwise provided for, action taken under section 104(b) of CERCLA, and any emergency assistance which may be provided under the Disaster Relief Act of 1974. A, L

renal
Pertaining to the kidney. N

renovation
Altering in any way one or more facility components. Operations in which load-supporting structural members are wrecked or taken out are excluded. A

rent
Use of another's property in return for regular payment. N

rep
A measurement of radiation by energy development in human tissue. (Acronym for roentgen equivalent physical.) N

replacement
Expenditures for obtaining and installing equipment, accessories, or appurtenances during the useful life of the treatment works necessary to maintain the capacity and performance for which such works are designed and constructed. D The term "operation and maintenance" includes replacement. A

replacement cost
The capital needed to purchase all the depreciable components in a facility. A

replicate
Two or more duplicate tests, samples, organisms, concentrations or exposure chambers. A

reportable quantities
Quantities of hazardous substances that may be harmful as set forth in 40 CFR § 117.3, the discharge of which is a violation of section 311(b)(3) of the FWPCA and requires notice as set forth in 40 CFR § 117.21 or requires notice pursuant to § 304.7 CERCLA. A

Reportable Quantity
RQ. (1) The quantity of a hazardous substance that triggers reports under CERCLA. If a substance is released in amounts exceeding its RQ, the release must be reported to the National Response Center, the SERC, and community emergency coordinators for areas likely to be affected. N (2) The quantity of material that when spilled must be reported to the DOT (Section 311 of the Clean Water Act). D

reporting agency
The applicable State agency or, in metropolitan areas, a local air pollution control agency designated by the State to carry out the provisions of 40 CFR § 58.40. A

reporting area
The geographical area for which the daily index is representative for the reporting period. This area(s) may be the total urban area (or subpart thereof) or each of any number of distinct geographical subregions of the urban area deemed necessary by the reporting agency for adequate presentation of local air quality conditions. A

reporting day
The calendar day during which the daily report is given. A

reporting period
The time interval for which the daily report is representative. Normally, the reporting period is the 24-hour period immediately preceding the time of the report and should coincide to the extent practicable with the reporting day. In cases where the index will be forecasted the reporting period will include portions of the reporting day for which no monitoring data are available at the time of the report. A

representative
Any person, including an authorized employee representative, authorized by a party or intervenor to represent him in a proceeding. O

representative point
(a) A location in surface waters or

ground waters at which specific conditions or parameters may be measured in such a manner as to characterize or approximate the quality or condition of the water body; or (b) A location in process or waste waters at which specific conditions or parameters are measured and will adequately reflect the actual condition of those waters or waste waters for which analysis was made. A

representative sample
(1) Any sample of the waste, which is equivalent to the total waste in composition, and physical and chemical properties. (2) A sample of a universe or whole (e.g., waste pile, lagoon, ground water) which can be expected to exhibit the average properties of the universe or whole. A

reprocessing
The action of changing the condition of a secondary material.

reproductive health hazard
Any agent that has a harmful effect on the adult male or female reproductive system or the developing fetus or child. Such hazards affect people in several ways, including loss of sexual drive, mental disorders, impotence, infertility, sterility, mutagenic effects on germ cells, teratogenic effects on the fetus, and transplacental carcinogenesis. N

requestor
An industrial user or a POTW or other interested person seeking a variance from the limits specified in a categorical pretreatment standard. A

reregistration
The reevaluation and relicensing of existing pesticides originally registered prior to current scientific and regulatory standards. EPA reregisters pesticides through its Registration Standards Program. N

rescission
Enacted legislation cancelling budget authority previously provided by the Congress.

Research Octane Number
RON. A measurement of a gasoline's knock characteristics which is determined by American Society for Testing and Materials analytical method designated D-2699. A

reseller
Any person who purchases gasoline identified by the corporate, trade, or brand name of a refiner from such refiner or a distributor and resells or transfers it to retailers or wholesale purchaser-consumers displaying the refiner's brand, and whose assets or facilities are not substantially owned, leased, or controlled by such refiner. A

reservoir
Any natural or artificial holding area used to store, regulate, or control water. N

residential application
Application of a pesticide (other than application by a commercial applicator) directly to humans or pets or application of a pesticide in, on, or around all structures, vehicles or areas associated with the household or

homelife or non-commercial areas where children spend time, including, but not limited to: (i) Gardens, non-commercial greenhouses, yards, patios, houses, pleasure marine craft, mobile homes, campers and recreational vehicles, non-commercial campsites, home swimming pools and kennels; (ii) Articles, objects, devices or surfaces handled or contacted by humans or pets in all structures, vehicles or areas listed above; and (iii) Educational, lounging and recreational areas of preschools, nurseries and day camps. A

residential property

Any property that is used for any of the purposes described in the following standard land use codes (ref. *Standard Land Use Coding Manual*. U.S. DOT/ FHWA Washington, D.C., reprinted March 1977): 1, Residential: 651, Medical and other Health Services; 68, Educational Services; 691, Religious Activities; and 711, Cultural Activities. A

residential use

Use of a pesticide directly: (1) On humans or pets; (2) In, on, or around any structure, vehicle, article, surface, or area associated with the household, including but not limited to areas such as non-agricultural outbuildings, non-commercial greenhouses, pleasure boats and recreational vehicles, or (3) In any preschool or day care facility. A

residual oil

A general term used to indicate a heavy viscous fuel oil. A

residual waste control needs; land disposal needs

(1) An identification of the necessary controls to be established over the disposition of residual wastes which could affect water quality and a description of the proposed actions necessary to achieve such controls. (2) An identification of the necessary controls to be established over the disposal of pollutants on land or in subsurface excavations to protect ground and surface water quality and a description of the proposed actions necessary to achieve such controls. A

residual wastes

Those solid, liquid, or sludge substances from man's activities in the urban, agricultural, mining and industrial environment remaining after collection and necessary treatment. A

residue

(1) The material that remains after completion of a chemical or physical process, such as combustion, distillation, evaporation, or filtration. (2) The active ingredient(s), metabolite(s) or degradation product(s) that can be detected in the crops, soil, water, or other component of the environment, including man, following the use of the pesticide. A

residue conveyor

Generally a drag or flight conveyor used to remove incinerator residue from a quench trough to a discharge point.

resistance

For plants and animals, the ability to withstand poor environmental conditions and/or attacks by chemical or disease. The ability may be inborn or developed. N

RESOLVE
Center for Environmental Conflict Resolution. N

resource conservation
Reduction of the amounts of solid waste that are generated, reduction of overall resource consumption, and utilization of recovered resources. I

resource recovery unit
A facility that combusts more than 75 percent non-fossil fuel on a quarterly (calendar) heat input basis. A

resource recovery facility
Any facility at which solid waste is processed for the purpose of extracting, converting to energy, or otherwise separating and preparing solid waste for reuse. Energy conversion facilities must utilize solid waste to provide more than 50 percent of the heat input to be considered a resource recovery facility under this ruling. A

resource recovery system
A solid waste management system which provides for collection, separation, recycling, and recovery of solid wastes, including disposal of nonrecoverable waste residues. I

resource recovery
The recovery of material or energy from solid waste. I

respirable
Of a size small enough to be inhaled deep into the lung.

respiratory protection
Devices that will protect the wearer's respiratory system from overexposure by inhalation to airborne contaminants. Respiratory protection is used when a worker must work in an area where he/she might be exposed to concentration in excess of the allowable exposure limit. N

respond or response
Remove, removal, remedy and remedial action. L

response action
A CERCLA-authorized action involving either a short-term removal action or a long-term removal response that may include but is not limited to: removing hazardous materials from a site to an EPA-approved hazardous waste facility for treatment, containment, or destruction; containing the waste safely on-site; destroying or treating the waste on-site; and identifying and removing the source of ground-water contamination and halting further migration of contaminants. (See: cleanup.) N

response time
The time interval from a stepchange in pollutant concentration at the input to the continuous monitoring system to the time at which 95 percent of the corresponding final value is reached as displayed on the continuous monitoring system data recorder. A

restoration
Measures taken to return a site to pre-violation conditions. N

restricted use
When a pesticide is registered, some or all of its uses may be classified (under FIFRA regulations) for restricted use if the pesticide requires special handling because of its toxicity. Restricted-use pesticides may be applied only by trained, certified applicators or those under their direct supervision. N

restriction enzymes
Enzymes that recognize certain specific regions of a long DNA molecule and then cut the DNA into smaller pieces. N

retailer
Any person who owns, leases, operates, controls, or supervises a retail outlet. A

retan-wet finish
The final processing steps performed on a tanned hide including, but not limited to, the following wet processes: retan, bleach, color, and fatliquor. A

retarder (active)
A device or system for decelerating rolling rail cars and controlling the degree of deceleration on a car by car basis. A

retarder sound
A sound which is heard and identified by the observer as that of a retarder, and that causes a sound level meter indicator at fast meter response [201.1(l)] to register an increase of at least ten decibels above the level observed immediately before hearing the sound. A

retort-type incinerator
A multiple-chamber incinerator in which the gases travel from the end of the ignition chamber, then pass through the mixing and combustion chamber.

retrofit
The addition or removal of an item of equipment, or a required adjustment, connection, or disconnection of an existing item of equipment, for the purpose of reducing emissions. A

retrofit device
Any component, equipment, or other device: (1) Which is designed to be installed in or on an automobile as an addition to, as a replacement for, or through alteration or modification of, any original component, equipment, or other device; and (2) Which any manufacturer, dealer, or distributor of such device represents will provide higher fuel economy than would have resulted with the automobile as originally equipped. The term also includes fuel and oil additives for use in an automobile. The term does not include fuel flow measuring instruments or other driving aids which will not be evaluated in this program. A

retrofitted configuration
The test configuration after adjustment of engine calibrations to the retrofit specifications and after all retrofit hardware has been installed. A

reuse
The reintroduction of a waste material or product into the economic stream without any chemical or physical change. An example is the empty soft drink bottle that is returned to the bottling company, sterilized, and refilled.

reverberation time
The time that would be required for the mean-square sound pressure level, originally in a steady state, to fall 60 dB after the source is stopped. A

reverberatory furnace
Includes the following types of reverberatory furnaces: stationary, rotating, rocking, and tilting.

reverse osmosis
An advanced method of waste treatment that uses a semi-permeable membrane to separate water from pollutants. N

review
Refers to the process of examining documents located in response to a request that is for a commercial use (see paragraph (e) of this section) to determine whether any portion of any document located is permitted to be withheld. It also includes processing any documents for disclosure, e.g., doing all that is necessary to excise them and otherwise prepare them for release. Review does not include time spent resolving legal or policy issues regarding the application of exemptions. (Documents must be reviewed in responding to all requests; however, review time may only be charged to Commercial Use Requesters). A

RFI
Remedial Field Investigation. N

RFP
Reasonable Further Progress. N

RI
Remedial Investigation. N

RI/FS
Remedial Information/Feasibility Study. N

RIA
Regulatory Impact Assessment. N

Ribonucleic Acid
RNA. A molecule that carries the genetic message from DNA to a cell's protein-producing mechanisms; similar to, but chemically different from, DNA. N

RIMs
See: Regulatory Interpretative Memoranda.

RIN
Regulation Identifier Number.

ring rolls
A class for forging equipment used for shaping weldless rings from pierced discs or thick-walled, ring-shaped blanks between rolls which control wall thickness, ring diameter, height and contour. O

Ringelmann chart
Actually, a series of charts, numbered from 0 to 5, that simulate various smoke densities, by presenting different percentages of black. A

Ringelmann No. 1 is equivalent to 20 percent black; a Ringelmann No. 5, to 100 percent. They are used for measuring the opacity of smoke arising from stacks and other sources by matching the actual emission with the various numbers, or densities, indicated by the charts. Ringelmann numbers are sometimes used in setting emission standards.

RIP
RCRA Implementation Plan.

riparian rights
Entitlement of a land owner to the water on or bordering his property, including the right to prevent diversion or misuse of upstream waters. Generally, a matter of state law. N

rise
The vertical distance from the top of a tread to the top of the next higher tread. O

riser
The upright member of a step situated at the back of a lower tread and near the leading edge of the next higher tread. O

rising current separator
A separator that uses a form of elutriation to sort mixed materials by a countercurrent flow of water or other fluid.

risk
The potential for realization of unwanted negative consequences or events. N

risk assessment
A qualitative or quantitative evaluation of the environmental and/or health risk resulting from exposure to a chemical or physical agent (pollutant); combines exposure assessment results with toxicity assessment results to estimate risk. N

risk communication
The exchange of information about health or environmental risks between risk assessors, risk managers, the general public, news media, interest groups, etc. N

risk estimate
A description of the probability that organisms exposed to a specified dose of chemical will develop an adverse response (e.g., cancer). N

risk factor
Characteristic (e.g., race, sex, age, obesity) or variable (e.g., smoking, occupational exposure level) associated with increased probability of a toxic effect. N

risk management
The process of evaluating alternative regulatory and non-regulatory reponses to risk and selecting among them. The selection process necessarily requires the consideration of legal, economic and social factors. N

river basin
The land area drained by a river and its tributaries. N

RMCL

Recommended Maximum Contaminant Level. The maximum level of a contaminant in drinking water at which no known or anticipated adverse affect on human health would occur, and which includes an adequate margin of safety. Recommended levels are nonenforceable health goals. (See: maximum contaminant level.) N

roadways

Surfaces on which motor vehicles travel. This term includes highways, roads, streets, parking areas, and driveways. A

ROC

Record of Communication. N

rocking-grate stoker

A stoker with a bed of bars or plates on axles. When the axles are rocked in a coordinated manner, the solid waste is lifted and advanced along the surface of the grate. G

ROD

Record of Decision (CERCLA). N

rodenticide

A chemical or agent used to destroy rats or other rodent pests, or to prevent them from damaging food, crops, etc. N

rodenticides

All substances or mixtures of substances intended for preventing, destroying, repelling, or mitigating animals belonging to the Order Rodentia of the Class Mammalia, and closely related species, declared to be pests. Rodenticides include, but are not limited to: (i) Baits, tracking powders, and fumigants intended to kill or repel rodents; (ii) Repellents intended for use on plants, surfaces, in premises, or in or on packaging or other materials such as food containers, plastic pipe, telephone cables, and building materials, for the purpose of repelling rodents; and (iii) Reproductive inhibitors intended to reduce or otherwise alter the reproductive capacity or potential of rodents. A

Roentgen

R. The special unit of exposure. One roentgen equals 2.58×10^{-4} coulomb per kilogram of air.

Roentgen Equivalent Man

REM. The unit of dose equivalent from ionizing radiation to the human body, used to measure the amount of radiation to which a person or a part of a human has been exposed. N

ROG

Reactive Organic Gases. N

rolling

The reduction in thickness or diameter of a workpiece by passing it between lubricated steel rollers. There are two subcategories based on the rolling process. In the rolling with neat oils subcategory, pure or neat oils are used as lubricants for the rolling process. In the rolling with emulsions subcategory, emulsions are used as lubricants for the rolling process. A

roof
The exterior surface on the top of a building. This does not include floors which, because a building has not been completely built, temporarily become the top surface of a building. O

roof monitor
That portion of the roof of a potroom where gases not captured at the cell exit from the potroom. A

roofing bracket
A bracket used in sloped roof construction, having provisions for fastening to the roof or supported by ropes fastened over the ridge and secured to some suitable object. O

root crops
Plants whose edible parts are grown below the surface of the soil. A

rotary kiln stoker
A cylindrical, inclined device that rotates, thus causing the solid waste to move in a slow cascading and forward motion. H

rotary screen
An inclined, meshed cylinder that rotates on its axis and screens material placed in its upper end.

rotary spin
A process used to produce wool fiberglass insulation by forcing molten glass through numerous small orifices in the side wall of a spinner to form continuous glass fibers that are then broken into discrete lengths by high velocity air flow. A

rotogravure print station
Any device designed to print or coat inks on one side of a continuous web or substrate using the intaglio printing process with a gravure cylinder. A

rotogravure printing unit
Any device designed to print one color ink on one side of a continuous web or substrate using a gravure cylinder. A

rotory lime kiln
A unit with an inclined rotating drum that is used to produce a lime product from limestone by calcination. A

rough fish
Those fish not prized for eating, such as gar and suckers. Most are more tolerant of changing environmental conditions than game species. N

rounded
A number shortened to the specific number of decimal places in accordance with the "Round Off Method" specified in ASTM E 29-67. A

route of exposure
The avenue by which a chemical comes into contact with an organism (e.g., inhalation, ingestion, dermal contact, injection). N

routine use
With respect to the disclosure of a record, the use of such record for a purpose which is compatible with the purpose for which it was collected. O

RP
Responsible Party. N

RPAR
Rebuttable Presumption Against Registration of a pesticide (FIFRA). N

RPM
(1) Remedial Project Manager. (2) Revolutions Per Minute.

RQ
Reportable Quantity. The quantity of a hazardous substance or oil spilled that triggers reporting under CERCLA and section 311 of the Clean Water Act. If a substance is released in amounts exceeding its RQ, the release must be reported to the National Response Center, the SERC, and community emergency coordinators for areas likely to be affected. N

RQG
Reduced Quantity Generator.

RRC
Regional Response Center. (EPA) N

RRT
Regional Response Team. Is composed of representatives of Federal agencies and a representative from each State in the Federal region. During a response to a major hazardous materials incident involving transportation or a fixed facility, the OSC may request that the RRT be convened to provide advice or recommendations in specific issues requiring resolution. Under the NCP, RRTs may be convened by the chairman when a hazardous materials discharge or release exceeds the response capability available to the OSC in the place where it occurs; crosses regional boundaries; or may pose a substantial threat to the public health, welfare, or environment; or the regionally significant amounts of property. Regional contingency plans specify detailed criteria for activation of RRTs. RRTs may review plans developed in compliance with Title III, if the local emergency planning committee so requests. N

RSD
Risk Specific Dose.

RTECS
Registry of Toxic Effects of Chemical Substances.

run
The net period of time during which an emission sample is collected. Unless otherwise specified, a run may be either intermittent or continuous within the limits of good engineering practice. A

run-on
Any rainwater, leachate, or other liquid that drains over land onto any part of a facility. A

rungs
Ladder crosspieces of circular or oval cross-section on which a person may step in ascending or descending. O

runner
The lengthwise horizontal bracing or bearing members or both. O

running loss

Fuel evaporative emissions resulting from an average trip in an urban area or the simulation of such a trip. A

runoff

(1) That portion of precipitation that flows over the ground surface and returns to streams. It can collect pollutants from air or land and carry them to the receiving waters. N (2) Any rainwater, leachate, or other liquid that drains over land from any part of a facility. A

runway

A passageway for persons, elevated above the surrounding floor or ground level, such as a footwalk along shafting or a walkway between buildings. O

RVP

Reid Vapor Pressure.

S

SAB

Science Advisory Board. A

SAE

Society of Automotive Engineers.

safety belt

A device, usually worn around the waist which, by reason of its attachment to a lanyard and lifeline or a structure, will prevent a worker from falling. O

safety block

A prop that, when inserted between the upper and lower dies or between the bolster plate and the face of the slide, prevents the slide from falling of its own deadweight. O

safety can

An approved closed container, of not more than 5 gallons capacity, having a flash-arresting screen, spring-closing lid and spout cover and so designed that it will safely relieve internal pressure when subjected to fire exposure. O

safety guard

An enclosure designed to restrain the pieces of the grinding wheel and furnish all possible protection in the event that the wheel is broken in operation. O

safety-monitoring system

A safety system in which a competent person monitors the safety of all employees in a roofing crew, and warns them when it appears to the monitor that they are unaware of the hazard or are acting in an unsafe manner. The competent person must be on the same roof as and within visual sighting distance of the employees, and must be close enough to verbally communicate with the employees. O

safety screen

An air- and water-tight diaphragm placed across the upper part of a compressed air tunnel between the face and bulkhead, in order to prevent flooding the crown of the tunnel between the safety screen and the bulkhead, thus providing a safe means of refuge and exit from flooding or flooded tunnel. O

saline estuarine waters
Those semi-enclosed coastal waters which have a free connection to the territorial sea, undergo net seaward exchange with ocean waters, and have salinities comparable to those of the ocean. Generally, these waters are near the mouth of estuaries and have cross-sectional annual mean salinities greater than twenty-five (25) parts per thousand. A

salinity
The degree of salt in water. N

salt water intrusion
The invasion of fresh surface or ground water by salt water. If the salt water comes from the ocean, it is called sea water intrusion. N

sample system
The system which provides for the transportation of the gaseous emission sample from the sample probe to the inlet of the instrumentation system. A

sampler
A device used with or without flow measurement to obtain an adequate portion of water or waste for analytical purposes. May be designed for taking a single sample (grab), composite sample, continuous sample, or periodic sample.

S&A
Surveillance and Analysis.

sand filters
Devices that remove some suspend-

ed solids from sewage. Air and bacteria decompose additional wastes filtering through the sand so that cleaner water drains from the bed. N

sanitary landfill liner
An impermeable barrier, manufactured, constructed, or existing in a natural condition, that is utilized to collect leachate. The component parts of a sanitary landfill liner consist of but are not limited to the natural subgrade which is the undisturbed in place earth upon which construction will commence, the subbase, the impermeable membrane, the protective cover, and drainage facilities.

sanitary landfill density
Sanitary landfill density is the ratio of the combined weight of solid waste and the soil cover to the combined volume of the solid waste and the soil cover, $(W_{sw} + W_{soil}/V_{sw} + V_{soil})$.

sanitary landfill
A facility for the disposal of solid waste which meets the criteria published under section 4004 [of RCRA]; a land disposal site employing an engineered method of disposing of solid wastes on land in a manner that minimizes environmental hazards by spreading the solid wastes in thin layers, compacting the solid wastes to the smallest practical volume, and applying and compacting cover material at the end of each operating day. A, I

sanitary landfilling methods
See area method, quarry method,

ramp method, trench method, and wet area method.

sanitary sewer
(1) Underground pipes that carry only domestic or commercial waste, not storm-water. N (2) A conduit intended to carry liquid and water-carried wastes from residences, commercial buildings, industrial plants and institutions together with minor quantities of ground, storm and surface waters that are not admitted intentionally. A

sanitary survey
An onsite review of the water source, facilities, equipment, operation and maintenance of a public water system for the purpose of evaluating the adequacy of such source, facilities, equipment, operation and maintenance for producing and distributing safe drinking water. A

sanitation
Control of physical factors in the human environment that can harm development, health, or survival. N

SARA
Superfund Amendments and Reauthorization Act of 1986. N

SAROAD
Storage And Retrieval of Aerometric Data. A

SAROAD site identification form
One of the several forms in the SAROAD system. It is the form which provides a complete description of the site (and its surroundings) of an ambient air quality monitoring station. A

saturated zone (zone of saturation)
A subsurface area in which all pores and cracks are filled with water under pressure equal to or greater than that of the atmosphere. N

saturator
The equipment in which asphalt is applied to felt to make asphalt roofing products. The term saturator includes the saturator, wet looper, and coater. A

scaffold
Any temporary elevated platform and its supporting structure used for supporting workmen or materials or both. O

scavenger
One who participates in the uncontrolled removal of materials at any point in the solid waste system; an organism that feeds upon refuse or carrion.

scavenging
The uncontrolled and unauthorized removal of materials at any point in the solid waste management system. A

scf.
Standard cubic feet.

scfh.
Standard cubic feet per hour.

scfm.
Standard cubic feet per minute.

schedule and timetable of compliance
A schedule of required measures including an enforceable sequence of actions or operations leading to compliance with an emission limitation, other limitation, prohibition, or standard. B

schedule of compliance
(1) A schedule of remedial measures included in a "permit," including an enforceable sequence of interim requirements (for example, actions, operations, or milestone events) leading to compliance with the "appropriate Act and regulations). A (2) A schedule of remedial measures including an enforceable sequence of actions or operations leading to compliance with an effluent limitation, other limitation prohibition, or standard. D

scheduled maintenance
Any adjustment, repair, removal,disassembly, cleaning, or replacement of facility components or systems which is performed on a periodic basis to prevent part failure or malfunction, or anticipated as necessary to correct an overt indication of malfunction or failure for which periodic maintenance is not appropriate. A

scope of work
A document similar in content to the program of requirements but substantially abbreviated. It is usually prepared for small-scale projects. A

scoping
A preliminary public discussion of the information to be developed, alternatives to be considered, and issues to be discussed in an EIS.

scrap
Materials discarded from manufacturing operations that may be suitable for reprocessing. N

screen
A device for separating material according to size by passing undersize material through one or more mesh surfaces (screens) in series and retaining oversize material on the mesh surfaces (screens). A

screw conveyor
A rotating helical shaft that moves material, such as incinerator siftings, along a trough or tube.

scrubber
A device that uses a liquid spray to remove aerosol and gaseous pollutants from an air stream. The gases are removed either by absorption or chemical reaction. Solid and liquid particulates are removed through contact with the spray. Scrubbers are used for both the measurement and control of pollution.

scrubbing
The washing of impurities from any process gas stream. A

SCUBA diving
A diving mode independent of surface supply in which the diver uses open circuit self-contained underwater breathing apparatus. O

scuppers

Openings around the deck of a vessel which allow water falling onto the deck to flow overboard. Should be plugged during fuel transfer. A

SD

Standard Deviation.

SDWA

Safe Drinking Water Act.

SEA

State-EPA Agreements.

sealable equipment

Equipment enclosed in a case or cabinet that is provided with a means of sealing or locking so that live parts cannot be made accessible without opening the enclosure. The equipment may or may not be operable without opening the enclosure. O

search

Includes all time spent looking for material that is responsive to a [FOIA] request, including page-by-page or line-by-line identification of material within documents. Searching for material must be done in the most efficient and least expensive manner so as to minimize costs for both the EPA and the requestor. For example, EPA will not engage in line-by-line search when merely duplicating an entire document would prove the less expensive and quicker method of complying with a request. "Search" will be distinguished, moreover, from "review" of material in order to determine whether the material is exempt from

disclosure. Searches may be done manually or by computer using existing programming. A

SEC

Securities and Exchange Commission.

secator

A separating device that throws mixed material onto a rotating shaft; heavy and resilient materials bounce off one side of the shaft, whereas light and elastic materials land on the other and are cast in the opposite direction.

secondary burner

A burner installed in the secondary combustion chamber of an incinerator to maintain a minimum temperature and to complete the combustion of incompletely burned gases. See afterburner.

secondary combustion air

The air introduced above or below a fuel bed by a natural, induced, or forced draft. See overfire air and underfire air.

secondary control system

An air pollution control system designed to remove gaseous and particulate fluorides from gases which escape capture by the primary control system. A

secondary drinking water regulation

A regulation which applies to public water systems and which specifies the maximum contaminant levels which, in the judgment of the Administrator [of

EPA], are requisite to protect the public welfare. Such regulations may apply to any contaminant in drinking water (A) which may adversely affect the odor or appearance of such water and consequently may cause a substantial number of the persons served by the public water system providing such water to discontinue its use, or (B) which may otherwise adversely affect the public welfare. Such regulations may vary according to geographic and other circumstances. J

secondary emissions

(1) Emissions which would occur as a result of the construction or operation of a major stationary source or major modification, but do not come from the major stationary source or major modification itself.   (2) Secondary emissions must be specific, well defined, quantifiable, and impact the same general area as the stationary source or modification which causes the secondary emissions.   (3) Secondary emissions include emissions from any offsite support facility which would not be constructed or increase its emissions except as a result of the construction or operation of the major stationary source or major modification. Secondary emissions do not include any emissions which come directly from a mobile source, such as emis sions from the tailpipe of a motor vehicle, from a train, or from a ves sel. Secondary emissions also do not include any emissions from ships or trains coming to or from the new or modified stationary source. A

secondary industry category

Any industry category which is not a "primary industry category." A

secondary materials

Recovered resources that are used as raw materials in some manufacturing processes.   See feedstock, exchange, and recycling.

Secondary Maximum Contaminant Levels

SMCLs which apply to public water systems and which, in the judgement of the Administrator, are requisite to protect the public welfare. The SMCL means the maximum permissible level of a contaminant in water which is delivered to the free flowing outlet of the ultimate user of public water system.   Contaminants added to the water under circumstances controlled by the user, except those resulting from corrosion of piping and plumbing caused by water quality, are excluded from this definition. A

secondary pollutant

A pollutant formed in the atmosphere by chemical changes taking place between primary pollutants and sometimes other substances present in the air.

secondary standard

A national secondary ambient air quality standard promulgated pursuant to section 109 of the [Clean Air] Act. A   [ed.   A secondary standard establishes that ambient concentration of the pollutant that, with an adequate margin of safety, will protect the public welfare (i.e. all parts of the environment other than human health) from adverse impacts].

secondary treatment

The second step in most publicly owned waste treatment systems in which bacteria consume the organic parts of the waste. It is accomplished by bringing together waste, bacteria, and oxygen in trickling filters or in the activated sludge process. This treatment removes floating and settleable solids and about 90 percent of the oxygen-demanding substances and suspended solids. Disinfection is the final stage of secondary treatment. (See: primary, tertiary treatment). N

Section 208 plan

An areawide waste treatment management plan prepared under Section 208 of the Federal Water Pollution Control Act (FWPCA), as amended. See 40 CFR Part 126 and 40 CFR Part 35, Subpart F. A

Section 404 program or **State 404 program** or **404**

An "approved State Program" to regulate the "discharge of dredged material" and in the "discharge of fill material" under section 404 of the Clean Water Act in "State regulated waters." A

sectional ladder

A non-self-supporting portable ladder, nonadjustable in length, consisting of two or more sections of ladder so constructed that the sections may be combined to function as a single ladder. Its size is designated by the overall length of the assembled sections. O

sectionally supported wall

A furnace or boiler wall of special refractory blocks or shapes that are mounted on and supported at intervals of height by metallic hangers.

secure maximum contaminant level

Maximum permissible level of a contaminant in water which is delivered to the free flowing outlet of the ultimate user of a water supply, the consumer, or of contamination resulting from corrosion of piping and plumbing caused by water quality. N

sedimentation

Letting solids settle out of waste water by gravity during waste water treatment. N

sedimentation tanks

Holding areas for waste water where floating wastes are skimmed off and settled solids are pumped out for disposal. N

sediments

Soil, sand, and minerals washed from land into water usually after rain. They pile up in reservoirs, rivers and harbors, destroying fish-nesting areas and holes of water animals, and clouding the water so that needed sunlight might not reach aquatic plants. Careless farming, mining, and building activities will expose sediment materials, contributing to their being washed off the land after rainfalls. N

seeding

The sowing of seed and placement of seedlings to produce farm, ranch, or forest crops and includes the placement of soil beds for seeds or seedlings on established farm and forest lands. A

seepage
The movement of liquids or gases through soil without the formation of definite channels.

seeps
Small springs of discolored, malodorous leachate that are frequently formed along the lower edges of many landfills.

segment
A portion of an approved planning area, the surface waters of which have common hydrologic characteristics (or flow regulation patterns); common natural physical, chemical and biological characteristics and processes; and common reactions to external stresses, such as the discharge of pollutants. Segments will be classified as either a water quality segment or an effluent limitation segment as follows: (1) Water quality segment. Any segment where it is known that water quality does not meet applicable water quality standards and/or is not expected to meet applicable water quality standards even after the application of the effluent limitations required by sections 301(b)(1)(B) and 301(b)(2)(A) of the [Clean Water] Act. (2) Effluent limitation segment. Any segment where it is known that water quality is meeting and will continue to meet applicable water quality standards or where there is adequate demonstration that water quality will meet applicable water quality standards after the

application of the effluent limitations required by sections 301(b)(1)(B) and 301(b)(2)(A) of the [Clean Water] Act. A

selective pesticide
A chemical designed to affect only certain types of pests leaving other plants and animals unharmed. N

self-contained breathing apparatus
A respiratory protection device that consists of a supply or means of respirable air, oxygen, or oxygen-generating material, carried by the wearer. N

self-purification
The natural processes occurring in a stream or other body of water that result in the reduction of bacteria, satisfaction of the BOD, stabilization of organic constituents, replacement of depleted dissolved oxygen, and the return of the stream biota to normal. Also called natural purification.

semiannual
A 6-month period; the first semiannual period concludes on the last day of the last month during the 180 days following initial startup for new sources; and the first semiannual period concludes on the last day of the last full month during the 180 days after the effective date of a specific subpart that references this subpart for existing sources. A

semiautomatic feeding
Feeding wherein the material or part being processed is placed within or removed from the point of operation

by an auxiliary means controlled by operator on each stroke of the press. O

semiconductors
Solid state electrical devices which perform functions such as information processing and display, power handling, and interconversion between light energy and electrical energy. A

semi-confined aquifer
An aquifer that is partially confined by a soil layer (or layers) of low permeability through which recharge and discharge can occur. N

semipermeable membrane
A barrier, usually thin, that permits passage of particles up to a certain size or of special nature. Often used to separate colloids from their suspending liquid, as in dialysis.

semi-wet
Those steelmaking air cleaning systems that use water for the sole purpose of conditioning the temperature and humidity of furnace gases such that the gases may be cleaned in dry air pollution control systems. A

senescence
Term for the aging process. Sometimes used to describe lakes or other bodies of water in advanced stages of eutrophication. N

sensitizer
A chemical that causes a substantial proportion of exposed people or animals to develop an allergic reaction in normal tissue after repeated exposure to the chemical. N

sensor
A device that measures a physical quantity or the change in a physical quantity, such as temperature, pressure, flow rate, pH, or liquid level. A

separate collection
Collecting recyclable materials which have been separated at the point of generation and keeping those materials separate from other collected solid waste in separate compartments of a single collection vehicle or through the use of separate collection vehicles. A

separate storm sewer
A conveyance or system of conveyances (including but not limited to pipes, conduits, and channels) located in an urbanized area and primarily operated for the purpose of collecting and conveying storm water runoff. It does not include any conveyance which discharges process waste water or storm water runoff contaminated by contact with aggregations of wastes, raw materials, or pollutant-contaminated soil, from lands or facilities used for industrial or commercial activities, into navigable waters or into another conveyance or system of conveyances defined as a separate storm sewer. A

separately derived system
A premises wiring system whose power is derived from generator,

transformer, or converter winding and has no direct electrical connection, including a solidly connected grounded circuit conductor, to supply conductors originating in another system. O

separation
The process of dividing solid waste into designated categories, which may be as general as paper from metals from glass or as specific as clear glass from colored glass. Also called segregation.

separator
A mechanical device or system for the separation of solid waste.

septic tank
An underground storage tank for wastes from homes having no sewer line to a treatment plant. The waste goes directly from the home to the tank, where the organic waste is decomposed by bacteria and the sludge settles to the bottom. The effluent flows out of the tank into the ground through drains; the sludge is pumped out periodically. N

SERC
State Emergency Response Commission.

serial number
The identification number assigned by the manufacturer to a specific production unit. A

serious chronic effects
Human disease processes or other adverse effects that have a long latency period for development, result from long-term exposure, are long-term illnesses, or are a combination of these factors and that are likely to result in death, severe or prolonged incapacitation, disfigurement, or severe or prolonged loss of the ability to use a normal bodily or intellectual function with a consequent impairment of normal activities. A

serious hazard
Any condition or practice which would be classified as a serious violation of applicable federal or state statutes, regulations or standards, based on criteria contained in the current OSHA Field Operations Manual or an approved state plan counterpart, except that the element of employer knowledge shall not be considered. O

service
The conductors and equipment for delivering energy from the electricity supply system to the wiring system of the premises served. O

service cable
Service conductors made up in the form of a cable. O

service conductors
The supply conductors that extend from the street main or from transformers to the service equipment of the premises supplied. O

service connector
The pipe that carries tap water from the public water main to a building. N

service drop
The overhead service conductors from the last pole or other aerial

support to and including the splices, if any, connecting to the service-entrance conductors at the building or other structure. O

service equipment
The necessary equipment, usually consisting of a circuit breaker or switch and fuses, and their accessories, located near the point of entrance of supply conductors to a building or other structure, or an otherwise defined area, and intended to constitute the main control and means of cutoff of the supply. O

service life
The period of time during which a component of a waste treatment management system will be capable of performing a function. A

service-entrance cable
A single conductor or multiconductor assembly provided with or without an overall covering, primarily used for services. O

SETS
Site Enforcement Tracking System. N

settleable solids
(1) That matter in wastewater which will not stay in suspension during a preselected period, such as one hour, but either settles to the bottom or floats to the top. (2) In the Imhoff cone test, the volume of matter that settles to the bottom of the cone in one hour.

settlement
The sinking of the surface of a sanitary landfill because of such factors as decomposition, consolidation, drainage, and underground failures. The degree and uniformity of settlement depends on the kind of refuse and how thoroughly it was compacted.

settling chamber
(1) Any chamber designed to reduce the velocity of the products of combustion and thus to promote the settling of fly ash from the gas stream before it is discharged into the environment. Also called expansion, separation, or subsidence chamber. (2) A series of screens placed in the way of flue gases to slow the stream of air, thus helping gravity to pull particles out of the emission into a collection area. N

settling tank
(1) A container that gravimetrically separates oils, grease, and dirt from petroleum solvent, together with the piping and ductwork used in the installation of this device. A (2) A holding area for waste water, where heavier particles sink to the bottom and can be siphoned off. N

settling velocity
The velocity at which a given dust will fall out of dust-laden gas under the influence of gravity only. Also called terminal velocity.

7-day average

The arithmetic mean of pollutant parameter values for samples collected in a period of 7 consecutive days. A

severe property damage

Substantial physical damage to property, damage to the treatment facilities which causes them to become inoperable, or substantial and permanent loss of natural resources which can reasonably be expected to occur in the absence of a bypass. Severe property damage does not mean economic loss caused by delays in production. A

sewage

(1) The waste and wastewater produced by residential and commercial establishments and discharged into sewers. N (2) Human body wastes and the wastes from toilets and other receptacles intended to receive or retain body wastes except that, with respect to commercial vessels on the Great Lakes such term shall include graywater. D

sewage collection system

Common lateral sewers, within a publicly-owned treatment system, which are primarily installed to receive wastewaters directly from facilities which convey wastewater from individual structures or from private property, and which include service connection "Y" fittings designed for connection with those facilities. The facilities which convey wastewater from individual structures or from private property to the public lateral sewer, or its equivalent, are specifically excluded from the definition, with the exception of pumping units, and

pressurized lines, for individual structures or groups of structures when such units are cost effective and are owned and maintained by the grantee. A

sewage from vessels (NPDES)

Human body wastes and the wastes from toilets and other receptacles intended to receive or retain body wastes that are discharged from vessels and regulated under section 312 of CWA, except that with respect to commercial vessels on the Great Lakes this term includes graywater. For the purposes of this definition, "graywater" means galley, bath, and shower water. A

sewage sludge

(l) The solids, residues, and precipitate separated from or created in sewage by the unit processes of a "publicly owned treatment works. "Sewage" as used in this definition means any wastes, including wastes from humans, households, commercial establishments, industries, and storm water runoff, that are discharged to or otherwise enter a publicly owned treatment works. A (2) Any solid, semisolid or liquid waste generated by a municipal wastewater treatment plant the ocean dumping of which may unreasonably degrade or endanger human health, welfare, or amenities, or the marine environment, ecological systems, and economic potentialities. A, E

sewage treatment works

Municipal or domestic waste treatment facilities of any type which are publicly owned or regulated to the extent that feasible compliance schedules are determined by the availability of funding provided by Federal, State, or local governments. A

sewer
A channel that carries waste water and stormwater runoff from the source to a treatment plant or receiving stream. Sanitary sewers carry household and commercial waste. Storm sewers carry runoff from rain or snow. Combined sewers are used for both purposes. N

sewerage
The entire system of sewage collection, treatment, and disposal. Also applies to all effluent carried by sewers. N

shaft horsepower
Only the measured shaft power output of an auxiliary power unit, turboprop, or piston engine. N

shear shredder
A shredder that cuts material between two large blades or between a blade and a stationary edge.

sheaves
Grooved pulleys, and shall be so classified unless used as flywheels. O

sheen
An iridescent appearance on the surface of water; a quantity of oil that creates a sheen is a harmful quantity subject to regulation under section 311 of the Clean Water Act. A

Shielded Nonmetallic-Sheathed Cable
Type SNM, shielded nonmetallic-sheathed cable is a factory assembly of two or more insulated conductors in an extruded core of moisture-resistant, flame-resistant nonmetallic material, covered with an overlapping spiral metal tape and wire shield and jacketed with an extruded moisture-, flame-, oil-, corrosion-, fungus-, and sunlight-resistant nonmetallic material. O

shift
The regular production work period for one group of workers. A

shipping losses
Discharges resulting from loading tank cars or tank trucks; discharges resulting from cleaning tank cars or tank trucks; and discharges from air pollution control scrubbers designed to control emissions from loading or cleaning tank cars or tank trucks. A

shore
A supporting member that resists a compressive force imposed by a load. O

shotgun
Non-scientific term for the process of breaking up the DNA derived from an organism and then moving each separate and unidentified DNA fragment into a bacterium. N

show window
Any window used or designed to be used for the display of goods or

advertising material, whether it is fully or partly enclosed or entirely open at the rear and whether or not it has a platform raised higher than the street floor level. O

SHP
Shaft Horsepower. A

shredder
A machine used to break up waste materials into smaller pieces by cutting or tearing.

shutdown
The cessation of operation of an affected facility for any purpose. A

SI
(1) Surface Impoundments. (2) Spark Ignition. N

SIC
The Standard Industrial Classification Manual, published by the Office of Management and Budget in the Executive Office of the President, defines industries in accordance with the composition and structure of the economy and covers the entire field of economic activities. The Calendar of Federal Regulations uses SIC terminology whenever possible throughout the "Sectors Affected" sections.

SICEA
Steel Industry Compliance Extension Act. N

sick building syndrome
A set of symptoms that affect a number of building occupants during the time they spend in the building and diminish or go away during periods when they leave the building. Cannot be traced to specific pollutants or sources within the building. (Compare to: "building-related illness.") N

side-rolling ladder
A semifixed ladder, nonadjustable in length, supported by attachments to a guide rail, which is generally fastened to shelving, the plane of the ladder being also its plane of motion. O

side-step ladder
One from which a man getting off at the top must step sideways from the ladder in order to reach the landing. O

siftings
The fine materials that fall from a fuel bed through its grate openings during incineration.

signal words
The words used on a pesticide label--Danger, Warning, Caution--to indicate the level of toxicity of the chemicals. N

signaling circuit
Any electric circuit that energizes signaling equipment. O

signals
Moving signs, provided by workers, such as flagmen, or by devices, such as flashing lights, to warn of possible or existing hazards. O

significant
(1) In reference to a net emissions increase or the potential of a source to emit any of the following pollutants, a rate of emissions that would

equal or exceed any of the following rates: Pollutant and Emissions Rate: Carbon monoxide, 100 tons per year (tpy); Nitrogen oxides, 40 tpy; Sulphur dioxide, 40 tpy; Particulate matter, 25 tpy; Ozone, 40 tpy of volatile organic compounds; Lead, 0.6 tpy; Asbestos, 0.007 tpy; Beryllium, 0.0004 tpy; Mercury, 0.1 tpy; Vinyl chloride, 1 tpy; Fluorides, 3 tpy; Sulfuric acid mist: 7 tpy; Hydrogen sulfide (H_2S), 10 tpy; Total reduced sulfur (including H_2S), 10 tpy; Reduced sulfur compounds (including H_2S), 10 tpy. (2) Significant, in reference to a net emissions increase or the potential of a source to emit a pollutant subject to regulation under the CAA, the preceding paragraph does not list any emissions rate. (3) Significant also means any emissions rate or any net emissions increase associated with a major stationary source or major modification, which would construct within 10 kilometers of a Class I area, and have an impact on such area equal to or greater than 1 ug/m^3, (24-hour average). [ed. Emissions below the significant levels are considered to be minimum and not subject to new source review pursuant to the PSD and nonattainment programs of the CAA]. A

significant adverse reactions

Reactions that may indicate a substantial impairment of normal activities or long-lasting or irreversible damage to health or the environment. A

significant biological treatment

The use of an aerobic or anaerobic biological treatment process in a treatment works to consistently achieve a 30-day average of at least 65 percent removal of BOD. A

significant deterioration

Pollution from a new source in previously "clean" areas. N [ed. An increase in air pollution in an area meeting a national ambient air quality standards, when the increase equals or exceeds allowable increments for that pollutant established by the Congress or EPA].

significant discharge

Any point source discharge for which timely management action must be taken in order to meet the water quality objectives within the period of the operative water quality management plan. The significant nature of the discharge is to be determined by the State, but must include any discharge which is causing or will cause water quality problems. A

significant economic loss

Under emergency conditions, for a productive activity, the profitability would be substantially below the expected profitability for that activity; or, for other types of activities, where profits cannot be calculated, the value of public or private fixed assets would be substantially below the expected value for those assets. Only losses caused by the emergency conditions, specific to the impacted site, and specific to the geographic area affected by the emergency conditions are included. The contribution of obvious mismanagement to the loss will not be considered in determining loss. In evaluating the significant of an economic loss for productive activities, the Agency will consider whether the expected reduction in profitability exceeds what would be expected as a result of normal fluctuations over a number of years, and whether the loss would affect the long-term financial viability expected from the productive activity. In evaluating the significance of an economic loss for situations other than productive activities, the Agency will consider reasonable measures of expected loss. A

significant environmental effects
(i) Any irreversible damage to biological, commercial, or agricultural resources of importance to society; (ii) Any reversible damage to biological, commercial, or agricultural resources of importance to society if the damage persists beyond a single generation of the damaged resource or beyond a single year, or (iii) Any known or reasonably anticipated loss of members of an endangered or threatened species. "Endangered" or "threatened" species are those species identified as such by the Secretary of the Interior. A

significant hazard to public health
Any level of contaminant which causes or may cause the aquifer to exceed any maximum contaminant level set forth in any promulgated National Primary Drinking Water Standard at any point where the water may be used for drinking purposes or which may otherwise adversely affect the health of persons, or which may re-

quire a public water system to install additional treatment to prevent such adverse effect. A

significant impairment
Visibility impairment which, in the judgment of the Administrator, interferes with the management, protection, preservation or enjoyment of the visitor's visual experience of the mandatory Class I Federal area. This determination must be made on a case-by-case basis taking into account the geographic extent, intensity, duration, frequency and time of the visibility impairment, and how these factors correlate with (1) times of visitor use of the mandatory Class I Federal area, and (2) the frequency and timing of natural conditions that reduce visibility. A

significant municipal facilities
Those publicly owned sewage treatment plants that discharge a million gallons per day or more and are therefore considered by states to have the potential for substantial effect on the quality of receiving waters. N

significantly more stringent limitation
BOD_5 and SS limitations necessary to meet the percent removal requirements of at least 5 mg/l more stringent than the otherwise applicable concentration-based limitations (e.g., less than 25 mg/l in the case of the secondary treatment limits for BOD_5 and SS) or the percent removal limitations in 40 CFR 133.102 and 133.105, if such limits would, by themselves, force significant construction

or other significant capital expenditure. A

signs

The warnings of a hazard, temporarily or permanently affixed or placed, at locations where hazards exist. O

silica

SiO2. Silicon dioxide, which is a major constituent of fireclay refractory materials either alone or in chemical combinations.

silicomanganese zirconium

That alloy containing 60 to 65 percent by weight silicon, 1.5 to 2.5 percent by weight calcium, 5 to 7 percent by weight zirconium, 0.75 to 1.25 percent by weight aluminum, 5 to 7 percent by weight manganese, and 2 to 3 percent by weight barium. A

silicon metal

Any silicon alloy containing more than 96 percent silicon by weight. A

silt

Fine particles of soil or rock that can be picked up by air or water and deposited as sediment. N

silviculture

Management of forest land for timber. Sometimes contributes to water pollution, as in clear-cutting. N

silviculture point source

Any discernible, confined and discrete conveyance related to rock crushing, gravel washing, log sorting or log storage facilities which are operated in connection with silvicultural activities and from which pollutants are discharged into navigable waters. This term does not include nonpoint source activities inherent to silviculture such as nursery operations, site preparation, reforestation and subsequent cultural treatment, thinning, prescribed burning, pest and fire control, harvesting operations, surface drainage, and road construction and maintenance from which runoff results from precipitation events. N

similar composition

A pesticide product which contains only the same active ingredient(s), or combination of active ingredients, and which is in the same category of toxicity, as a federally registered pesticide product. A

similar product

A pesticide product which, when compared to a federally registered product, has a similar composition and a similar use pattern. A

similar use pattern

Use of a pesticide product which, when compared to a federally registered use of a product with a similar composition, does not require a change in precautionary labeling under 40 CFR 162.10(h), and which is substantially the same as the federally registered use. Registrations involving changed use patterns are not included in this term. A

simple cycle gas turbine

Any stationary gas turbine which does not recover heat from the gas turbine exhaust gases to preheat the inlet combustion air to the gas turbine, or which does not recover heat from the gas turbine exhaust gases to heat water or generate steam. A

simple leachate collection

This system consists of a gravity flow drainfield installed under the waste disposal facility liner. This design is recommended for use when semi-solid or leachable solid wastes are placed in a lined pit excavated into a relatively thick, unsaturated, homogeneous layer of low permeability soil. A

SIMS

Secondary Ion-Mass Spectometry. N

single cleat ladder

One which consists of a pair of side rails, usually parallel, but with flared side rails permissible, connected together with cleats that are joined to the side rails at regular intervals. O

single ladder

A single ladder is a non-self-supporting portable ladder, nonadjustable in length, consisting of but one section. Its size is designated by the overall length of the side rail. O

single stroke mechanism

An arrangement used on a full revolution clutch to limit the travel of the slide to one complete stroke at each engagement of the clutch. O

single-point adjustable suspension scaffold

A manually or power-operated unit designed for light duty use, supported by a single wire rope from an overhead support so arranged and operated as to permit the raising or lowering of platform to desired working positions. O

single-pole scaffold

Platforms resting on putlogs or cross beams, the outside ends of which are supported on ledgers secured to a single row of posts or uprights, and the inner ends of which are supported on or in a wall. O

single stroke

One complete stroke of the slide, usually initiated from a full open (or up) position, followed by closing (or down), and then a return to the full open position. O

sinking

Controlling oil spills by using an agent to trap the oil. Both sink to the bottom of the body of water and biograde there. N

sinking agents

Those materials which are applied to oil and hazardous substance spills to sink floating pollutants below the water surface. A

sintering

A heat treatment that causes adjacent particles of a material to cohere below a temperature that would cause them to melt.

sintering machine

Any furnace in which a lead sulfide ore concentrate charge is heated in the presence of air to eliminate sulfur contained in the charge and to agglomerate the charge into a hard porous mass called "sinter." A

sintering machine discharge end
Any apparatus which receives sinter as it is discharged from the conveying grate of a sintering machine. A

SIP
State Implementation Plans. EPA-approved state plans for the establishment, regulation, and enforcement of air pollution standards. N

SITE
Superfund Innovative Technology Evaluation, EPA-supported research, development and demonstration projects designed to develop new remediation technologies.

site
(1) The land or water area where any "facility or activity" is physically located or conducted, including adjacent land used in connection with the facility or activity. A (2) A contiguous property unit. Property divided only by a public right-of-way shall be considered one site. There may be more than one manufacturing plant on a single site. A

site buffer zone
The area of land between the active portion of a hazardous waste treatment, storage, or disposal facility and its property boundary line. Its purpose is to protect human health and the environment.

site inspection
The collection of information from a Superfund site to determine the extent and severity of hazards posed by the site. It follows and is more extensive than a preliminary assessment. The purpose is to gather information necessary to score the site, using the Hazard Ranking System, and to determine if the site presents an immediate threat that requires prompt removal action. N

site of construction
The general physical location of any building, highway, or other change or improvement to real property which is undergoing construction, rehabilitation, alteration, conversion, extension, demolition, and repair and any temporary location or facility at which a contractor, subcontractor, or other participating party meets a demand or performs a function relating to the contract or subcontract. A

site quality assurance and sampling plan
A written document, associated with site sampling activities, which presents in specific terms the organization (where applicable), objectives, functional activities, and specific quality assurance (QA) and quality control (QC) activities designed to achieve the data quality goals of a specific project(s) or continuing operation(s). The QA Project Plan is prepared for each specific project or continuing

operation (or group of similar projects of continuing operations). The QA Project Plan will be prepared by the responsible program office, regional office, laboratory, contractor, recipient of an assistance agreement, or other organization. A

siting
The process of choosing a location for a facility. N

six-minute period
Any one of the 10 equal parts of a one-hour period. A

size classes of discharges
The following sizes of oil discharges which are provided as guidance to the On-Site Coordinator (OSC), and serve as the criteria for the actions delineated in Subpart E. They are not meant to imply associated degrees of hazard to public health or welfare, nor are they a measure of environmental damage. Any oil discharge that poses a substantial threat to the public health or welfare or results in critical public concern shall be classified as a major discharge regardless of the following quantitative measures. (a) Minor Discharge. A discharge to the inland waters of less than 1,000 gallons of oil or a discharge to the coastal waters of less than 10,000 gallons of oil. (b) Medium Discharge. A discharge of 1,000 to 10,000 gallons of oil in the inland waters or a discharge of 10,000 to 100,000 gallons of oil to the coastal waters. (c) Major Discharge. A discharge of more than 10,000 gallons of oil to the inland waters or more than 100,000 gallons of oil to the coastal waters. A

skimming
Using a machine to remove oil or scum from the surface of the water. N

skimming tank
A tank so designed that floating matter will rise and remain on the surface of the wastewater until removed, while the liquid discharges continuously under curtain walls or scum boards.

skyshine
Radiation emitted through the roof of the shield (or unshielded roof) that scatters back to the ground level due to its deviation by the atmosphere.

slag
The more or less completely fused and vitrified matter separated during the reduction of a metal from its ore. A

slagging of refractory materials
Destructive chemical action that forms slag on refractory materials subjected to high temperatures; or, a molten or viscous coating produced on refractory materials by ash particles.

SLAMS
State or Local Air Monitoring Station(s). The SLAMS make up the ambient air quality monitoring network which is required by 40 CFR 58.20 to be provided for in the State's implementation plan. This definition places no restrictions on the use of the physical structure or facility housing the SLAMS. Any combination of SLAMS and any other monitors (Special Purpose, NAMS, PSD) may

occupy the same facility or structure without affecting the respective definitions of those monitoring station. A

slide
The main reciprocating press member. A slide is also called a ram, plunger, or platen. O

sliding damper
A plate normally installed perpendicular to the flow of gas in a breeching and arranged to slide across it to regulate the flow.

slimicides
All substances or mixtures of substances intended for use in preventing or inhibiting the growth of, or destroying biological slimes composed of combinations of algae, bacteria or fungi declared to be pests. Slimicides include, but are not limited to, slime control agents for use in industrial water cooling systems and in pulp and paper mill wet end systems. A

slough
A wet or marshy area.

slow meter response
The slow response of the sound level meter shall be used. The slow dynamic response shall comply with the meter dynamic characteristics in paragraph 5.4 of the American National Standard Specification for Sound Level Meters. ANSI S1.4-1971. This publication is available from the American National Standards Institute

Inc., 1430 Broadway, New York, New York 10018. A

slow sand filtration
Treatment process involving passage of raw water through a bed of sand at low velocity which results in the substantial removal of chemical and biological contaminants. N

sludge
Any solid, semisolid or liquid waste generated from a municipal, commercial, or industrial wastewater treatment plant, water supply treatment plant, or air pollution control facility exclusive of the treated effluent from a wastewater treatment plant. A

sludge digestion
The process by which organic or volatile matter in sludge is gasified, liquified, mineralized, or converted into more stable organic matter through the activities of either anaerobic or aerobic organisms.

sludge dryer
A device used to reduce the moisture content of sludge by heating to temperatures above 65° C (ca. 150° F) directly with combustion gases. A

sludge oil
Muddy impurities and acid which have settled from a mineral oil. A

slurry
A watery mixture of insoluble matter that results from some pollution control techniques. N

small commercial establishments

Private establishments such as restaurants, hotels, stores, filling stations, or recreational facilities and private, non-profit entities such as churches, schools, hospitals, or charitable organizations with dry weather wastewater flows less than 25,000 gallons per day. A

small manufacturer, processor, or importer

(1) A manufacturer or importer whose total annual sales are less than $500,000, based upon the manufacturer's or importer's latest complete fiscal year, except that no manufacturer or importer is a small manufacturer or importer with respect to PBBs or Tris which such person manufactured at one site or imported in quantities greater than 10,000 pounds during the latest calendar year. In the case or a company which is owned or controlled by another company, total annual sales shall be based on the total annual sales of the owned or controlled company, the parent company, and all companies owned or controlled by the parent company taken together. A (2) A manufacturer or processor who employed no more than 10 full-time employees at any one time in 1981. A

small quantities for research and development

Quantities of a chemical substance manufactured, imported, processed or proposed to be manufactured, imported, or processed that (1) are no greater than reasonably necessary for such purposes and (2) after the publication of the revised inventory, are used by, or directly under the super-

vision of, a technically qualified individual(s). Any chemical substances manufactured, imported or processed in quantities less than 1,000 pounds annually shall be presumed to be manufactured, imported or processed for research and development purposes. No person may report for the inventory any chemical substance in such quantities unless that person can certify, that the substance was not manufactured, imported, or processed solely in small quantities for research and development, as defined in this section. A

small quantity generator

Under RCRA, a facility that generates less than 1,000 kg but more than 100 kg per month of hazardous wastes.

small refinery

A refinery: (1) The gasoline producing capacity of which was either: (i) in operation at any time during the one-year period immediately preceding October 1, 1976, as evidenced by submittal to EPA prior to January 1, 1977, of a report for any compliance period during such period, pursuant to 40 CFR 80.20(a)(3); or (ii) in operation at any time prior to October 1, 1979 (as evidenced by submittal to EPA by January 1, 1980, of a report for any compliance period ending prior to that date, pursuant to 40 CFR 80.20(a)(3)) and under construction at any time during the one-year period immediately preceding October 1, 1976; (2) Which has an average daily production of 10,000 barrels of gasoline or less during each compliance period since July 1, 1981;

(3) Which is not owned or controlled by any refiner that has a total combined average daily production of greater than 70,000 barrels of gasoline during any compliance period since July 1, 1981, and was not owned or controlled by a refiner with such production during any period of ownership or control since July 1, 1981; and (4) Which has produced gasoline during the period July 1, 1981, to June 30, 1982, as evidenced by submittal to EPA prior to August 27, 1982, of a report for any two compliance periods during this period, pursuant to 40 CFR § 80.20(b)(2). A

SMCL
Secondary Maximum Contaminant Levels. The maximum permissible level of contaminant in water which is delivered to the free flowing outlet of the ultimate user of public water system. Contaminants added to the water under circumstances controlled by the user, except those resulting from corrosion of piping and plumbing caused by water quality, are excluded from this definition. A

smelting
The treatment of an ore by heat to separate out the desired metal.

smelting furnace
Any vessel in which the smelting of copper sulfide ore concentrates or calcines is performed and in which the heat necessary for smelting is provided by an electric current, rapid oxidation of a portion of the sulfur contained in the concentrate as it passes through

an oxidizing atmosphere, or the combustion of a fossil fuel. A

smog
(1) The irritating haze resulting from the sun's effect on certain pollutants in the air, notably those from automobile exhaust; see photochemical process. (2) Also a mixture of fog and smoke.

smoke
(1) Solid or liquid particles under 1 micron in diameter. (2) Particles suspended in air after incomplete combustion of materials containing carbon. N (3) The matter in the exhaust emissions which obscures the transmission of light. A

smoke density
The amount of solid matter contained in smoke. It is often measured by systems that relate the grayness of the smoke to an established standard. See Ringelmann chart.

Smoke Number
SN. The dimensionless term quantifying smoke emissions. A

SMSA
Standard Metropolitan Statistical Area. N

SNAAQS
Secondary National Ambient Air Quality Standards. N

snagging
Grinding which removes relatively

large amounts of material without regard to close tolerances or surface finish requirements. O

SNAP
Significant Non-Compliance Action Plan. D

SNC
Significant Noncompliance.

SNUR
Significant New Use Rule (TSCA). N

SO₂
Sulfur dioxide.

SO₃
Sulfur trioxide.

SOCMA
Synthetic Organic Chemical Manufacturers Association.

SOCs
Synthetic Organic Chemicals. Man-made organic chemicals. Some SOCs are volatile, others tend to stay dissolved in water rather than evaporate out of it. N

soda-lime recipe
Glass product composition of the following ranges of weight proportions: 60 to 75 percent silicon dioxide, 10 to 17 percent total R_2O (e.g., Na_2O and K_2O), 8 to 20 percent total RO but not to include any PbO (e.g., CaO, and MgO), 0 to 8 percent total R_2O_3 (e.g., Al_2O_3), and 1 to 5 percent other oxides. A

soft water
Any water that is not "hard", i.e.,

does not contain a significant amount of dissolved minerals such as salts containing calcium or magnesium. N

soil
All unconsolidated materials normally found on or near the surface of the earth including, but not limited to, silts, clays, sands, gravel, and small rocks. A

soil adsorption field
A sub-surface area containing a trench or bed with clean stones and a system of distribution piping through which treated sewage may seep into the surrounding soil for further treatment and disposal. N

soil cohesion
The mutual attraction exerted between soil particles by molecular forces and moisture films.

soil conditioner
An organic material like humus or compost that helps soil absorb water, build a bacterial community, and distribute nutrients and minerals. N

soil flushing
The process of site restoration by flooding the area of contamination and collecting the seepage with a series of shallow well points. It is a practical approach only when contamination is fairly shallow and confined to a fairly small area.

soil gas
Gaseous elements and compounds that occur in the small spaces between particles of the earth and soil. Such gases can move through or leave the

soil or rock, depending on changes in pressure. N

soil horizon
A layer of soil or soil material approximately parallel to the land surface and differing from adjacent genetically related layers in physical, chemical, and biological properties or characteristics (e.g., color, structure, and texture). N

soil injection
The emplacement of pesticides by ordinary tillage practices within the plow layer of a soil. A

soil matrix
The portion of a given soil having the dominant color; in most cases, the matrix will be the portion of the soil having more than 50 percent of the same color. N

soil permeability
The ease with which gases, liquids, or plant roots penetrate or pass through a layer of soil. N

soil pH
The value obtained by sampling the soil to the depth of cultivation or solid waste placement, whichever is greater, and analyzing by the electrometric method. ("Methods of Soil Analysis, Agronomy Monograph No. 9," C.A. Black, ed., American Society of Agronomy, Madison, Wisconsin, pp. 914-926, 1965). A

soil phase
A subdivision of a soil series having

features (e.g. slope, surface texture, and stoniness) that affect the use and management of the soil, but which do not vary sufficiently to differentiate it as a separate series. N

soil plasticity
The property of a soil that allows it to be deformed or molded while moist without cracking or falling apart.

soil pore
An area within soil occupied by either air or water, resulting from the arrangement of individual soil particles or peds. N

soil profile
A vertical section of the soil through all its horizons and extending into the parent material. N

soil, renovating soil
Soil material that exists or is placed beneath a landfill that will provide the natural renovation of leachate emanating from the landfill.

soil sealant
A chemical or physical agent used to plug porous soils to prevent leaching or percolation.

soil series
A group of soils having horizons similar in differentiating characteristics and arrangements in the soil profile, except for texture of the surface layer. N

soil structure
The combination or arrangement of

primary soil particles into secondary particles, units, or peds. N

soil surface
The upper limits of the soil profile; for mineral soils, the upper limits of the highest mineral horizon (A-horizon); for organic soils, the upper limit of undecomposed organic matter. N

soil texture
The relative proportions of the various sizes of particles (silt, sand and clay) in a soil. N

sole or principal source aquifer
(1) An aquifer which has been designated by the Administrator pursuant to sections 1424 (a) or (e) of the SDWA. A (2) An aquifer that is the sole source of drinking water for an area. Upon designation by the Administrator of EPA, development around a sole source aquifer that could contaminate the drinking water can be curtailed.

solid-derived fuel
Any solid, liquid, or gaseous fuel derived from solid fuel for the purpose of creating useful heat and includes, but is not limited to, solvent refined coal, liquified coal, and gasified coal. A

solidification and stabilization
Removal of wastewater from a waste or changing it chemically to make the waste less permeable and susceptible to transport by water. N

solid waste
Any garbage, refuse, sludge from a waste treatment plant, water supply treatment plant, or air pollution control facility and other discarded material, including solid, liquid, semisolid, or contained gaseous material resulting from industrial, commercial, mining, and agricultural operations, and from community activities, but does not include solid or dissolved material in domestic sewage, or solid or dissolved materials in irrigation return flows or industrial discharges which are point sources subject to permits under section 402 of the Federal Water Pollution Control Act, as amended (86 Stat. 880), or source, special nuclear, or byproduct material as defined by the Atomic Energy Act of 1954, as amended (68 Stat. 923). I

solid waste boundary
The outermost perimeter of the solid waste (projected in the horizontal plane) as it would exist at completion of the disposal activity. A

solid-waste-derived fuel
A fuel that is produced from solid waste that can be used as a primary or supplementary fuel in conjunction with or in place of fossil fuels. The solid-waste-derived fuel can be in the form of raw (unprocessed) solid waste, shredded (or pulped) and classified solid waste, gas or oil derived from pyrolyzed solid waste, or gas derived from the biodegradation of solid waste. A

solid waste disposal
The final placement of refuse that cannot be salvaged or recycled. N

solid waste management
The systematic administration of activities which provide for the col-

lection, source separation, storage, transportation, transfer, processing, treatment, and disposal of solid waste. I

solid waste management facility

Includes--(A) any resource recovery system or component thereof, (B) any system, program, or facility for resource conservation, and (C) any facility for the collection, source separation, storage, transportation, transfer, processing, treatment or disposal of solid wastes, including hazardous wastes, whether such facility is associated with facilities generating such wastes or otherwise. I

solid waste product charge

A Federal, virgin materials tax built into an article's original purchase price in order to finance municipal collection and disposal of the article after it is discarded and becomes solid waste. Also called product disposal charge and solid waste disposal charge.

solid waste storage container

A receptacle used for the temporary storage of solid waste while awaiting collection. A

solvent

(1) Substance (usually liquid) capable of dissolving or dispersing one or more other substances. N (2) A mixture that can dissolve other materials to form a uniform mixture. N

solvent-borne

A coating which contains five percent or less water by weight in its volatile fraction. A

solvent-borne ink systems

Ink and related coating mixtures whose volatile portion consists essentially of VOC solvent with not more than five weight percent water, as applied to the gravure cylinder. A

solvent feed

The solvent introduced into the spinning solution preparation system or precipitation bath. This feed stream includes the combination of recovered solvent and makeup solvent. A

solvent filter

A discrete solvent filter unit containing a porous medium that traps and removes contaminants from petroleum solvent, together with the piping and ductwork used in the installation of this device. A

solvent inventory variation

The normal changes in the total amount of solvent contained in the affected facility. A

solvent of high photochemical reactivity

Any solvent with an aggregate of more than 20 percent of its total volume composed of the chemical compounds classified below or which exceeds any of the following individual percentage composition limitations in reference to the total volume of solvent: (i) A combination of hydrocarbons, alcohols, aldehydes, esters, ethers, or ketones having an olefinic or cycloolefinic type of unsaturation: 5 percent; (ii) A combination of aromatic compounds with eight or more carbon atoms to the molecule except ethylbenzene: 8 percent; (iii) A combination of ethylbenzene, ketones having branched hydrocarbon structures, tri-chloroethylene or toluene: 20 percent. Whenever any organic solvent or any constituent of an organic solvent may be classified from its chemical structure into more than one of the above groups of organic compounds, it shall be considered as a member of the most reactive chemical group, that is, that group having the least allowable percentage of total volume of solvents. A

solvent recovery dryer
A class of dry cleaning dryers that employs a condenser to condense and recover solvent vapors evaporated in a closed-loop stream of heated air, to-gether with the piping and ductwork used in the installation of this device. A

solvent recovery system
(1) The equipment associated with capture, transportation, collection, concentration, and purification of organic solvents. It may include enclosures, hoods, ducting, piping, scrubbers, condensers, carbon ad-sorbers, distillation equipment, and associated storage vessels. A (2) An air pollution control system by which VOC solvent vapors in air or other gases are captured and directed through a condenser(s) or a vessel(s) containing beds of activated carbon or

other adsorbents. For the condensa-tion method, the solvent is recovered directly from the condenser. For the adsorption method, the vapors are ad-sorbed, then desorbed by steam or other media, and finally condensed and recovered. A

solvent-spun synthetic fiber process
The total of all equipment having a common spinning solution prepara-tion system or a common solvent recovery system, and that is used in the manufacture of solvent-spun synthetic fiber. It includes spinning solution preparation, spinning, fiber processing and solvent recovery, but does not include the polymer production equipment. A

solvent-spun synthetic fiber
Any synthetic fiber produced by a process that uses an organic solvent in the spinning solution, the precipitation bath, or processing of the sun fiber. A

sonic boom
The thunderous noise made when shock waves reach the ground from a jet airplane exceeding the speed of sound. N

soot
Carbon dust formed by incomplete combustion. N

sorbents
Essentially inert and insoluble materials which are used to remove oil and hazardous substances from water through a variety of sorption mechanisms. Examples include: straw, expanded perlite, polyurethane foams, reclaimed paper fibers, peat moss. A

sorption
The action of soaking up or attracting substances; used in many pollution control processes. N

sound exposure level
The level in decibels calculated as ten times the common logarithm of time integral of squared A-weighted sound pressure over a given time period or event divided by the square of the standard reference sound pressure of 20 micropascals and a reference duration of one second. A

sound level
The level in decibels measured by instrumentation which satisfies the requirements of American National Standards Specification for Sound Level Meters S1.4-1971 Type 1 or (S1A) or Type 2 if adjusted as shown in Table 1 (40 CFR § 201.1). This publication is available from the American National Standards Institute, Inc., 1430 Broadway, New York, New York 10018. For the purpose of these procedures the sound level is to be measured using the A-weighting of spectrum and either the FAST or SLOW dynamic averaging characteristics, as designated. It is abbreviated as L_A. A

sound pressure level
In decibels, 20 times the logarithm to the base ten of the ratio of a sound pressure to the reference sound pressure of 20 micropascals (20 micronewtons per square meter). In the absence of any modifier, the level is understood to be that of a root-mean-square pressure. A

source
Any building, structure, facility, or installation from which there is or may be the discharge of pollutants. D

source control remedial action
Measures that are intended to contain the hazardous substances or pollutants or contaminants where they are located or eliminate potential contamination by transporting the hazardous substances or pollutants or contaminants to a new location. Source control remedial actions may be appropriate if a substantial concentration or amount of hazardous substances or pollutants or contaminants remains at or near the area where they are originally located and inadequate barriers exist to retard migration of hazardous substances or pollutants or contaminants into the environment. Source control remedial actions may not be appropriate if most hazardous substances or pollutants or contaminants have migrated from the area where originally located or if the lead agency determines that the hazardous substances or pollutants or contaminants are adequately contained. A

source material
Any material except special nuclear material, which contains 0.05 percent or more of uranium, thorium, or any combination of the two.

source operation

The last operation preceding the emission of an air contaminant, which operation (a) results in the separation of the air contaminant from process materials or in the conversion of the process materials into air contaminants, as in the case of combustion of fuel; and (b) is not primarily an air pollution abatement operation. A

source separation

The separation of individual recyclable components of solid waste at their point of generation for segregated collection and transport to specialized waste-processing sites or final manufacturing markets.

source/receptor area

For each episode occurrence based on air monitoring, geographical, and meteorological factors: Source area is that area in which contaminants are discharged and a receptor area is that area in which the contaminants accumulate and are measured. A

SO$_x$

Sulfur Oxide.

sp.

Speed.

spalling of refractory materials

The breaking or crushing of refractory materials due to thermal, mechanical, or structural decomposition.

span

The value of opacity at which the continuous monitoring system is set to produce the maximum data display output. The span shall be set at an opacity specified in each applicable regulation. A

span drift

The change in instrument output over a stated time period, usually 24 hours, of unadjusted continuous operation, when the input concentration is a stated upscale value; usually expressed as percent full scale, e.g., span drift (maximum)-Not to exceed 1 percent/24 hours. A

span gas

A gas of known concentration which is used routinely to set the output level of an analyzer. A

spandex fiber

A manufactured fiber in which the fiber-forming substance is a long chain synthetic polymer comprised of at least 85 percent of a segmented polyurethane. A

spare flue gas desulfurization system module

A separate system of sulfur dioxide emission control equipment capable of treating an amount of flue gas equal to the total amount of flue gas generated by an affected facility when operated cat maximum capacity divided by the total number of nonspare flue gas desulfurization modules in the system. A

SPCC

Spill Prevention Control and Countermeasure [plan].

special decompression chamber

A chamber to provide greater comfort of employees when the total decompression time exceeds 75 minutes. O

special features enabling off-street or off-highway operation and use

(1) That has 4-wheel drive; and (2) That has at least four of the following characteristics calculated when the automobile is at curb weight, on a level surface, with the front wheels parallel to the vehicle's longitudinal centerline and the tires inflated to the manufacturer's recommended pressure: (i) Approach angle of not less than 28 degrees. (ii) Breakover angle of not less than 14 degrees. (iii) Departure angle of not less than 20 degrees. (iv) Running clearance of not less than 8 inches. (v) Front and rear axle clearances of not less than 7 inches each. A

special local need

An existing or imminent pest problem within a state for which the state lead agency, based upon satisfactory supporting information, has determined that an appropriate federally registered pesticide product is not sufficiently available. A

special nuclear material

This term refers to plutonium-239, uranium-233, uranium containing more than the natural abundance of uranium-235, or any material artificially enriched in any of these substances.

special packaging

Packaging that is designed and constructed to be significantly difficult for children under five years of age to open or obtain a toxic or harmful amount of the substance contained therein within a reasonable time, and that is not difficult for normal adults to use properly. A

special permission

The written consent of the authority having jurisdiction. O

special purpose facility

A building or space, including land incidental to its use, which is wholly or predominantly utilized for the special purpose of an agency and not generally suitable for other uses, as determined by the General Services Administration. A

special purpose equipment

Maintenance-of-way equipment which may be located on or operated from rail cars including: ballast cribbing machines, ballast regulators, conditioners and scarifiers, bolt machines, brush cutters, compactors, concrete mixers, cranes and derricks, earth boring machines, electric welding machines, grinders, grouters, pile drivers, rail heaters, rail layers, sandblasters, snow plows, spike drivers, sprayers and other types of such maintenance-of-way equipment. A

special review

(1) Formerly known as Rebuttable Presumption Against Registration (RPAR), this is the regulatory process

through which existing pesticides suspected of posing unreasonable risks to human health, non-target organisms, or the environment are referred to for review by EPA. The review requires an intensive risk/benefit analysis with opportunity for public comment. If the risk of any use of a pesticide is found to outweigh social and economic benefits, regulatory actions--ranging from label revisions and use-restriction to cancellation or suspended registration--can be initiated. N (2) Refers to any interim administrative review of the risks and benefits of the use of a pesticide conducted pursuant to the provisions of EPA's Rebuttable Presumption Against Registration rules, 40 CFR 162.11(a), or any subsequent version of those rules. A

special track work
Track other than normal tie and ballast bolted or welded rail or containing devices such as retarders or switching mechanisms. A

special waste
Waste materials that require different management than other hazardous wastes because they occur in very large volumes but the potential hazard posed by the materials is relatively low and thus the materials are generally not amenable to the management techniques developed for hazardous waste. The waste includes cement kiln dust, utility waste (fly ash, bottom ash, scrubber sludge), phosphate mining and processing waste, uranium and other mining waste, and gas and oil drilling muds and oil production brines.

specially designated landfill
A landfill at which complete long term protection is provided for the quality of surface and subsurface waters from pesticides, pesticide containers, and pesticide-related wastes deposited therein, and against hazard to public health and the environment. Such sites should be located and engineered to avoid direct hydraulic continuity with surface and subsurface waters, and any leachate or subsurface flow into the disposal area should be contained within the site unless treatment is provided. Monitoring wells should be established and a sampling and analysis program conducted. The location of the disposal site should be permanently recorded in the appropriate local office of legal jurisdiction. Such facility complies with the Agency Guidelines for the Land Disposal of Solid Wastes as prescribed in 40 CFR Part 241. A

species
A reproductively isolated aggregate of interbreeding populations of organisms. N

specific gravity
The ratio of the weight of a given volume of the material at a stated temperature to the weight of an equal volume of distilled water at a stated temperature. A

specification
A clear and accurate description of the technical requirement for materials, products or services, which specifies the minimum requirement for quality and construction of materials and equipment necessary for an

acceptable product. In general, specifications are in the form of written descriptions, drawings, prints, commercial designations, industry standards, and other descriptive references. A

specified work object
The specific process, method, machine, manufacture or composition of matter (including relatively minor modifications thereof) which is the subject of the experimental, developmental, research or demonstration work performed under an EPA grant. A

spectral uncertainty
Possible variation in exposure to the noise spectra in the workplace. (To avoid the underprotection that would result from these variations relative to the assumed "Pink Noise" used to determine the NRR, an extra three decibel reduction is included when computing the NRR). A

spill
(1) Any unplanned discharge or release of hazardous waste onto or into the land, air, or water. (2) The accidental spilling, leaking, pumping, emitting, emptying, or dumping of hazardous wastes or materials which, when spilled, become hazardous wastes into or on any land or water. A

spill event
A discharge of oil into or upon the navigable waters of the United States or adjoining shorelines in harmful

quantities, as defined in 40 CFR Part 110. A

spill prevention control and countermeasure plan
A plan required to be developed and implemented by onshore facilities that includes physical structures and other measures to respond to and prevent spills of oil or hazardous substances from reaching navigable waters.

spinning reserve
The sum of the unutilized net generating capability of all units of the electric utility company that are synchronized to the power distribution system and that are capable of immediately accepting additional load. The electric generating capability of equipment under multiple ownership is prorated based on ownership unless the proportional entitlement to electric output is otherwise established by contractual arrangement. A

spinning solution
The mixture of polymer, prepolymer, or copolymer and additives dissolved in solvent. The solution is prepared at a viscosity and solvent-to-polymer ratio that is suitable for extrusion into fibers. A

spiral classifier
A mechanical device for performing two types of wet separation of fine solids: same-density solids according to size and same-size solids according to density. The larger or denser

solids are delivered up the spiral, somewhat drained.

spirometer
An instrument that measures the flow and volume of air in and out of the lungs.

SPMS
(1) Strategic Planning Management Strategy. B (2) Special Purpose Monitoring Stations.

spoil
Dirt or rock that has been removed from its original location, destroying the composition of the soil in the process, as with strip-mining or dredging. N

Spontaneous Ignition Temperature
SIT. The temperature at which an oil ignites of its own accord in the presence of air oxygen under standard conditions. A

sprawl
Unplanned development of open land. N

spray application
Any method of projecting a jet of vapor of finely divided liquid onto a surface to be coated; whether by compressed air, hydraulic pressure, electrostatic forces, or other methods of generating a spray. A

spray booth
A structure housing automatic or manual spray application equipment where a coating is applied to components of automobile, light-duty truck

bodies, or large appliance parts or products. A

spray chamber
A chamber equipped with water sprays that cool and clean the combustion products passing through it.

sq. ft.
Square feet.

SQG
Small Quantity Generator.

SS
The pollutant parameter total suspended solids. A

SSA
Social Security Administration.

SSCD
Stationary Source Compliance Division.

SSUR
Stop, Sales, Use or Restriction. C

stability
The atmospheric condition existing when the temperature of the air rises rather than falls with altitude. It allows for little or no vertical air movement.

stabilization
To convert the active organic matter in sludge into inert, harmless material. N

stabilization pond
A large shallow basin (usually 2 to 4 feet) for purifying many types of industrial wastes by allowing climatic

conditions which favor the growth of bacteria and algae to convert organic materials into nontoxic organic substances. This method has been used extensively in the treatment of industrial waste-waters when a high degree of purification is not required. They have also proven successful in treating steel mill wastes.

stabilization (reduction)
Processes aimed at converting raw (untreated) sludges into a less offensive form with regard to odor, putrescibility rate, and pathogenic organism content. Major types of processes are: anaerobic digestion, aerobic digestion, lime treatment, chlorine oxidation.

stable air
An air mass that remains in the same position rather than moving in its normal horizontal and vertical directions. Stable air does not disperse pollutants and can lead to high buildups of air pollution.

stack
(1) Any chimney, flue, vent, roof monitor, conduit or duct arranged to vent emissions to the ambient air. A (2) Any point in a source designed to emit solids, liquids, or gases into the air, including a pipe or duct but not including flares. A

stack effect
Used air, as in a chimney, that moves upward because it is warmer than the surrounding atmosphere. N

stack emissions
The particulate matter captured and released to the atmosphere through a stack, chimney, or flue. A

stack gas
See flue gas.

stack sampling
The collecting of representative samples of gaseous and particulate matter that flows through a duct or stack.

stagnation
Lack of wind in an air mass or lack of motion in water. Both cases tend to entrap and concentrate pollutants.

stair platform
An extended step or landing breaking a continuous run of stairs. O

stair railing
A vertical barrier erected along exposed sides of a stairway to prevent fall of persons. O

stairs, stairways
A series of steps leading from one level or floor to another, or leading to platforms, pits, boiler rooms, crossovers, or around machinery, tanks, and other equipment that are used more or less continuously or routinely by employees or only occasionally by specific individuals. For the purpose of this subpart, a series of steps and landings having three or more rises constitutes stairs or stairway. O

STALAPCO
State and Local Air Pollution Control Officials. N

standard day conditions
Standard ambient conditions as described in the United States Standard Atmosphere, 1976, (i.e., temperature = 15° C, specific humidity = 0.00 kg/H$_2$O/kg dry air, and pressure = 101325 Pa). A

Standard Metropolitan Statistical Areas
SMSA. Such areas as designated by the U.S. Bureau of the Budget in the following publication: "Standard Metropolitan Statistical Area," issued in 1967, with subsequent amendments. A

standard of performance
(1) (A) With respect to any air pollutant emitted from a category of fossil fuel fired stationary sources to which subsection (b) applies, a standard--(B) With respect to any air pollutant emitted from a category of stationary sources (other than fossil fuel fired sources) to which [§ 111] subsection (b) [of the CAA] applies, a standard such as that referred to in subparagraph (A)(i); and (C) With respect to any air pollutant emitted from a particular source to which [§ 111] subsection (d) [of the CAA] applies, a standard which the State (or the Administrator [of EPA]) under the conditions specified in subsection (d)(2) determines is applicable to that source and which reflects the degree of emission reduction achievable through the application of the best system of continuous emission reduction which (taking into consideration the cost of achieving such

emission reduction, and any nonair quality health and environmental impact and energy requirements) the Administrator [of EPA] determines has been adequately demonstrated for that category of sources. B (2) A standard for the control of the discharge of pollutants which reflects the greatest degree of effluent reduction which the Administrator [of EPA] determines to be achievable through application of the best available demonstrated control technology, processes, operating methods, or other alternatives, including, where practicable, a standard permitting no discharge of pollutants. D

standard operating procedure
A document which describes in detail an operation, analysis, or action which is commonly accepted as the preferred method for performing certain routine or repetitive tasks. A

standard railing
A vertical barrier erected along exposed edges of a floor opening, wall opening, ramp, platform, or runway to prevent falls of persons. O

standard sample
The aliquot of finished drinking water that is examined for the presence of coliform bacteria. A

standard strength and construction
Any construction of railings, covers, or other guards that meets the requirements of this subpart. O

standards for the development of test data
A prescription of (A) the (i) health

and environmental effects, and (ii) information relating to toxicity, persistence, and other characteristics which affect health and the environment, for which test data for a chemical substance or mixture are to be developed and any analysis that is to be performed on such data, and (B) to the extent necessary to assure that data respecting such effects and characteristics are reliable and adequate (i) the manner in which such data are to be developed, (ii) the specification of any test protocol or methodology to be employed in the development of such data, and (iii) such other requirements as are necessary to provide such assurance. K

standby trust fund

A trust fund which must be established by an owner or operator who obtains a letter of credit or surety bond as specified in these regulations. The institution issuing the letter of credit or surety bond will deposit into the standby trust fund any drawings by the Regional Administrator on the credit or bond. A

STAPPA

State and Territorial Air Pollution Program Administrators. N

starting material

A substance used to synthesize or purify a technical grade of active ingredient (or the practical equivalent of the technical grade ingredient if the technical grade cannot be isolated) by chemical reaction. A

startup

The setting in operation of a source for any purpose. A

state

For most environmental statutes, the term state includes any one of the states of the United States as well as the District of Columbia, the Commonwealth of Puerto Rico, the Virgin Islands, Guam, American Samoa, the Trust Territory of the Pacific Islands (except in the case of RCRA), and the Commonwealth of the Northern Mariana Islands (except in the case of CWA). A, C, D, G, H, J, K

state agency

The air pollution control agency primarily responsible for development and implementation of a state implementation plan under the Clean Air Act. A

state air pollution control agency

A single state agency designated by the governor of that state as the official state air pollution control agency for purposes of the Clean Air Act. A

state certifying authority

(1) For water pollution control facilities, the state pollution control agency as defined in section 502 of the Act. (2) For air pollution control facilities, the air pollution control agency designated pursuant to section 302(b)(1) of the Act; or (3) For both air and water pollution control facilities, any interstate agency authorized

to act in place of the certifying agency of a state. A

state continuing planning process
The continuing planning process required by Section 303(e) of the [Clean Water] Act, as developed and approved pursuant to 40 CFR Part 130. A

State Emergency Response Commission
SERC. Commission appointed by each state governor according to the requirements of SARA Title III. The SERCs designate emergency planning districts, appoint local emergency planning committees, and supervise and coordinate their activities. N

State Implementation Plans
SIP. EPA-approved state plans for the establishment, regulation, and enforcement of air pollution standards. N

state planning agency
That state agency designated to prepare a state water planning process pursuant to section 208(a)(6) of the Federal Water Pollution Control Act. A

state planning area
That area of the state that is not designated pursuant to section 208(a) (2), (3), or (4) of the Clean Water Act. State planning areas are to be identified in the planning process description that is submitted by the state for approval by the Regional Administrator. Depending upon the requirement being considered, the state planning area may be subdivided into "approved planning areas" that may include the entire state or por-

tions of the state defined by hydrologic, political, or other boundaries. A

state primary drinking water regulation
A drinking water regulation of a state which is comparable to a national primary drinking water regulation. A

state program grant
The amount of federal assistance awarded to a state or interstate agency to assist in administering approved programs for the prevention, reduction and elimination of pollution. A

state regulated waters
"Waters of the United States" in which the Corps of Engineers suspends the issuance of section 404 [of CWA] permits upon approval of a state's section 404 permit program by the Administrator under section 404(h). These waters shall be identified in the program description as required by 40 CFR § 233.22(h)(1). The Secretary of Defense shall retain jurisdiction over the following waters (see CWA section 404(g)(1)): (a) Waters which are subject to the ebb and flow of the tide; (b) Waters which are presently used, or are susceptible to use in their natural condition or by reasonable improvement as a means to transport interstate or foreign commerce shoreward to their ordinary high water mark; and (c) "Wetlands" adjacent to waters in paragraphs (a) and (b). A

state water pollution control agency
The state agency designated by the

governor having responsibility for enforcing state laws relating to the abatement of pollution. D

static loaded radius arc
A portion of a circle whose center is the center of a standard tire-rim combination of an automobile and whose radius is the distance from that center to the level surface on which the automobile is standing, measured with the automobile at curb weight, the wheel parallel to the vehicle's longitudinal centerline, and the tire inflated to the manufacturer's recommended pressure. A

static system
A test chamber in which the test solution is not renewed during the period of the test. A

station wagon
A passenger automobile with an extended roof line to increase cargo or passenger capacity, cargo compartment open to the passenger compartment, a tailgate and one or more rear seats readily removed or folded to facilitate cargo carrying. A

stationary casting
The pouring of molten aluminum into molds and allowing the metal to air cool. A

stationary compactor
A powered machine which is designed to compact solid waste or recyclable materials, and which remains stationary when in operation. A

stationary gas turbine
Any simple cycle gas turbine, regenerative cycle gas turbine or any gas turbine portion of a combined cycle steam/electric generating system that is not self propelled. It may, however, be mounted on a vehicle for portability. A

stationary source fuel or emission limitation
Any emission limitation, schedule or timetable of compliance, or other requirement, which is prescribed under the Clean Air Act (other than section 112 or section 303 of the Act) or contained in any applicable implementation plan (other than a requirement imposed pursuant to section 110(a)(2)(F)(v) of the Act), and which limits, or is designed to limit, stationary source emissions resulting from combustion of fuels, including a prohibition on, or specification of, the use of any fuel of any type, grade or pollution characteristic. A

stationary source
Any stationary building, facility, equipment, installation or operation (or combination thereof) which is located on one or more contiguous or adjacent properties and which is owned or operated by the same person (or by persons under common control), and which emits an air pollutant for which a national ambient air quality standards promulgated under section 109 of the Act is in effect or which has been designated a hazardous waste in § 112 of the Act. O

statistical significance
The statistical significance determined by using appropriate standard techniques of multivariate analysis with results interpreted at the 95 percent confidence level and based on data relating species which are present in sufficient numbers at control areas to permit a valid statistical comparison with the areas being tested. A

statistical sound level
The level in decibels that is exceeded in a stated percentage (x) of the duration of the measurement period. It is abbreviated as L_x. A

steam generating unit
A device that combusts any fuel or byproduct/waste to produce steam or to heat water or any other heat transfer medium. This term includes any municipal-type solid waste incinerator with a heat recovery steam generating unit or any steam generating unit that combusts fuel and is part of a cogeneration system or a combined cycle system. This term does not include process heaters as they are defined in this subpart. A

steam hammers
A type of drop hammer where the ram is raised for each stroke by a double-action steam cylinder and the energy delivered to the workpiece is supplied by the velocity and weight of the ram and attached upper die driven downward by steam pressure. Energy delivered during each stroke may be varied. O

steel basis material
Cold rolled steel, hot rolled steel, and chrome, nickel and tin coated steel which are processed in coil coating. A

steel production cycle
The operations required to produce each batch of steel and includes the following major functions: Scrap charging, preheating (when used), hot metal charging, primary oxygen blowing, additional oxygen blowing (when used), and tapping. A

STEL
Short-Term Exposure Limit. N

Step 1 facilities planning
Preparation of a plan for facilities as described in 40 CFR Part 35, Subpart E or I. A

Step 1 grant
A Federal grant for preparation of a waste water treatment facilities plan as described in 40 CFR § 35.930-1. A

Step 2 plus Step 3 grant
Grant assistance for a project which combines grants as described in 40 CFR 35.930-1(a)(4).

Step 2
A project to prepare design drawings and specifications as described in 40 CFR Part 35, Subpart E or I. A

Step 2 + 3
A project which combines preparation of design drawings and specifications as described in [40 CFR] 6.501(b) and building as described in 6.501(c). A

Step 2 grant
A Federal grant for preparation of construction drawings and specifications for a waste water treatment facility as described in 40 CFR § 35.930-1. A

Step 3
A project to build a publicly owned treatment works as described in 40 CFR Part 35, Subpart E or I. A

Step 3 grant
A federal grant for fabrication and building of a publicly owned treatment works as described in 40 CFR 35.930-1. A

stepladder
A self-supporting portable ladder, nonadjustable in length, having flat steps and a hinged back. Its size is designated by the overall length of the ladder measured along the front edge of the side rails. O

steps
The flat crosspieces of a ladder on which a person may step in ascending or descending. O

sterilization
(1) In pest control, the use of radiation and chemicals to damage body cells needed for reproduction. (2) The destruction of all living organisms in water or on the surface of various materials. In contrast, disinfection is the destruction of **most** living organisms in water or on surfaces. N

still
(1) A device used to volatilize, separate, and recover petroleum solvent from contaminated solvent, together with the piping and ductwork used in the installation of this device. A (2) A closed chamber in which heat is applied to vaporize a substance; chemical decomposition may or may not take place.

stochastic
Based on the assumption that the actions of a chemical substance result from probabilistic events. N

stock solution
The source of the test solution prepared by dissolving the test substance in dilution water or a carrier which is then added to dilution water at a specified, selected concentration by means of the test substance delivery system. A

stoke
The unit of kinematic viscosity. A

stoker
A mechanical device to feed solid fuel or solid waste to a furnace.

stone feed
Limestone feedstock and millscale or other iron oxide additives that become part of the product. A

stone setters' adjustable multiple-point suspension scaffold
A swinging type scaffold having a platform supported by hangers suspended at four points so as to

permit the raising or lowering of the platform to the desired working position by the use of hoisting machines. O

stop control
An operator control designed to immediately deactivate the clutch control and activate the brake to stop slide motion. O

storage
Temporary holding of waste pending treatment or disposal. Storage methods include containers, tanks, waste piles, and surface impoundments.N

Storage And Retrieval of Aerometric Data
SAROAD. A computerized system which stores and reports information relating to ambient air quality. A

storage bin
A facility for storage (including surge bins and hoppers) for metallic minerals prior to further processing or loading. A

storage for disposal
Temporary storage of PCBs that have been designated for disposal. A

storage of hazardous waste
The containment of hazardous waste, either on a temporary basis or for a period of years, in such a manner as not to constitute disposal of such hazardous waste. A

storage pit
A hole in the ground in which solid waste is held prior to processing.

storage vessel
Each tank, reservoir, or container used for the storage of petroleum liquids, but does not include: (1) Pressure vessels which are designed to operate in excess of 204.9 kPa (15 psig) without emissions to the atmosphere except under emergency conditions, (2) Subsurface caverns or porous rock reservoirs, or (3) Underground tanks if the total volume of petroleum liquids added to and taken from a tank annually does not exceed twice the volume of the tank. A

STORET
Storage and Retrieval of Water-Related Data. N

storm sewer
A sewer designed to carry only storm waters, surface runoff, street wash waters, and drainage. A

storm water runoff
Water discharged as a result of rain, snow, or other precipitation. N

stratification
(1) A condition identified by a difference in excess of 10 percent between the average concentration in the duct or stack and the concentration at any point more than 1.0 meter from the duct or stack wall. A (2) Separating into layers. N

stratosphere
The portion of the atmosphere that is 10-to-25 miles above the earth's surface. N

stratum (plural strata)
A single sedimentary bed or layer, regardless of thickness, that consists of generally the same kind of rock material. A

street motorcycle
(1) Any motorcycle that: (a) With an 80 kg (176 lb) driver, is capable of achieving a maximum speed of at least 40 km/h (25 mph) over a level paved surface; and (b) Is equipped with features customarily associated with practical street or highway use, such features including but not limited to any of the following: stoplight, horn, rear view mirror, turn signals; or (2) Any motorcycle that: (a) Has an engine displacement less than 50 cubic centimeters; (b) Produces no more than two brake horse power; (c) With an 80 kg (176 lb) driver, cannot exceed 48 km/h (30 mph) over a level paved surface. A

street refuse
Solid waste picked up when streets and sidewalks are swept manually and mechanically.

street wastes
Materials picked up by manual or mechanical sweepings of alleys, streets, and sidewalks; wastes from public waste receptacles; and material removed from catch basins. A

stressed waters
Those receiving environments in which an applicant can demonstrate, to the satisfaction of the Administrator, that the absence of a balanced, indigenous population is caused solely by human perturbations other than the applicant's modified discharge. A

strip
To take off friable asbestos materials from any part of a facility. A

stripcropping
Growing crops in a systematic arrangement of strips or bands which serve as barriers to wind and water erosion. N

strip-mining
A process that uses machines to scrape soil or rock away from mineral deposits just under the earth's surface. N

stripper
A mechanism or die part for removing the parts or material from the punch. O

stroking selector
The part of the clutch/brake control that determines the type of stroking when the operating means is actuated. The stroking selector generally includes positions for "Off" (Clutch Control), "Inch," "Single Stroke," and "Continuous" (when Continuous is furnished). O

structural member
Any load-supporting member of a facility, such as beams and load

supporting walls; or any nonload-supporting member, such as ceilings and nonload-supporting walls. A

stud, pin, or fastener
A fastening device specifically designed and manufactured for use in explosive-actuated fastening tools. O

subacute dietary LC$_{50}$
A concentration of a substance, expressed as parts per million in food that is lethal to 50 percent of the test population of animals under test conditions. A

subacute toxicity
The property of a substance or mixture of substances to cause adverse effects in an organism upon repeated or continuous exposure within less than one-half the lifetime of that organism. A

subagreements
A written agreement between an EPA grantee and another party (other than another public agency) and any tier of agreement thereunder for the furnishing of services, supplies, or equipment necessary to complete the project for which a grant was awarded. These agreements include contracts and subcontracts for personal and professional services, agreements with consultants, and purchase orders. A

subbituminous coal
Coal that is classified as subbituminous A, B, or C according to the American Society of Testing and Materials (ASTM) Standard

Specification for Classification of Coals by Rank D388-77. A

subchronic
Of intermediate duration, usually used to describe studies or levels of exposure between five and 90 days. N

subject invention
Any invention, discovery, improvement or development (whether or not patentable) made in the course of or under a grant or any subagreement (at any tier) thereunder. A

subject to the jurisdiction of the United States
Subject to the jurisdiction of the United States by virtue of United States citizenship, United States vessel documentation or numbering, or as provided for by international agreement to which the United States is a party. N

submission
(1) A request by a POTW for approval of a Pretreatment Program to the EPA or a Director; (2) a request by a POTW to the EPA or a Director for authority to revise the discharge limits in categorical Pretreatment Standards to reflect POTW pollutant removals; or (3) a request to the EPA by an NPDES state for approval of its state pretreatment program. A

subsidence
The lowering of the natural land surface in response to: Earth movements; lowering of fluid pressure; removal of underlying supporting

material by mining or solution of solids, either artificially or from natural causes; compaction due to wetting (hydrocompaction); oxidation of organic matter in soils; or added load on the land surface. A

subsoil
The layer of earth beneath the topsoil, which is usually lacking in appreciable quantities of organic matter.

subsurface soil injection
A special method of landfarming hazardous waste with vapor pressures exceeding 78 millimeters of mercury. See deep-well disposal.

suction manometers
This system consists of a network of porous "stones" connected by hoses/tubing to a vacuum pump. The porous "stones" or suction manometers are installed along the sides and under the bottom of the waste disposal facility liner. This type of system works best when installed in relatively permeable unsaturated soil immediately adjacent to the disposal facility's bottom and/or sides. A

sudden accident
An unforeseen and unexpected occurrence which is not continuous or repeated in nature. A

sudden accidental occurrence
An occurrence which is not continuous or repeated in nature. A

sulfate
A compound in which the hydrogen of sulfuric acid is replaced by either a metal or by an organic radical, to become a sulfate salt or sulfate ester, respectively.

sulfite
A compound in which the hydrogen of sulfurous acid is replaced by either a metal or by an organic radical, to become a sulfite salt or sulfite ester, respectively.

Sulfur Dioxide
$SO2$. A heavy, pungent, colorless gas formed primarily by the combustion of fossil fuels. This major air pollutant is unhealthy for plants, animals, and people. N

sulfur oxide/particulate complex
The primary pollutant emissions of sulfur dioxide and the secondary particulate compounds that are formed from them in the atmosphere. Abbreviated SPC.

sulfur recovery plant
Any plant that recovers elemental sulfur from any gas stream. A

sulfuric acid production unit
Any facility producing sulfuric acid by the contact process by burning elemental sulfur, alkylation acid, hydrogen sulfide, organic sulfides and mercaptans, or acid sludge, but does not include facilities where conversion to sulfuric acid is utilized primarily as a means of preventing emissions to

the atmosphere of sulfur dioxide or other sulfur compounds. A

sump
A depression or tank that catches liquid runoff for drainage or disposal, like a cesspool. N

Superfund
The program operated under the legislative authority of CERCLA and SARA that funds and carries out the EPA solid waste emergency and long-term removal remedial activities. These activities include establishing the National Priorities List investigating sites for inclusion on the list, determining their priority level on the list, and conducting and/or supervising the ultimately determined cleanup and other remedial actions. N

supernatant
The liquid remaining above a layer of settleable solids after the solids collected at the bottom of a vessel.

supplemental appropriation
An appropriation enacted as an addition to a regular annual appropriation act. Supplemental appropriations acts provide additional budget authority beyond original estimates for programs or activities (including new programs authorized after the date of the original appropriation act) for which the need for funds is too urgent to be postponed until the next regular appropriation.

supplementary control system
Any technique for limiting the concentration of a pollutant in the ambient air by varying the emissions of that pollutant according to atmospheric conditions, particularly when the conditions are conducive to ground level concentrations in excess of natural ambient standards. The term supplementary control system may not include any dispersion technique based solely on the use of a stack the height of which exceeds good engineering practice (as determined under regulations implementing section 123 of the CAA). A

supplier of water
Any person who owns or operates a public water system. A, J

suppressed combustion
Those basic oxygen furnace steelmaking wet air cleaning systems which are designed to limit or suppress the combustion of carbon monoxide in furnace gases by restricting the amount of excess air entering the air pollution control system. A

surface casing
The first string of well casing to be installed in the well. A

surface coating operation
(1) Any prime coat, guide coat, or topcoat operation on an automobile or light-duty truck surface coating line. A (2) The system on a metal furniture or on a large appliance surface coating line used to apply and dry or cure an organic coating on the surface of the metal furniture part or product. The surface coating operation may be a prime coat or a top

coat operation and includes the coating application station(s), flash-off area, and curing oven. A

surface collecting agents
Those chemical agents that form a surface film to control the layer thickness of oil. A

surface cracking
Discontinuities that develop in the cover material of a sanitary landfill due to the surface drying or settlement of the solid waste. These discontinuities may result in the exposure of solid waste and thus lead to the entrance or egress of vectors, intrusion of water, and venting of decomposition gases.

surface feet per minute
s.f.p.m. The distance in feet any one abrasive grain on the peripheral surface of a grinding wheel travels in 1 minute. O

Surface Impoundment
SI. A facility or part of a facility which is a natural topographic depression, man-made excavation, or diked area formed primarily of earthen materials (although it may be lined with man-made materials), which is designed to hold an accumulation of liquid wastes or wastes containing free liquids, and which is not an injection well. Examples of surface impoundments are holding, storage, settling, and aeration pits, ponds, and lagoons. A

surface moisture
Water that is not chemically bound to a metallic mineral or metallic mineral concentrate. A

surface water
Water that flows exclusively across the surface of the land from the point of application to the point of discharge. A

surfacing material
Material in a school building that is sprayed-on, troweled-on, or otherwise applied to surfaces such as acoustical plaster on ceilings and fireproofing materials on structural members, or other materials on surfaces for acoustical, fireproofing, or other purposes. A

surfactant
A surface active chemical agent, usually made up of phosphates, used in detergents to cause lathering. The phosphates may contribute to water pollution.

surgical waste
The waste generated by surgical techniques in the treatment of disease, injury, or deformity.

surveillance system
(1) A series of monitoring devices designed to determine environmental quality. (2) A required part of state implementation plans, established to monitor all aspects of progress toward attainment of air quality standards and to identify potential episodes of high

pollutant concentrations in time to take prevention action.

susceptibility
The degree to which an organism is affected by a pesticide at a particular level of exposure. A

suspended solids
Small particles of solid pollutants that float on the surface of, or are suspended in, sewage or other liquids. They resist removal by conventional means. (See: Total Suspended Solids.) N

suspension
The act of suspending the use of a pesticide when EPA deems it necessary to do so in order to prevent an imminent hazard resulting from continued use of the pesticide. An emergency suspension takes effect immediately; under an ordinary suspension, a registrant can request a hearing before the suspension goes into effect. Such a hearing process might take six months. N

suspension culture
Individual cells or small clumps of cells growing in a liquid nutrient medium. N

swamp
A type of wetland that is dominated by woody vegetation and does not accumulate appreciable peat deposits. Swamps may be fresh or salt water and tidal or non-tidal. N

SWDA
Solid Waste Disposal Act of 1980 (P.L. 96-482). N

sweep device
A single or double arm (rod) attached to the upper die or slide of the press and designed to move the operator's hands to a safe position as the dies close, if the operator's hands are inadvertently within the point of operation. O

switch
A device for opening and closing or changing the connection of a circuit. O

switchboard
A large single panel, frame, or assembly of panels which have switches, buses, instruments, overcurrent and other protective devices mounted on the face or back or both. Switchboards are generally accessible from the rear as well as from the front and are not intended to be installed in cabinets. O

switcher locomotive
Any locomotive designated as a switcher by the builder or reported to the ICC as a switcher by the operator-owning-railroad and including, but not limited to, all locomotives of the builder/model designations listed in Appendix A to this subpart. A

SWMU
Solid Waste Management Unit.

SWU
Standard Work Units.

synergism
The cooperative action of separate substances such that the total effect

entirely of materials made by chemical synthesis, or made partially or entirely from chemically-modified naturally-occurring materials. A

synthetic organic chemicals manufacturing industry

The industry that produces, as intermediates or final products, one or more of the chemicals listed in 40 CFR § 60.489. A

Synthetic Organic Chemicals

SOCs. Man-made organic chemicals. Some SOCs are volatile, others tend to stay dissolved in water rather than evaporate out of it. N

system emergency reserves

An amount of electric generating capacity equivalent to the rated capacity of the single largest electric generating unit in the electric utility company (including steam generating units, internal combustion engines, gas turbines, nuclear units, hydroelectric units, and all other electric generating equipment) which is interconnected with the affected facility that has the malfunctioning flue gas desulfurization system. The electric generating capability of equipment under multiple ownership is prorated based on ownership unless the proportional entitlement to electric output is otherwise established by contractual arrangement. A

system load

The entire electric demand of an electric utility company's service area interconnected with the affected facility that has the malfunctioning flue gas desulfurization system plus firm contractual sales to other electric utility companies. Sales to other electric utility companies (e.g., emergency power) not on a firm contractual basis may also be included in the system load when no available system capacity exists in the electric utility company to which the power is supplied for sale. A

system of records

A group of any records under the control of any agency from which information is retrieved by the name of the individual or by some identifying number, symbol, or other identifying particular assigned to the individual. O

system response

The time interval from a step change in opacity in the stack at the input to the continuous monitoring system to the time at which 95 percent of the corresponding final value is reached as displayed on the continuous monitoring system data recorder. A

systemic

Relating to the whole body, rather than its individual parts. N

systemic pesticide

A chemical that is taken up from the ground or absorbed through the surface and carried through the systems of the organism being protected, making it toxic to pests.

T

T
Temperature, degrees Fahrenheit or Kelvin.

t1/2
First-order half-life. The time required for the concentration of the chemical to be reduced to one-half its initial value. A

Table z
OSHA's Toxic and Hazardous Substances Tables Z-1, Z-2, and Z-3 of air contaminants, found in 29 CFR 1910.1000. These tables record PELs, TWAs, and ceiling concentrations for the materials listed. N

tag
1) Stiff paper, metal or other hard material that is tied or otherwise affixed to the packaging of a protector. A 2) Temporary signs, usually attached to a piece of equipment or part of a structure, to warn of existing or immediate hazards. A

tail-end techniques
Methods for controlling air pollution by treating the polluted air stream after the pollutants have been formed.

tailings
Residue of raw materials or waste separated out during the processing of crops or mineral ores. N

tampering
The removal or rendering inoperative by any person, other than for purposes of maintenance, repair, or replacement, of any device or element of design incorporated into any product in compliance with regulations under Section 6 of the Noise Control Act, prior to its sale or delivery to the ultimate purchaser or while it is in use; or the use of a product after such device or element of design has been removed or rendered inoperative by any person. A

tangible net worth
Tangible assets that remain after deducting liabilities; such assets would not include intangibles such as goodwill and rights to patents or royalties. A

tank

A stationary device, designed to contain an accumulation of hazardous waste which is constructed primarily of non-earthen materials (e.g., wood, concrete, steel, plastic) which provide structural support. A

tank fuel volume

The volume of fuel in the fuel tank(s), which is determined by taking the manufacturer's nominal fuel tank(s) capacity and multiplying by 0.40, the result rounded using ASTM E 29-67 to the nearest tenth of a U.S. gallon. A

tank system

A hazardous waste storage or treatment tank and its associated ancillary equipment and containment system. A

tape sampler

A device used in the measurement of both gases and fine particulates. It allows air sampling to be made automatically at predetermined times.

tapping

The removal of slag or product from the electric submerged arc furnace under normal operating conditions such as removal of metal under normal pressure and movement by gravity down the spout into the ladle. A

tapping period

The time duration from initiation of the process of opening the tap hole until plugging of the tap hole is complete. A

target abatement dates

Target abatement dates or schedules of compliance for all significant dischargers, nonpoint source control measures, residual and land disposal controls, and stormwater system needs, including major interim and final completion dates, and requirements that are necessary to assure an adequate tracking of progress toward compliance. A

target organ effects

The following is a target organ categorization of effects which may occur, including examples of signs and symptoms and chemicals which have been found to cause such effects. These examples illustrate the range and diversity of effects and hazards found in the workplace, and the broad scope employers must consider in this area, but are not intended to be all inclusive.

a. Hepatoxins - Chemicals which produce liver damage.

Signs and Symptoms - Jaundice; liver enlargement.

Chemicals - Carbon tetrachloride; nitrosamines.

b. Nephrotoxins - Chemicals which produce kidney damage.

Signs and Symptoms - Edema; proteinuria.

Chemicals - Halogenated hydrocarbons; uranium.

c. Neurotoxins -Chemicals which produce their primary toxic effects on the nervous system.

Signs and Symptoms - Narcosis, behavioral changes; decrease in motor functions.

Chemicals - Mercury, carbon disulfide.

d. Agents which act on blood hematopoietic system -Decrease hemoglobin function; deprive the body

tissues of oxygen.
Signs and Symptoms - Cyanosis; loss of consciousness.
Chemicals - Carbon monoxide; cyanides.
    e. Agents which damage the lung - Chemicals which irritate or damage the pulmonary tissue.
Signs and Symptoms - Cough, tightness of chest, shortness of breath.
Chemicals - Silica; asbestos.
    f. Reproductive toxins - Chemicals which affect the reproductive capabilities including chromosomal damage (mutations) and effects on fetuses (teratogenesis).
Signs and Symptoms - Birth defects; sterility.
Chemicals - Lead; DBCP.
    g. Cutaneous hazards - Chemicals which affect the dermal layer of the body.
Signs and Symptoms - Defatting of the skin; rashes; irritation.
Chemicals - Ketones; chlorinated compounds.
    h. Eye hazards - Chemicals which affect the eye or visual capacity.
Signs and Symptoms - Conjunctivitis; corneal damage.
Chemicals - Organic solvents; acids.
N

target organ toxin
A toxic substance that attacks a specific organ of the body. For example, overexposure to carbon tetrachloride can cause liver damage. N

TARs
Technical Amendment Regulations. See regulatory interpretative memoranda for description.

TAT
Technical Assistance Team. N

TCDD
2,3,7,8-Tetrachlorodibenzo-p-dioxin. A

TCE
Trichloroethylene. A stable, low-boiling colorless liquid, toxic by inhalation. TCE is used as a solvent, metal degreasing agent, and in other industrial applications. N

TCL
Target Cleanup Levels.

TC$_{Lo}$
Toxic Concentration Low.

TCLP
Toxicity Characteristic Leaching Procedure.

TCP
Transportation Control Plan.

TD
Toxic Dose.

TD$_{Lo}$
Lowest Dose of a Substance. The lowest dose of a substance introduced by any route other than inhalation over any given period of time and reported to produce any toxic effect in humans or to produce tumorigenic or reproductive effects in animals or humans. N

Technical Assistance Team
TAT. N

technical grade of active ingredient

A material containing an active ingredient: (1) Which contains no inert ingredient, other than one used for purification of the active ingredient; and (2) Which is produced on a commercial or pilot-plant production scale (whether or not it is ever held for sale). A

Technical Review Criteria

TRC. D

technically qualified individual

A person or persons (1) who, because of training, or experience, or a combination of these factors, is capable of understanding the health and environmental risks associated with the chemical substance which is used under his or her supervision, (2) who is responsible for enforcing appropriate methods of conducting scientific experimentation, analysis, or chemical research to minimize such risks, and (3) who is responsible for the safety assessments and clearances related to the procurement, storage, use, and disposal of the chemical substance as may be appropriate or required within the scope of conducting a research and development activity. A

Technologically Enhanced Natural Radioactivity

TENR. Naturally radioactive nuclides whose relationship to the location of persons has been altered through man's activities such as by the activities of mining, tunneling, development of underground caverns, development of wells, and travel in space or at high altitudes.

technology-based standards

Effluent limitations applicable to direct and indirect sources which are developed on a category-by-category basis using statutory factors, not including water-quality effects. N

TEL

Tetraethyl Lead.

ten-year 24-hour precipitation event

The maximum 24-hour precipitation event with a probable recurrence interval of once in 10 years as defined by: (1) The National Weather Service and Technical Paper No. 40, "Rainfall Frequency Atlas of the U.S.," May 1961, or equivalent regional or rainfall probability information developed therefrom. (2) The U.S. Department of Commerce, National Oceanic and Atmospheric Administration, National Weather Service, or equivalent regional or rainfall probability information. A

ten-year 24-hour rainfall event

The maximum precipitation event with a probable recurrence interval of once in 10 years as defined by the National Weather Service in technical paper no. 40, "Rainfall Frequency Atlas of the U.S.," May 1961, and subsequent amendments or equivalent regional or State rainfall probability information developed therefrom. A

teratogenic

Substances that are suspected of causing malformations or serious deviations from the normal type, which can not be inherited in or on animal embryos or fetuses. N

teratogenicity

The capacity of a physical or chemical agent to cause non-hereditary congenital malformations (birth defects) in offspring. N

termination

The cancellation of Federal assistance, in whole or in part, under a grant prior to the scheduled date.

terms and conditions of registration

The terms and conditions governing lawful sale, distribution, and use approved in conjunction with registration including labeling, use classification, composition, and packaging. A

terracing

Dikes built along the contour of agricultural land to hold runoff and sediment, thus reducing erosion. N

terrestrial radiation

Radiation emitted by naturally occurring radionuclides such as potassium-40; the natural decay chains uranium-238, uranium-235, or thorium-232; or from cosmic-ray induced radionuclides in the soil.

territorial seas

The belt of the seas measured from the line of ordinary low water along that portion of the coast which is in direct contact with the open sea and the line marking the seaward limit of inland waters, and extending seaward a distance of three miles. A, D

tertiary treatment

Advanced cleaning of waste water that goes beyond the secondary or biological stage. It removes nutrients such as phosphorus and nitrogen and most suspended solids.

test data

Data from a formal or informal test or experiment, including information concerning the objectives, experimental methods and materials, protocols, results, data analyses (including risk assessments), recorded observations, monitoring data, measurements, and conclusions from a study, test or experiment, recorded observation, monitoring, or measurement. A

test engine

An engine in a test sample. A

test hearing protector

A hearing protector that has been selected for testing to verify the value to be put on the label, or which has been designated for testing to determine compliance of the protector with the labeled value. A

test marketing

The distribution in commerce of no more than a predetermined amount of a chemical substance, mixture, or article containing that substance or mixture, by a manufacturer or processor to no more than a defined number of potential customers to explore market capability in a competitive situation during a predetermined testing period prior to the broader distribution of that chemical substance, mixture or article in commerce. A

test sample size

The number of vehicles of the same category or configuration in a test sample.

test sample

(1) The collection of vehicles of the same configuration which have been drawn from the population of vehicles of that configuration and which will receive exhaust emission testing. (2) The collection of light-duty trucks or heavy-duty engines of the same configuration which have been selected to receive exhaust emission testing. A

test substance

The form of chemical substance or mixture that is specified for use in testing. A

test vehicle

A vehicle in a test sample or a production verification vehicle. A

test weight

The weight, within an inertia weight class, which is used in the dynamometer testing of a vehicle, and which is based on its loaded vehicle weight in accordance with the provisions of Part 86. A

testing agent

Any person who develops test data on a retrofit device. A

testing exemption

An exemption from the prohibitions of Section 10(a)(1), (2), (3), and (5) of FIFRA, which may be granted under Section 10(b)(1) of the Act for research, investigations, studies, demonstrations, or training, but not for national security. A

textile fiberglass

Fibrous glass in the form of continuous strands having uniform thickness. A

theoretical air

The quantity of air, calculated from the chemical composition of a waste, required to burn the waste completely. Also referred to as theoretical combustion air and stoichiometric air.

therapeutic index

The ratio of the dose required to produce toxic or lethal effect to dose required to produce non-adverse or therapeutic response. N

thermal conductivity

The specific rate of heat flow per hour through refractory materials or other substances expressed in British thermal units per square feet of area for a temperature difference of 1° F and for a thickness of 1 foot (30.48 centimeters) expressed as British thermal units per square feet per hour per degree Fahrenheit per foot.

thermal dryer

A unit in which the surface moisture content of a metallic mineral or a metallic mineral concentrate is reduced by direct or indirect contact with a heated gas stream. A

thermal efficiency

The ratio of heat used to total heat generated.

thermal pollution

Discharge of heated water from industrial processes that can affect the life processes of aquatic plants and animals. N

thermal processing

Processing of waste material by means of heat. A

thermal shock resistance

The ability of a material to withstand sudden heating or cooling, or both, without cracking or spalling.

thermal treatment

The treatment of hazardous waste in a device which uses elevated temperatures as the primary means to change the chemical, physical, or biological character or composition of the hazardous waste. Examples of thermal treatment processes are incineration, molten salt, pyrolysis, calcination, wet air oxidation, and microwave discharge.

thermal turbulence

Air movement and mixing caused by convection.

thermocouple

Two lengths of wire, made from different kinds of homogeneous metals, that are connected to form a complete electric circuit; they develop an electromotive force when one junction is at a different temperature from the other.

third party

A method for preparing EPA's environmental impact statement whereby the applicant retains a consultant, the responsible official exercises a concurrence review, and then the responsible official supervises the approved consultant in the preparation of the EIS. This method is optional and requires approval of both the new source applicant and the responsible official prior to the execution of an agreement to prepare the EIS. Generally, the preparation of the EIS under the third party method would be initiated prior to the preparation of the environmental impact assessment by the applicant and would thereby serve the purpose of any such environmental assessment analyses. A

30-day average

The arithmetic mean of pollutant parameter values of samples collected in a period of 30 consecutive days. A

thixotropic

Describes a material which appears and acts as a solid when undisturbed but will change to a semi-liquid when agitated; describes a material whose viscosity is a function of shear rate.

THM

Trihalomethane. A

threshold dose

The minimum application of a given substance required to produce a measurable effect. F

Threshold Limit Value

TLV. Represents the air concentrations of chemical substances to which it is believed that workers may be daily exposed without adverse effect. N

threshold planning quantity

A quantity designated for each chemical on the list of extremely hazardous substances that triggers notification by facilities to the state emergency response commission that such facilities are subject to emergency planning under SARA Title III. N

tidal

A situation in which the water level periodically fluctuates due to the action of lunar (moon) and solar (sun) forces upon the rotating earth. N

tidal marsh

Low, flat marshlands traversed by interlaced channels and tidal sloughs and subject to tidal inundation; normally, the only vegetation present is salt-tolerant bushes and grasses. N

tidal volume

The volume of air that is inspired or expired in a single breath during regular breathing. The symbol is VT.

tiering

The coverage of general matters in broader environmental impact statements (such as national program or policy statements) with subsequent narrower statements or environmental analyses (such as regional or basinwide program statements or ultimately site-specific statements) incorporating by reference the general discussions and concentrating solely on the issues specific to the statement subsequently prepared. Tiering is appropriate when the sequence of statements or analyses is: (a) From a program, plan, or policy environmental impact statement to a program, plan, or policy statement or analysis of lesser scope or to a site-specific statement or analysis. (b) From an environmental impact statement on a specific action at an early stage (such as need and site selection) to a supplement (which is preferred) or a subsequent statement or analysis at a later stage (such as environmental mitigation). Tiering in such cases is

appropriate when it helps the lead agency to focus on the issues which are ripe for decision and exclude from consideration issues already decided or not yet ripe. A

TIM

Time In Mode. A

time to 90 percent response

The time interval from a step change in the input concentration at the instrument inlet to a reading of 90 percent of the ultimate recorded concentration. A

Time-Weighted Average

TWA exposure is the airborne concentration of a material to which a person is exposed, averaged over the total exposure time--generally the total workday (8 to 12 hours). Also see "TLV." N

tipping

The unloading of refuse from a collection truck.

tipping floor

The unloading area for vehicles that are delivering solid waste to an incinerator or other processing plant.

tissue

A group of similar cells. N

titration

The determination of a constituent in a known volume of solution by the measured addition of a solution of known strength to completion of the reaction as signaled by observation of an end point.

TLV
Threshold Limit Value.

TME
Test Marketing Exemption.

TML
Tetramethyl Lead.

to chamber
To fit properly without the use of excess force, the case being duly supported. O

to commence construction
To engage in a continuous program of on-site construction including site clearance, grading, dredging, or land filling specifically designed for an indirect source in preparation for the fabrication, erection, or installation of the building components of the indirect source. For the purpose of this paragraph, interruptions resulting from acts of God, strikes, litigation, or other matters beyond the control of the owner shall be disregarded in determining whether a construction or modification program is continuous. A

to commence modification
To engage in a continuous program of on-site modification, including site clearance, grading, dredging, or land filling in preparation for a specific modification of the indirect source. A

to use any registered pesticide in a manner inconsistent with its labeling
To use any registered pesticide in a manner not permitted by the labeling: Provided, That the term shall not include (1) applying a pesticide at any

dosage, concentration, or frequency less than that specified on the labeling, (2) applying a pesticide against any target pest not specified on the labeling if the application is to the crop, animal, or site specified on the labeling, unless the Administrator [of EPA] has required that the labeling specifically state that the pesticide may be used only for the pests specified on the labeling after the Administrator [of EPA] has determined that the use of the pesticide against other pests would cause an unreasonable adverse effect on the environment, (3) employing any method of application not prohibited by the labeling, or (4) mixing a pesticide or pesticides with a fertilizer when such mixture is not prohibited by the labeling: Provided further, That the term also shall not include any use of a pesticide in conformance with section 5, 18, or 24 of this Act [FIFRA], or any use of a pesticide in a manner that the Administrator [of EPA] determines to be consistent with the purposes of this Act: And provided further, That after March 31, 1979, the term shall not include the use of a pesticide for agricultural or forestry purposes at a dilution less than label dosage unless before or after that date the Administrator [of EPA] issues a regulation or advisory opinion consistent with the study provided for in section 27(b) of the Federal Pesticide Act of 1978, which regulation or advisory opinion specifically requires the use of definite amounts of dilution. C

toe
The bottom of the working face of a sanitary landfill, where deposited solid

waste is in contact with virgin ground or previous lift.

toeboard
A vertical barrier at floor level erected along exposed edges of a floor opening, wall opening platform, runway, or ramp to prevent falls of materials. O

tolerance
1) The ability of an organism to cope with changes in its environment. 2) The safe level of any chemical applied to crops that will be used as food or feed. N 3) The permissible residue levels for pesticides in raw agricultural produce and processed foods. Whenever a pesticide is registered for use on a food or a feed crop, a tolerance (or exemption from the tolerance requirement) must be established. EPA establishes the tolerance levels, which are enforced by the Food and Drug Administration and the Department of Agriculture. N

tool
An explosive-actuated fastening tool, unless otherwise indicated, and all accessories pertaining thereto. O

topcoat operation
The topcoat spray booth, flash-off area, and bake oven(s) which are used to apply and dry or cure the final coating(s) on components of automobile and light-duty truck bodies. A

topography
The physical features of a surface area including relative elevations and the position of natural and man-made features. N

topsoil
The surface layer of soil, which usually refers to soil that contains humus and is capable of supporting good plant growth.

total dissolved solids
The total dissolved (filterable) solids as determined by use of the method specified in 40 CFR Part 136. A

total fluorides
Elemental fluorine and all fluoride compounds as measured by reference methods specified 40 CFR 60.195 or by equivalent or alternative methods (see 60.8(b)). A

total maximum daily loads
(1) For each water quality segment, or appropriate portion thereof, the total allowable maximum daily load of relevant pollutants during critical flow conditions for each specific water quality criterion being violated or expected to be violated. (i) Such total maximum daily loads shall be established at levels necessary to achieve compliance with applicable water quality standards. (ii) Such loads shall take into account: (A) Provision for seasonal variation; and (B) Provision of a margin of safety which takes into account any lack of knowledge concerning the relationship between effluent limitations and water quality. (2) For each water quality segment where thermal water quality criteria are being violated or expected to be violated, the total daily thermal load during critical flow conditions allowable in each segment. (i) Such loads shall be established at a level necessary to assure the protection and

propagation of a balanced, indigenous population of fish, shellfish, and wildlife. (ii) Such loads shall take into account: (A) Normal water temperature; (B) Flow rates; (C) Seasonal variations; (D) Existing sources of heat input; and (E) The dissipative capacity of the waters within the identified segment. (iii) Each estimate shall include an estimate of the maximum heat input that can be made into the waters of each segment where temperature is one of the criteria being violated or expected to be violated and shall include a margin of safety which takes into account lack of knowledge concerning the development of thermal water quality criteria for protection and propagation of fish, shellfish and wildlife in the waters of the identified segments. (3) For each water quality segment, a total allocation for point sources of pollutants and a gross allotment for nonpoint sources of pollutants. (i) A specific allowance for growth shall be included in the allocation for point sources and the gross allotment for nonpoint sources. (ii) The total of the allocation for point sources and the gross allotment for nonpoint sources shall not exceed the total maximum daily load. (4) Where predictive mathematical models are used in the determination of total maximum daily loads, an identification and brief description of the model, and the specific use of the model. (Note: Total maximum daily loads shall not be determined by designated areawide planning agencies except where the State has delegated such responsibility to the designated agency. In those cases where the responsibility has not been delegated, the State shall deter-

mine total maximum daily loads for a designated areawide planning area). (5) No point source load allocation developed pursuant to this section shall be less stringent than effluent limitations standards, or prohibitions required to be established pursuant to Sections 301, 302, 304, 306, 307, 311, and 316 of the [Clean Water] Act. A

total project cost
The sum of the direct and indirect costs allocable to the project incurred or to be incurred, less allocable credits.

total rated capacity
The sum of the rated capacities of all fuel-burning equipment connected to a common stack. The rated capacity shall be the maximum guaranteed by the equipment manufacturer or the maximum normally achieved during use as determined by the Administrator, whichever is greater. A

total solids
The sum of dissolved and undissolved constituents in water or wastewater, usually stated in milligrams per liter.

Total Suspended Solids
TSS. A measure of the suspended solids in wastewater, effluent, or water bodies, determined by using tests for "total suspended nonfilterable solids." (See: suspended solids). N

Total Suspended Nonfilterable Solids
TSNS as measured by the technique utilizing glass fiber disks as specified in "Standard Methods for the Exami-

nation of Water and Wastewater" (13th Edition). A

Total Toxic Organics
TTO. The sum of the concentrations for each of the following toxic organic compounds which is found in the discharge at a concentration greater than ten (10) micrograms per liter: 1,1,1 chloroform, trichloroethane, methylene chloride, bis (2-ethylhexyl) phthlate, toluene, trichloroethylene. A

Total Trihalomethanes
TTHM. The sum of the concentration in milligrams per liter of the trihalomethane compounds (trichloromethane [chloroform], dibromochloromethane, bromodichloromethane and tribromomethane [bromoform]), rounded to two significant figures. A

totally enclosed treatment facility
A facility for the treatment of hazardous waste which is directly connected to an industrial production process and which is constructed and operated in a manner which prevents the release of any hazardous waste or any constituent thereof into the environment during treatment. An example is a pipe in which waste acid is neutralized. A

totally enclosed manner
Any manner that will ensure no exposure of human beings or the environment to any concentration of PCBs. A

toxaphene
A material consisting of technical grade chlorinated camphene having the approximate formula of $C_{10}H_{10}Cl_8$

and normally containing 67-69 percent chlorine by weight. A

toxaphene formulator
A person who produces, prepares or processes a formulated product comprising a mixture of toxaphene and inert materials or other diluents into a product intended for application in any use registered under the Federal Insecticide, Fungicide and Rodenticide Act, as amended (7 U.S.C. 135, et seq.). A

toxaphene manufacturer
A manufacturer, excluding any source which is exclusively a toxaphene formulator, who produces, prepares or processes toxaphene or who uses toxaphene as a material in the production, preparation or processing of another synthetic organic substance. A

toxic
A chemical falling within any of the following categories:
(a) A chemical with a median lethal dose (LD_{50}) or more than 50 milligrams per kilogram but not more than 500 milligrams per kilogram of body weight when administered orally to albino rats weighing between 200 and 300 grams each. (b) A chemical that has a median lethal dose (LD_{50}) or more than 200 milligrams per kilogram but not more than 1,000 milligrams per kilogram of body weight when administered by continuous contact for 24 hours (or less if death occurs within 24 hours) with the bare skin of albino rabbits weighing between two and three kilograms each.
(c) A chemical that has a median

lethal concentration (LC_{50}) in air of 200 parts per million by volume or less of gas or vapor, or 2 milligrams per liter or less of mist, fume, or dust, when administered by continuous inhalation for 1 hour (or less if death occurs within 1 hour) to albino rats weighing between 200 and 300 grams each. N

toxic chemical release form
Information form required to be submitted by facilities that manufacture, process, or use (in quantities above a specific amount) chemicals listed under SARA Title III. N

toxic cloud
Airborne mass of gases, vapors, fumes, or aerosols containing toxic materials. N

Toxic Concentration Low
TC_{Lo}. The lowest concentration of a substance in air to which humans or animals have been exposed for any given period of time that has produced any toxic effect in humans or produced a tumorigenic or reproductive effect in animals or humans. N

toxic pollutant
(1) Those pollutants, or combinations of pollutants, including disease-causing agents, which after discharge and upon exposure, ingestion, inhalation or assimilation into any organism, either directly from the environment or indirectly by ingestion through food chains, will, on the basis of information available to the Administrator of EPA, cause death, disease, behavioral abnormalities, cancer, genetic mutations,

physiological malfunctions (including malfunctions in reproduction) or physical deformations, in such organisms or their offspring. D (2) Any pollutant listed as toxic under Section 307(a)(1) of the Clean Water Act. N

toxic substances
A chemical or mixture that may present an unreasonable risk of injury to health or the environment. N

toxicant
(1) A chemical that controls pests by killing rather than repelling them. (2) A harmful substance or agent that may injure an exposed organism. N

toxicity
(1) The property of a substance to cause any adverse physiological effects. A (2) The quality or degree of being poisonous or harmful to plant, animal or human life. N

toxicology
The study of the nature, effects, and detection of poisons in living organisms. N

TPQ
Threshold Planning Quantity.

traceable
A local standard that has been compared and certified, either directly or via not more than one intermediate standard, to a primary standard such as a Natl. Bureau of Standards Standard Reference Material (NBS SRM) or a USEP/NBS-approved Certified Reference Material (CRM). A

tracer

(1) A foreign substance mixed with or attached to a given substance for the determination of the location or distribution of the substance. (2) An element or compound that has been made radioactive so that it can be easily followed (traced) in biological and industrial processes. Radiation emitted by the radioisotope pinpoints its location.

trade name

The trademark name or commercial trade name for a material or product. N

traditional pollutant

Biochemical oxygen demand (BOD), suspended solids (SS) and pH. A

traffic flow measure

Any measure, such as signal light synchronization, freeway metering and curbside parking restrictions, that is taken for the purpose of improving the flow of traffic and thereby reducing emissions of air pollutants from motor vehicles. A

training

The planned and organized activity of a consultant to impart skills, techniques and methodologies to employers and their employees to assist them in establishing and maintaining employment and a place of employment which is safe and healthful. O

transfer and loading system

Any facility used to transfer and load coal for shipment. A

transfer efficiency

The ratio of the amount of coating solids transferred onto the surface of a part or product to the total amount of coating solids used. A

transfer facility

Any transportation related facility including loading docks, parking areas, storage areas and other similar areas where shipments of hazardous waste are held during the normal course of transportation. A

transfer station

A site at which solid wastes are concentrated for transport to a processing facility or land disposal site. A transfer station may be fixed or mobile. A

transformation

(1) A resource recovery method including the collection and physical treatment of a waste product for use as raw material in the manufacture of a different product (e.g., glass that is collected, ground, and then used to make bricks). (2) The process of placing new genes into a host cell, thereby inducing the host cell to exhibit functions encoded by the DNA. N

transit incentive program

A mix of incentive or disincentive provisions most likely to obtain maximum use of carpooling and mass transit so as to reduce vehicle miles traveled (VMT). Some incentive examples are: subsidies to employees using mass transit, preferential parking or other benefits for those who travel in carpools, provision of vanpooling services, provision of special charter or employer buses to and from mass transit stops and formal information systems so that employees can select optimum carpool arrangements. Some examples of disincentive provisions are: reduction in employee parking spaces, surcharges on use of parking spaces for single passenger drivers and non-preferential parking for single passenger drivers. **A**

translocation
The transfer of matter from one location to another within the soil. **N**

transmission class
A group of transmissions having the following common features: basic transmission type (manual, automatic, or semi-automatic), number of forward speeds (e.g., manual, four speed, three speed automatic, two speed semiautomatic), and other characteristics determined to be significant by the Administrator (e.g., "creeper" first gear, overdrive final gear ratio, or overdrive unit) considering factors such as the manufacturer's recommendation for use and/or the numerical gear ratios. **A**

transmission configuration
A unique combination, within a transmission class, of the number of forward gears, and, if applicable, overdrive. The Administrator may further subdivide a transmission configuration (based on such criteria as gear ratios, torque converter multiplication ratio, stall speed, shift calibration, etc.) if he determines that significant fuel economy differences exist within that transmission configuration. **A**

transmissivity
The hydraulic conductivity integrated over the saturated thickness of an underground formation. The transmissivity of a series of formations is the sum of the individual transmissivities of each formation comprising the series. **A**

transmissometer
The portions of a continuous monitoring system for opacity that include the sampling interface and the analyzer. **A**

transmittance
The fraction of incident light that is transmitted through an optical medium of interest. **A**

transpiration
The process by which water vapor is lost to the atmosphere from living plants. The term can also be applied to the quantity of water thus dissipated. **N**

transport or transportation
The carriage and related handling of any material by a vessel, or by any other vehicle, including aircraft. **E**

transport or transportation of hazardous substances
The movement of a hazardous substance by any mode, including pipeline (as defined in the Pipeline Safety Act), and in the case of a hazardous substance which has been accepted for transportation by a common or contract carrier, the term "transport" or "transportation" shall include any stoppage in transit which is temporary, incidental to the transportation move-

ment, and at the ordinary operating convenience of a common or contract carrier, and any such stoppage shall be considered as a continuity of movement and not as the storage of a hazardous substance. L

transport vehicle
A motor vehicle or rail car used for the transportation of cargo by any mode. Each cargo-carrying body (e.g., trailer, railroad freight car) is a separate transport vehicle. A

transportation control measure
Any measure, such as reducing vehicle use, changing traffic flow patterns, decreasing emissions from individual motor vehicles, or altering existing modal split patterns that is directed toward reducing emissions of air pollutants from transportation sources. A

transportation-related onshore and offshore facilities
(A) Onshore and offshore terminal facilities including transfer hoses, loading arms and other equipment and appurtenances used for the purpose of handling or transferring oil in bulk to or from a vessel as well as storage tanks and appurtenances for the reception of oily ballast water or tank washings from vessels, but excluding terminal waste treatment facilities and terminal oil storage facilities. (B) Transfer hoses, loading arms and other equipment appurtenant to a nontransportation-related facility which is used to transfer oil in bulk to or from a vessel. (C) Interstate and intrastate onshore and offshore pipeline systems including pumps and appurtenances

related thereto as well as in-line or breakout storage tanks needed for the continuous operation of a pipeline system, and pipelines from onshore and offshore oil production facilities, but excluding onshore and offshore piping from wellheads to oil separators and pipelines which are used for the transport of oil exclusively within the confines of a nontransportation-related facility or terminal facility and which are not intended to transport oil in interstate or intrastate commerce or to transfer oil in bulk to or from a vessel. (D) Highway vehicles and railroad cars which are used for the transport of oil in interstate or intrastate commerce and the equipment and appurtenances related thereto, and equipment used for the fueling of locomotive units, as well as the rights-of-way on which they operate. Excluded are highway vehicles and railroad cars and motive power used exclusively within the confines of a nontransportation-related facility or terminal facility and which are not intended for use in interstate or intrastate commerce. A

transporter
(In the RCRA program) A person engaged in the off-site transportation of hazardous waste by air, rail, highway, or water. N

transuranic radioactive waste
Waste containing more than 100 nanocuries of alpha-emitting transuranic isotopes, with half-lives greater than twenty years, per gram of waste, except for: (1) High-level radioactive wastes; (2) wastes that the Department has determined, with

the concurrence of the Administrator, do not need the degree of isolation required by this part; or (3) wastes that the Commission has approved for disposal on a case-by-case basis in accordance with 10 CFR Part 61. A

transuranium
Nuclides having an atomic number greater than that of uranium (i.e., greater than 92).

trash-to-energy plan
Plan for putting waste back to work by burning trash to produce energy. N

traveling-grate stoker
A stoker that is essentially a moving chain belt carried on sprockets and covered with separated, small, metal pieces called keys. The entire top surface can act as a grate while moving through the furnace but can flex over the sprocket wheels at the end of the furnace, return under the furnace, and reenter the furnace over sprocket wheels at the front.

TRC
Technical Review Criteria (under NPDES). D

tread
The horizontal member of a step. O

tread run
The horizontal distance from the leading edge of a tread to the leading edge of an adjacent tread. O

tread width
The horizontal distance from front to back of tread including nosing when used. O

treatment
When used in connection with hazardous waste, any method, technique, or process, including neutralization, designed to change the physical, chemical, or biological character or composition of any hazardous waste so as to neutralize such waste or so as to recover energy or material resources from the waste, or so as to render such waste nonhazardous, or less hazardous; safer to transport, store, or dispose of; or amenable for recovery, amenable for storage, or reduced in volume. A

treatment plant
The land, buildings, machinery, apparatus, and fixtures employed in any method, technique, or process to change the physical, chemical, or biological character or composition of any solid waste to render it safe for transport, amenable for recovery or storage, reduced in volume, or ready for disposal.

Treatment, Storage, and Disposal Facility
TSD. Site where a hazardous substance is treated, stored, or disposed. TSD facilities are regulated by EPA and states under RCRA. N

treatment technique requirement
A requirement of the national primary drinking water regulations which specifies for a contaminant a specific treatment technique(s) known to the Administrator which leads to a reduction in the level of such contaminant sufficient to comply with the requirements of [40 CFR] Part 141. A

treatment works phase or segment

Any cost-effective portion of a complete waste treatment system described in a facilities plan under 40 CFR 35.2030, which can be identified as a contract or discrete subitem or subcontract. Completion of building of a treatment works phase or segment may, but need not in and of itself, result in an operable treatment works. **A**

treatment works

(A) Any devices and systems used in the storage, treatment, recycling, and reclamation of municipal sewage, domestic sewage, or industrial wastes of a liquid nature to implement section 201 of the [FWPCA], or necessary to recycle or reuse water at the most economical cost over the estimated or useful life of the works, including intercepting sewers, outfall sewers, sewage collection systems, individual systems, pumping power, and other equipment, and their appurtenances; extensions, improvements, remodeling, additions, and alterations thereof; elements essential to provide a reliable recycled supply such as standby treatment units and clear well facilities; and any works, including site acquisition of the land that will be an integral part of the treatment process (including land use for the storage of treated wastewater in land treatment systems prior to land application) or is used for ultimate disposal of residues resulting from such treatment (including land for composting sludge, temporary storage of such compost and land used for the storage of treated wastewater in land treatment systems before land application). (B) Also, any other method or system for preventing, abating, reducing, storing, treating, separating, or disposing of municipal waste, including storm water runoff, or industrial waste, including waste in combined storm water and sanitary sewer systems. Any application for construction grants which includes wholly or in part such methods or systems shall, in accordance with guidelines published by the pursuant to subparagraph (C) of this paragraph, contain adequate data and analysis demonstrating such proposal to be, over the life of such works, the most cost efficient alternative to comply with section 301 or 302 of the Clean Water Act, or the requirements of section 201 of the Clean Water Act. (C) For the purposes of subparagraph (B) of this paragraph, the Administrator shall, within one hundred and eighty days after the date of enactment of this title, publish and thereafter revise no less often than annually, guidelines for the evaluation of methods, including cost-effective analysis, described in subparagraph (B) of this paragraph. **A, D**

treatment zone

A soil area of the unsaturated zone of a land treatment unit within which hazardous constituents are degraded, transformed, or immobilized. **A**

trench method

Sanitary landfilling method in which the waste is spread and compacted in a trench. The excavated spoil is spread and compacted over the waste to form a basic cell structure.

trestle ladder

A trestle ladder is a self-supporting

portable ladder, non-adjustable in length, consisting of two sections hinged at the top to form equal angles with the base. The size is designated by the length of the side rails measured along the front edge. O

Trichloroethylene
TCE. A stable, low-boiling colorless liquid, toxic by inhalation. TCE is used as a solvent, metal degreasing agent, and in other industrial applications. N

trickling filter
A biological treatment device; wastewater is trickled over a bed of stones covered with bacterial growth, the bacteria break down the organic wastes in the sewage and produce cleaner water. N

Trihalomethane
THM. One of the family of organic compounds, named as derivatives of methane, wherein three of the four hydrogen atoms in methane are each substituted by a halogen atom in the molecular structure. A

trimming presses
A class of auxiliary forging equipment which removes flash or excess metal from a forging. This trimming operation can also be done cold, as can coining, a product sizing operation. O

trip or tripping
Activation of the clutch to "run" the press. O

trip type
Any class of vehicle trips possessing one or more characteristics (e.g., work, nonwork; peak, off-peak; freeway, nonfreeway) that distinguish vehicle trips in the class from vehicle trips not in the class. A

triple rinse
The flushing of containers three times, each time using a volume of the normal diluent equal to approximately ten percent of the container's capacity, and adding the rinse liquid to the spray mixture or disposing of it by a method prescribed for disposing of the pesticide. A

trippage
The number of round trips the average refillable bottle makes between the filler and the consumer.

Tris
Tris (2,3-dibromopropyl) phosphate (also commonly named DBPP, TBPP, and Tris-BP). A

trolley ladder
A semifixed ladder, nonadjustable in length, supported by attachments to an overhead track, the plane of the ladder being at right angles to the plane of motion. O

trommel
A perforated, rotating, horizontal cylinder that may be used in resource recovery facilities to break open trash bags, to remove glass and such small items as stones and dirt, and to remove cans from incinerator residue.

trophic condition
A relative description of a lake's biological productivity based on the availability of plant nutrients. The range of trophic conditions is charac-

terized by the terms of oligotrophic for the least biologically productive, to eutrophic for the most biologically productive. A

troposphere
The portion of the atmosphere between seven and ten miles from the Earth's surface, where clouds form.

truck loading station
That portion of a metallic mineral processing plant where metallic minerals or metallic mineral concentrates are loaded by a conveying system into trucks. A

truck unloading station
That portion of a metallic mineral processing plant where metallic ore is unloaded from a truck into a hopper, screen, or crusher. A

true vapor pressure
The equilibrium partial pressure exerted by a petroleum liquid as determined in accordance with methods described in American Petroleum Institute Bulletin 2517, Evaporation Loss from External Floating Roof Tanks, Second Edition, February 1980. A

trust fund
The Hazardous Substance Response Fund established by section 221 of CERCLA or, in the case of a hazardous waste disposal facility for which liability has been transferred under section 107(k) of this Act [CERCLA], the Post-closure Liability Fund established by section 232. L

TSCA
The Toxic Substances Control Act, 15 U.S.C. 2601 et seq. A

TSP
Total Suspended Particulates.

TSS
Total Suspended Solids. A measure of the suspended solids in wastewater, effluent, or water bodies, determined by using tests for "total suspended non-filterable solids". (See: suspended solids). N

TTHM
Total Trihalomethane. D

tube and coupler scaffold
An assembly consisting of tubing which serves as posts, bearers, braces, ties, and runners, a base supporting the posts, and special couplers which serve to connect the uprights and to join the various members. O

tubular welded sectional folding scaffold
A sectional, folding metal scaffold either of ladder frame or inside stairway design, substantially built of prefabricated welded sections, which consist of end frames, platform frame, inside inclined stairway frame and braces, or hinged connected diagonal and horizontal braces, capable of being folded into a flat package when the scaffold is not in use. O

tubular welded frame scaffold
A sectional panel or frame metal scaffold substantially built up of prefabricated welded sections which consists of posts and horizontal bearer

with intermediate members. O

tuck pointing
Removal, by grinding, of cement, mortar, or other nonmetallic jointing material. O

tuck pointing wheels
Tuck pointing wheels, usually Type 1, reinforced organic bonded wheels have diameter, thickness and hole size dimension. They are subject to the same limitations of use and mounting as Type 1 wheels. O

tundra
A type of ecosystem dominated by lichens, mosses, grasses, and woody plants. Tundra is found at high latitudes (arctic tundra) and high altitudes (alpine tundra). Arctic tundra is underlain by permafrost and is usually very wet. (See: wetlands). N

turbidimeter
A device that measures the amount of suspended solids in a liquid. N

turbidity
Hazy air due to the presence of particles and pollutants; a similar cloudy condition in water due to suspended silt or organic matter. N

turbine
An engine that forces a stream of gas or liquid through jets at high pressure against the curved blades of a wheel, thus forcing the blades to turn.

turbines employed in oil/gas production or oil/gas transportation
Any stationary gas turbine used to provide power to extract crude oil/ natural gas from the earth or to move crude oil/natural gas, or products refined from these substances through pipelines. A

turnover bar
A bar used in die setting to manually turn the crankshaft of the press. O

tuyeres
Openings or ports in a grate through which air can be directed to improve combustion.

TWA
Time-Weighted Average exposure is the airborne concentration of a material to which a person is exposed, averaged over the total exposure time--generally the total workday (8 to 12 hours). Also see "TLV." N

twenty-five-year 24-hour rainfall event
The maximum precipitation event with a probable recurrence interval of once in 25 years as defined by the National Weather Service in technical paper no. 40, "Rainfall Frequency Atlas of the United States," May, 1961, and subsequent amendments or equivalent regional or State rainfall probability information developed therefrom. A [ed. Similar events are established for 10-year, 50-year, 100-year and 500-year rainfall events].

24-hour period
The period of time between 12:01 a.m. and 12:00 midnight. A

two hand trip

A clutch actuating means requiring the concurrent use of both hands of the operator to trip the press. O

two hand control device

A two hand trip that further requires concurrent pressure from both hands of the operator during a substantial part of the die-closing portion of the stroke of the press. O

2-year, 24-hour precipitation event

The maximum 24-hour precipitation event with a probable recurrence interval of once in two years as defined by the National Weather Service and Technical Paper No. 40, "Rainfall Frequency Atlas of the U.S.," May 1961, or equivalent regional or rainfall probability information developed therefrom. A

TWPL

Total Weighted Pollutant Load.

Type A packaging

Containers designed to maintain their integrity, i.e., not allow any radioactive material to be released and to keep the shielding properties intact, under normal transportation conditions. The test conditions which must be met are defined in 49 CFR 173, 398b and include heat, cold, reduced air pressure, vibration, water spray endurance, free drop, penetration, and compression standards.

Type B packaging

Containers designed to meet the standards established for hypothetical transportation accident conditions, as well as meeting the Type A packaging standards, without reducing the effectiveness of the shielding or allowing releases in excess of those enumerated in 49 CFR 173.398c(1). The standards to be met by Type B packages, in addition to the Type A standards, are defined in 49 CFR 173.398c(2) and include puncture, thermal, water immersion, and higher free drop tests.

Type I sound level meter

A sound level meter which meets the Type I requirements of American National Standard Specification S1.4-1971 for sound level meters. This publication is available from the American National Standards Institute, Inc., 1430 Broadway, New York, New York 10018. A

type of resin

The broad classification of resin referring to the basic manufacturing process for producing that resin, including, but not limited to, the suspension, dispersion, latex, bulk, and solution processes. A

type of pesticide

Refers to each individual product as identified by the product name; EPA Registration Number (EPA File Symbol, if any, for planned products; Experimental Permit Number if the pesticide is produced under an Experimental Use Permit); production type (technical, formulation, repackaging, etc.); product classification (fungicide, insecticide, herbicide, etc.); market produced for (domestic, foreign, etc.); and use classification. In cases where a pesticide is not registered, registration is not applied for, or is not produced under an Experimental Use Permit, the term shall also include chemical formulation. A

Type SE

Having a flame-retardant, moisture-resistant covering, but not required to have inherent protection against mechanical abuse. O

Type USE

Recognized for underground use, having a moisture-resistant covering, but not required to have a flame-retardant covering or inherent protection against mechanical abuse. Single-conductor cables having an insulation specifically approved for the purpose do not require an outer covering. O

U

UAQI
Uniform Air Quality Index. N

UCATA
Uniform Contribution Among (Joint) Tortfeasors Act.

UCC
Ultra Clean Coal. Coal that has been washed, ground into fine particles, then chemically treated to remove sulfur, ash, silicone, and other substances; usually briquetted and coated with a sealant made from coal. N

UCFA
Uniform Comparative Fault Act (Section 6, Superfund).

UDDS
Urban Dynamometer Driving Schedule.

UEL, or UFL
Upper Explosive Limit or Upper Flammable Limit.

Ug/m³
Microgram per cubic meter.

UIAs
Urban Impact Analyses.

UIC
Underground Injection Control. Program under Part C of the Safe Drinking Water Act, including an "approved program." A

ultimate analysis
The chemical analysis of a solid, liquid, or gaseous fuel. In the case of coal, coke, or solid waste, the amounts of carbon, hydrogen, sulfur, nitrogen, oxygen, and ash are determined.

ultimate consumer
The first person who purchases an automobile for purposes other than resale, or leases an automobile. A

ultimate purchaser
With respect to any new motor vehicle or new motor vehicle engine, the first person who in good faith purchases such new motor vehicle or new engine for purposes other than resale. B, G

Ultra Clean Coal
UCC. Coal that has been washed, ground into fine particles, then chemically treated to remove sulfur, ash, silicone, and other substances; usually briquetted and coated with a sealant made from coal. N

ultraviolet rays
Radiation from the sun that can be useful or potentially harmful. UV rays from one part of the spectrum enhance plant life and are useful in some medical and dental procedures; UV rays from other parts of the spectrum to which humans are exposed (e.g., while getting a sun tan) can cause skin cancer or other tissue damage. The ozone layer in the atmosphere provides a protective shield that limits the amount of ultraviolet rays that reach the Earth's surface. N

unacceptable adverse effect
Impact on an aquatic or wetland ecosystem which is likely to result in significant degradation of municipal water supplies (including surface or ground water) or significant loss of or damage to fisheries, shell-fishing, or wildlife habitat or recreation areas. In evaluating the unacceptability of such impacts, consideration should be given to the relevant portions of the section 404(b)(1) guidelines (40 CFR part 230). A

unauthorized dispersion technique
Any dispersion technique which, under section 123 of the CAA and the regulations promulgated pursuant to that section, may not be used to reduce the degree of emission limitation otherwise required in the applicable SIP. A

under the direct supervision of [a certified applicator]
The act or process whereby the application of a pesticide is made by a competent person acting under the instructions and control of a certified applicator who is responsible for the actions of that person and who is available if and when needed, even though such certified applicator is not physically present at the time and place the pesticide is applied. A

underfire air
Forced or induced combustion air (quantity and direction are controlled) introduced under a grate to promote burning within a fuel bed.

underground drinking water source
See "underground source of drinking water."

Underground Injection Control
UIC. The program under the Safe Drinking Water Act that regulates the use of wells to pump fluids into the ground. N

underground injection
The subsurface emplacement of fluids through a bored, drilled or driven well; or through a dug well, where the depth of the dug well is greater than the largest surface dimension. (See also "injection well.") A

Underground Source of Drinking Water
USDW. As defined in the UIC program, this term refers to aquifers that are currently being used as a

source of drinking water, and those that are capable of supplying a public water system. They have a total dissolved solids content of 10,000 milligrams per liter or less, and are not "exempted aquifers." (See: exempted aquifer.) N

Underground Storage Tank

UST. Any one or combination of tanks (including underground pipes connected thereto) which is used to contain an accumulation of regulated substances, and the volume of which (including the volume of the underground pipes connected thereto) is 10 percent or more beneath the surface of the ground. Such term does not include any--(A) farm or residential tank of 1,100 gallons or less capacity used for storing motor fuel for noncommercial purposes; (B) tank used for storing heating oil for consumptive use on the premises where stored; (C) septic tank; (D) pipeline facility (including gathering lines) regulated under--(i) the Natural Gas Pipeline Safety Act of 1968, (49 U.S.C.App. 1671, et seq.), (ii) the Hazardous Liquid Pipeline Safety Act of 1979 (49 U.S.C.App. 2001, et seq.), or (iii) which is an intrastate pipeline facility regulated under state laws comparable to the provisions of law referred to in clause (i) or (ii) of this subparagraph; (E) surface impoundment, pit, pond, or lagoon; (F) storm water or waste water collection system; (G) flow-through process tank; (H) liquid trap or associated gathering lines directly related to oil or gas production and gathering operations; or; (I) storage tank situated in an underground area (such as a basement, cellar, mineworking, drift, shaft, or

tunnel) if the storage tank is situated upon or above the surface of the floor. The term "underground storage tank" shall not include any pipes connected to any tank which is described in subparagraphs (A) through (I). I

undisturbed performance

The predicted behavior of a radiation disposal system, including consideration of the uncertainties in predicted behavior, if the disposal system is not disrupted by human intrusion or the occurrence of unlikely natural events. A

UNEP

United Nations Environment Program. N

uniquely military equipment, systems, and operations

Excludes from the scope of the order the design of Department of Defense equipment and systems that are unique to the national defense mission, such as military aircraft, ships, submarines, missiles, and missile sites, early warning systems, military space systems, artillery, tanks, and tactical vehicles; and excludes operations that are uniquely military such as field maneuvers, naval operations, military flight operations, associated research test and development activities, and actions required under emergency conditions. The term includes within the scope of the Order Department of Defense workplaces and operations comparable to those of industry in the private sector such as: vessel, aircraft, and vehicle repair, overhaul, and modification (except for equipment trials); construction; supply services; civil engineering or public works; medical services; and office work. O

unit package
A package that is labeled with directions to use the entire contents of the package in a single application. A

unit-suspended wall
A furnace wall or panel that is hung from a steel structure.

unitized tooling
A type of die in which the upper and lower members are incorporated into a self-contained unit so arranged as to hold the die members in alignment. O

unleaded gasoline
Gasoline containing not more than 0.05 gram of lead per gallon and not more than 0.005 gram of phosphorus per gallon. A

unloading bulkhead
A steel plate that ejects waste out the rear doors of an enclosed transfer trailer. It is propelled by a telescoping, hydraulically powered cylinder that traverses the length of the trailer.

unloading leg
A device which includes a bucket-type elevator which is used to remove grain from a barge or ship. A

unprotected side or edge
Any side or edge of a roof perimeter where there is no wall three feet (.9 meters) or more in height. O

unreasonable adverse effects on the environment
Any unreasonable risk to man or the environment, taking into account the economic, social, and environmental costs and benefits of the use of any pesticide. A, C

unreasonable degradation of the marine environment
(1) Significant adverse changes in ecosystem diversity, productivity and stability of the biological community within the area of discharge and surrounding biological communities, (2) Threat to human health through direct exposure to pollutants or through consumption of exposed aquatic organisms, or (3) Loss of esthetic, recreational, scientific or economic values which is unreasonable in relation to the benefit derived from the discharge. A

unreclaimable residues
Residual materials of little or no value remaining after incineration. A

unsaturated zone or zone of aeration
The zone between the land surface and the water table. A

UNSCEAR
United Nations Scientific Committee on the Effects of Atomic Radiation.

unscheduled maintenance
Any inspection, adjustment, repair, removal, disassembly, cleaning, or replacement of vehicle components or systems which is performed to correct a part failure or vehicle (if the

engine were installed in a vehicle) malfunction. A

unsolicited contract proposal
An unsolicited request for support via the contract mechanism. At the discretion of the approving program an unsolicited request for support may be approved and funded by either the grant or contract mechanism within certain limitations.

unsolicited proposal
An informal written offer to perform funded work for which the government did not publish a solicitation. A

unstable
Tending toward decomposition or other unwanted chemical change during normal handling or storage. N

unstable material
Earth material, other than running, that because of its nature or the influence of related conditions, cannot be depended upon to remain in place without extra support, such as would be furnished by a system of shoring. O

unstable reactive
A chemical that, in the pure state, or as produced or transported, will vigorously polymerize, decompose, condense, or become self-reactive under conditions of shocks, pressure, or temperature. N

upland
Any area that does not qualify as a wetland because the associated hydrologic regime is not sufficiently wet to elicit development of vegetation, soils, and/or hydrologic characteristics asso-

ciated with wetlands. Such areas occurring in floodplains are more appropriately termed nonwetlands. N

Upper Explosive Limit or Upper Flammable Limit
UEL, or UFL of a vapor or gas; the highest concentration (highest percentage of the substance in air) that will produce a flash of fire when an ignition source (heat, arc, or flame) is present. At higher concentrations, the mixture is too "rich" to burn. Also see "LEL." N

uppermost aquifer
The geologic formation nearest the natural ground surface that is an aquifer, as well as lower aquifers that are hydraulically interconnected with this aquifer within the facility's property boundary. A

upset
An exceptional incident in which there is unintentional and temporary noncompliance with technology-based permit effluent limitations because of factors beyond the reasonable control of the permittee. An upset does not include noncompliance to the extent caused by operational error, improperly designed treatment facilities, inadequate treatment facilities, lack of preventive maintenance, or careless or improper operation. N

uranium
A radioactive heavy metal element used in nuclear reactors and the production of nuclear weapons. Term refers usually to U-238, the most abundant radium isotope, although a

small percentage of naturally-occurring uranium is U-235. N

uranium byproduct material (tailings)

The wastes produced by the extraction or concentration of uranium from any ore processed primarily for its source material content. Ore bodies depleted by uranium solution extractions and which remain underground do not constitute byproduct material. A

urban and industrial stormwater systems needs

(1) An identification of the required improvements to existing urban and industrial stormwater systems, including combined sewer overflows, that are necessary to attain and maintain applicable water quality standards. (2) An identification of the needed urban and industrial · stormwater systems for areas not presently served over at least a 20-year planning period (in 5-year increments) that are necessary to attain and maintain applicable water quality standards, emphasizing appropriate land management and other nonstructural techniques for control of urban and industrial stormwater runoff. (3) A cost estimate for the needs identified in paragraph (l)(1) and (2) of this section, the reduction in capital construction costs brought about by nonstructural control measures, and any capital and annual operating costs of such facilities and practices. A

urban area population

The population defined in "1970 Census of Population; Supplementary Report: Population of Urbanized Areas Established Since the 1970 Census, for the United States; 1970." U.S.

Bureau of Census, PC(S)-106, U.S. Government Printing Office, Washington, D.C., October 1976. A

urban bus

A heavy-duty diesel-powered passenger-carrying vehicle with a load capacity of fifteen or more passengers and intended primarily for intra-city operation, i.e., within the confines of a city or greater metropolitan area. Urban bus operation is characterized by short rides and frequent stops. To facilitate this type of operation, more than one set of quick-opening entrance and exit doors would normally be installed. Since fares are usually paid in cash or tokens rather than purchased in advance in the form of tickets, urban buses would normally have equipment installed for collection of fares. Urban buses are also typically characterized by the absence of equipment and facilities for long distance travel, e.g., rest rooms, large luggage compartments, and facilities for stowing carry-on luggage. A

urban runoff

Storm water from city streets, usually carrying litter and organic wastes. N

urban scale

The overall, citywide conditions with dimensions on the order of 4 to 50 kilometers. This scale would usually require more than one site for definition. A

USC

United States Code. It contains a consolidation and codification of all laws of the United States. The USC is divided into 50 titles which represent broad areas subject to Federal law.

USCG
United States Coast Guard.

USDA
United States Department of Agriculture.

USDW
Underground Source of Drinking Water. A

use
Any act of handling or release of a pesticide, or exposure of man or the environment to a pesticide through acts, including but not limited to: (1) Application of a pesticide, including mixing and loading and any required supervisory action in or near the area of application; (2) Storage actions for pesticides and pesticide containers; and (3) Disposal actions for pesticides and pesticide containers. [ed. "Use" as defined here incorporates application. However, the certification requirement for certain restricted use pesticides only applies with respect to applications of such pesticides. Many aspects of use do not include application (e.g., storage, transportation), and hence are outside the requirement for certification]. A

use-dilution
A dilution specified on the label or labeling which produces the concentration of the pesticide for a particular purpose or effect. A

used oil
Any oil which has been (A) refined

from crude oil, (B) used, and (C) as a result of such use, contaminated by physical or chemical impurities. I

useful life
(1) Estimated period during which a facility or piece of equipment will be operated. A (2) (a) For light-duty vehicles and light-duty trucks, a period of use of 5 years or 50,000 miles, whichever first occurs. (b) For gasoline-fueled heavy-duty engines a period of use of 5 years or 50,000 miles of vehicle operation or 1,500 hours of engine operation (or an equivalent period of 1,500 hours of dynamometer operation), whichever first occurs. (c) For diesel heavy-duty engines a period of use of 5 years or 100,000 miles of vehicle operation or 3,000 hours of engine operation (or an equivalent period of 1,000 hours of dynamometer operation), whichever first occurs. A

U.S. Environmental Protection Agency
EPA. Established in 1970 by Presidential Executive Order, bringing together parts of various government agencies involved with the control of pollution. N

use-pattern
The manner in which a pesticide is applied and includes the following parameters of pesticide application: (1) Target pest; (2) Crop or animals treated; (3) Application site; and (4) Application technique, rate and frequency. A

user charge
A charge levied on users of a treatment works, or that portion of

the advalorem taxes paid by a user, for the user's proportional share of the cost of operation and maintenance (including replacement) of such works under sections 204(b)(1)(A) and 201(h)(2) of the [Federal Water Pollution Control] Act and this subpart. A

user collection charge
The means for raising new or increased revenues for funding municipally operated solid waste systems.

USGS
United States Geological Survey. N

UST
Underground Storage Tank. Any one or combination of tanks (including underground pipes connected thereto) which is used to contain an accumulation of regulated substances, and the volume of which (including the volume of the underground pipes connected thereto) is 10 percent or more beneath the surface of the ground. Such term does not include any--(A) farm or residential tank of 1,100 gallons or less capacity used for storing motor fuel for noncommercial purposes; (B) tank used for storing heating oil for consumptive use on the premises where stored; (C) septic tank; (D) pipeline facility (including gathering lines) regulated under--(i) the Natural Gas Pipeline Safety Act of 1968, (49 U.S.C.App. 1671, et seq.), (ii) the Hazardous Liquid Pipeline Safety Act of 1979 (49 U.S.C.App. 2001, et seq.), or (iii) which is an intrastate pipeline facility regulated under state laws comparable to the provisions of law referred to in

clause (i) or (ii) of this subparagraph; (E) surface impoundment, pit, pond, or lagoon; (F) storm water or waste water collection system; (G) flow-through process tank; (H) liquid trap or associated gathering lines directly related to oil or gas production and gathering operations; or; (I) storage tank situated in an underground area (such as a basement, cellar, mineworking, drift, shaft, or tunnel) if the storage tank is situated upon or above the surface of the floor. The term "underground storage tank" shall not include any pipes connected to any tank which is described in subparagraphs (A) through (I). I

utilization equipment
Equipment which utilizes electric energy for mechanical, chemical, heating, lighting, or similar purpose. O

utilization system
A system which provides electric power and light for employee workplaces; includes the premises wiring system and utilization equipment. O

U-235
Uranium-235. Naturally occurring Uranium. A radioactive heavy metal element used in nuclear reactors and the production of nuclear weapons. N

U-238
Uranium-238. A radioactive heavy metal element used in nuclear reactors and the production of nuclear weapons. The most abundant radium isotope. N

UZM
Unsaturated Zone Monitoring. N

V

V
Volt(s).

v/v
Volume per volume.

vaccine
Dead or partial or modified antigen used to induce immunity to certain infectious diseases. N

vacuum spark advance disconnect retrofit
A device or system installed on a motor vehicle that prevents the ignition vacuum advance from operating either when the vehicle's transmission is in the lower gears, or when the vehicle is traveling below a predetermined speed, so as to achieve reduction in exhaust emissions of hydrocarbon and carbon monoxide from 1967 and earlier light-duty vehicles of at least 25 and 9 percent, respectively. A

valence
The chemical combining power of an atom. It indicates the number of electrons that can be lost, gained, or shared by an atom in a compound. Also called bond or chemical bond.

valid study
A study that has been conducted in accordance with the Good Laboratory Practice standards of 40 CFR Part 160 or generally accepted scientific methodology and that EPA has not determined to be invalid. A

validated test
A test determined by the Agency to have been conducted and evaluated in a manner consistent with accepted scientific procedures. A

valuable commercial and recreational species
Those [animal or fish] species for which catch statistics are compiled on a routine basis by the Federal or State agency responsible for compiling such statistics for the general geographical area impacted, or which are under current study by such Federal or State agencies for potential development for commercial or recreational use. A

Value Engineering

VE. A specialized cost control technique based on a systematic and creative approach which identifies and focuses on unnecessarily high cost in a project in order to arrive at a cost saving without sacrificing the reliability or efficiency of the project. A

value for pesticide purposes

That characteristic of a substance or mixture of substances which produces an efficacious action on a pest. A

van

A light-duty truck having an integral enclosure, fully enclosing the driver compartment and load carrying device, and having no body sections protruding more than 30 inches ahead of the leading edge of the windshield. A

vapor

The gaseous phase of substances that are liquid or solid at atmospheric temperature and pressure, such as steam. N

vapor capture system

Any device or combination of devices designed to contain, collect, and route organic solvent vapors emitted from the flexible vinyl or urethane rotogravure printing line. A

vapor collection system

A system which will collect no less than 90 percent by weight of vapors and gases of organic compounds discharged during any gasoline loading or unloading operation so as to reduce their emissions to the atmosphere. A

vapor density

The weight of a vapor or gas compared to the weight of an equal volume of air is an expression of the density of the vapor or gas. Materials lighter than air have vapor densities less than 1.0 (examples: acetylene, methane, hydrogen). Materials heavier than air (examples: propane, hydrogen, sulfide, ethane, butane, chlorine, sulfur dioxide) have vapor densities greater than 1.0. All vapors and gases will mix with air, but the lighter materials will tend to rise and dissipate (unless confined). Heavier vapors and gases are likely to concentrate in low places--along or under floors, in sumps, sewers, and manholes, in trenches and ditches--where they may create fire or health hazards. N

vapor dispersion

The movement of vapor clouds in air due to wind, gravity spreading, and mixing. N

vapor plume

The stack effluent consisting of flue gas made visible by condensed water droplets or mist.

vapor pressure

(1) The pressure, measured in pounds per square inch (absolute), exerted by a volatile liquid as determined by the "Standard Method of Test for Vapor Pressure of Petroleum Products (Reid Method)." (ASTM D-323-58). O (2) The pressure exerted by a saturated vapor above its own liquid in a closed container. When quality control tests are performed on products, the test temperature is usually 100° F, and the

vapor pressure is expressed as pounds per square inch (psig or psia), but vapor pressures reported on MSDS's are in millimeters of mercury (mmHg) at 68° F (20° C), unless stated otherwise. Three facts are important to remember: (A) Vapor pressure of a substance at 100° F will always be higher than the vapor pressure of the substance at 68° F (20° C). (B) Vapor pressures reported on MSDS's in mmHg are usually very low pressures; 760 mmHg is equivalent to 14.7 pounds per square inch. (C) The lower the boiling point of a substance, the higher its vapor pressure. N

vapor recovery disposal system
A system of processing vapors and gases of organic compounds discharged during gasoline loading or unloading operations. This system shall consist of one of the following: (i) A re-frigeration-condensation system, ad-sorption-absorption system, or the equivalent that processes all vapors and gases and ultimately converts no less than 90 percent by weight of the processed vapors and gases back to the liquid product, or (ii) A vapor handling system that directs all vapors and gases to a fuel gas system, which will dispose of no less than 90 percent by weight of the processed vapors and gases, or (iii) Other equipment of an efficiency equal to or greater than paragraphs (i) and (ii), if approved by the Administrator. A

vapor recovery system
(1) A closed system of pipes, valves, and compressor in which vapors that might otherwise escape into the atmosphere are compressed to liquid

form and returned to their source. (2) A vapor gathering system capable of collecting all hydrocarbon vapors discharged from the storage vessel and a vapor disposal system capable of processing such hydrocarbon vapors and gases so as to prevent their emission to the atmosphere. A

vapor-mounted seal
A foam-filled primary seal mounted continuously around the circumference of the tank so there is an annular vapor space underneath the seal. The annular vapor space is bounded by the bottom of the primary seal, the tank wall, the liquid surface, and the floating roof. A

vaporization
The change of a substance from the liquid to the gaseous state. One of the three basic contributing processes of air pollution, the others being attrition and combustion.

variance
(1) Government permission for a delay or exception in the application of a given law, ordinance, or regula-tion. N (2) (NPDES) Any mechanism or provision under section 301 or 316 of CWA or under 40 CFR part 125, or in the applicable "effluent limitations guidelines" which allows modification to or waiver of the generally applic-able effluent limitation requirements or time deadlines of CWA. This includes provisions which allow the establish-ment of alternative limitations based on fundamentally different factors or on sections 301(c), 301(g), 301(h), 301(i), or 316(a) of CWA. A

vault

An enclosure above or below ground which personnel may enter and is used for the purpose of installing, operating, and/or maintaining equipment and/or cable. O

vector

(1) An organism, often an insect or rodent, that carries disease. (2) An object that is used to transport genes into a host cell (vectors can be plasmids viruses, or other bacteria). A gene is placed in the vector; the vector infects the bacterium. N

vegetable tan

The process of converting hides into leather using chemicals either derived form vegetable matter or synthesized to produce effects similar to those chemicals. A

vehicle

Any motor vehicle, machine, or tractor, which is propelled by mechanical power and capable of transportation of property on a street or highway and which has a gross vehicle weight rating in excess of 10,000 pounds and a partially or fully enclosed operator's compartment. A

vehicle configuration

A unique combination of basic engine, engine code, inertia weight class, transmission configuration, and axle ratio. A

vehicle curb weight

The actual or the manufacturer's estimated weight of the vehicle in operational status and all standard equipment, and weight of fuel at nominal tank capacity, and the weight of optional equipment computed in accordance with 40 CFR 86.078-24; incomplete light duty trucks shall have vehicle curb weight specified by the manufacturer. A

vehicle for hire

Any chauffeur-driven, spark-ignition-powered motor vehicle used for the purpose of providing transportation for a fee or charge, such as taxicabs and limousine services. A

vehicle trip

Any movement of a motor vehicle from one location to another that results in the emission of air pollutants by the motor vehicle. A

vehicle type

Any class of motor vehicles (e.g., precontrolled, heavy duty vehicles, gasoline powered trucks) whose emissions characteristics are significantly different from the emissions characteristics of motor vehicles not in the class. A

vehicle useful life

(1) For light-duty vehicles and light-duty trucks a period of use of 5 years or 50,000 miles, whichever first occurs. (2) For gasoline-fueled heavy-duty engines a period of use of 5 years or 50,000 miles of vehicle operation or 1,500 hours of engine operation (or an equivalent period of 1,500 hours of dynamometer operation), whichever first occurs. (3) For diesel heavy-duty engines a period of use of 5 years or 100,000 miles of vehicle operation or 3,000 hours of engine operation (or an equivalent period of

1,000 hours of dynamometer operation), whichever first occurs. A

ventilated

Provided with a means to permit circulation of air sufficient to remove an excess of heat, fumes, or vapors. O

ventilated cell composting

A method in which the compost is mixed and aerated by being dropped through a vertical series of ventilated cells.

ventilation/suction

The act of admitting fresh air into a space in order to replace stale or contaminated air; achieved by blowing air into the space. Similarly, suction represents the admission of fresh air into an interior space by lowering the pressure outside of the space, thereby drawing the contaminated air outward. N

ventilatory volume

The volume of gas exchanged per unit of time between the lungs and the atmosphere that occurs in breathing.

vertical slip forms

Forms which are jacked vertically and continuously during placing of the concrete. O

vessel

Every description of watercraft or other artificial contrivance used, or capable of being used, as a means of transportation on water. A, L

VHAP

Volatile Hazardous Air Pollutant. A

VHS

Vertical and Horizontal Spread. A term used in relation to the transport of landfill wastes to nearby receptors.

vinyl chloride

A chemical compound used in producing some plastics. Excessive exposure to this substance may cause cancer. N [ed. Vinyl chloride has been designated a hazardous air pollutant under 112 of the CAA].

violating facility

Any facility that is owned, leased, or supervised by an applicant, recipient, contractor, or subcontractor that EPA lists under 40 CFR Part 15 as not in compliance with federal, state, or local requirements under the Clean Air Act or Clean Water Act. A facility includes any building, plant, installation, structure, mine, vessel, or other floating craft. A

violation

Any incident of excess emissions, regardless of the circumstances of the occurrence. A

virgin material

A raw material, including previously unused copper, aluminum, lead, zinc, iron, or other metal or metal ore, any undeveloped resource that is, or with new technology will become, a source of raw materials. I

virus

The smallest form of microorganisms capable of causing disease. N

viscose process

The fiber forming process where

cellulose and concentrated caustic soda are reacted to form soda or alkali cellulose. This reacts with carbon disulfide to form sodium cellulose xanthate, which is then dissolved in a solution of caustic soda. After ripening, the solution is spun into an acid coagulating bath. This precipitates the cellulose in the form of a regenerated cellulose filament. A

viscosity
The property of liquids which causes them to resist instantaneous change of shape, or instantaneous rearrangement of their parts, due to internal friction. The resistance which the particles of a liquid offer to a force tending to move them in relation to each other. Viscosity of oils is usually expressed as the number of seconds at a definite temperature required for a standard quality of oil to flow through a standard apparatus. A

viscous
Thick, resistant to flow, having a high viscosity. A

visibility impairment and impairment of visibility
Any humanly perceptible change in visibility (visual range, contrast, coloration) from that which would have existed under natural conditions. A

visible emissions
Any emissions containing particulate asbestos material that are visually detectable without the aid of instruments. This does not include condensed uncombined water vapor. A

vitrification
A process whereby high temperatures effect permanent chemical and physical changes in a ceramic body, most of which is transformed into glass.

VMT
Vehicle Miles Traveled. N

VOC
Volatile Organic Compound.

VOC content
All volatile organic compounds that are in a coating expressed as kilograms of VOC per liter of coating solids. A

VOC emission reduction system
A system composed of an enclosure, hood, or other device for containment and capture of VOC emissions and a VOC emission control device. A

VOC emission control device
Equipment that destroys or recovers VOC. A

VOC emissions
The mass of volatile organic compounds (VOC's), expressed as kilograms of VOC's per liter of applied coating solids, emitted from a surface coating operation. A

VOC solvent
An organic liquid or liquid mixture consisting of VOC components. A

volatile
Any substance that evaporates at a low temperature. N

volatile flammable liquid

A flammable liquid having a flash point below 38 degrees C (100 degrees F) or whose temperature is above its flash point. O

Volatile Hazardous Air Pollutant

VHAP. A substance regulated under the Clean Air Act for which a standard for equipment leaks of the substance has been proposed and promulgated. Benzene and vinyl chloride are VHAPs. A

Volatile Organic Compounds

VOC. (1) Any compound containing carbon and hydrogen or containing carbon and hydrogen in combination with any other element which has a vapor pressure of 1.5 pounds per square inch absolute (77.6mm Hg) or greater under actual storage conditions. A (2) Any reactive organic compounds as defined in 40 CFR § 60.2 definitions. A (3) Any organic compound which participates in atmospheric photochemical reactions except for those designated by the EPA Administrator as having negligible photochemical reactivity. N

volatile synthetic organic chemicals

Chemicals that tend to volatilize or evaporate from water. N

volatility

The property of a substance or substances to convert into vapor or gas without chemical change. A

volt

V. The unit of electromotive force (1 volt = 1 watt/1 ampere).

voltage

The effective (rms) potential difference between any two conductors or between a conductor and ground. Voltages are expressed in nominal values. The nominal voltage of a system or circuit is the value assigned to a system or circuit of a given voltage class for the purpose of convenient designation. The operating voltage of the system may vary above or below this value. O

voltage (nominal)

A nominal value assigned to a circuit or system for the purpose of conveniently designating its voltage class (as 120/240, 480Y/277, 600, etc.). The actual voltage at which a circuit operates can vary from the nominal within a range that permits satisfactory operation of equipment. O

voltage (of a circuit)

The greatest root-mean-square (effective) difference of potential between any two conductors of the circuit concerned. O

voltage to ground

For grounded circuits, the voltage between the given conductor and that point or conductor of the circuit that is grounded; for ungrounded circuits, the greatest voltage between the given conductor and any other conductor of the circuit. O

volume reduction processes

Those biological, chemical, mechanical and thermal methods used to reduce the amount of space that waste materials occupy and put them into a form suitable for reuse or disposal. See: biodegradable, compaction, incinerator, pyrolysis, and sanitary landfill.

voluntarily submitted information

Business information in EPA's possession--(1) The submission of which EPA had no statutory or contractual authority to require; and (2) The submission of which was not prescribed by state or regulation as a condition of obtaining some benefit (or avoiding some disadvantage) under a regulatory program of general applicability, including such regulatory programs as permit, licensing, registration, or certification programs, but excluding programs concerned solely or primarily with the award or administration by EPA of contracts or grants. A

voluntary emissions recall

A repair, adjustment, or modification program voluntarily initiated and conducted by a manufacturer to remedy any emission-related defect for which direct notification of vehicle or engine owners has been provided. A

vulnerability analysis

Assessment of elements in the community that are susceptible to damage should a release of hazardous materials occur. N

vulnerable zone

An area over which the airborne concentration of a chemical involved in an accidental release could reach the level of concern. N

W

W
   Watt(s).

wane
   Bark, or the lack of wood from any cause, on the corner of a piece. O

warning
   For air quality contingency plans, the warning level indicates that air quality is continuing to degrade and that additional control actions are necessary. A warning will be declared when any one of the following levels is reached at any monitoring site: (1) SO_2--1,600 ug/m^3 (0.6 ppm), 24-hour average. (2) particulate--625 ug/m^3, 24-hour average. (3) SO_2 and particulate combined--product of SO_2 ug/m^3, 24-hour average and particulate AG2 ug/m^3, 24-hour average equal to 261 x 10^3. (4) CO--34 mg/m^3 (30 ppm), 8-hour average. (5) Ozone (O_3)--800 ug/m^3 (0.4 ppm), 1-hour average. (6) NO_2--2,260 ug/m^3 (1.2 ppm), 1-hour average; 565 ug/m^3 (0.3 ppm), 24-hour average and meteorological conditions are such that pollutant concentrations can be expected to remain at the above levels for 12 or more hours or increase, or in the case of ozone, the situation is likely to reoccur within the next 24 hours unless control actions are taken. A

warning device
   A sound emitting device used to alert and warn people of the presence of railroad equipment. A

washer
   A machine which agitates fabric articles in a petroleum solvent bath and spins the articles to remove the solvent, together with the piping and ductwork used in the installation of this device. A

waste
   (1) Unwanted materials left over from manufacturing processes, refuse from places of human or animal habitation. N (2) Any solid liquid, semisolid, or contained gaseous material that results from the production of a chemical substance identified in paragraph (b) of this section and which is to be disposed. A

waste load allocation

The maximum load of pollutants each discharger of waste is allowed to release into a particular waterway. Discharge limits are usually required for each specific water quality criterion being, or expected to be, violated. N

waste material containing TCDD or waste(s) containing TCDD

Any waste material or waste(s) resulting from manufacture or processing of 2,4,5-Trichlorophenol or its pesticide derivatives, or any waste(s) resulting from manufacturing processes using equipment that was at some time used in the manufacture of 2,4,5-Trichlorophenol or its pesticide derivatives. A

waste material or waste

Any garbage, refuse, sludge from a waste treatment plant or water supply facility and other discarded material including solid, liquid, semisolid, or contained gaseous material resulting from industrial, commercial, mining and agricultural operations. A

waste oil

Used products primarily derived from petroleum, which include, but are not limited to, fuel oils, motor oils, gear oils, cutting oils, transmission fluids, hydraulic fluids, and dielectric fluids. A

waste pulper

A pulping system designed especially for solid waste processing.

waste reduction

The prevention or restriction of waste generation at its source by redesigning products or the patterns of production and consumption.

waste stabilization ponds

Large, shallow basins used to purify wastewaters by storage under climatic conditions that favor the growth of microorganisms, and thus promote the stabilization of organic waste.

waste stream

A general term for the total waste output of an area, location, or facility.

waste water

Water carrying dissolved or suspended solids from homes, farms, businesses, and industries. N

wastewater treatment process

Includes any process which modifies characteristics such as BOD, COD, TSS, and pH, usually for the purpose of meeting effluent guidelines and standards. B, K

wastewater treatment unit

A device which (a) is part of a wastewater treatment facility which is subject to regulation under either Section 402 or Section 307(b) of the Clean Water Act; and (b) receives and treats or stores an influent wastewater which is a hazardous waste as defined in 40 CFR § 261.3; or generates and accumulates a wastewater treatment sludge which is a hazardous waste as defined in 40 CFR § 261.3, or treats or stores a wastewater treatment sludge which is a hazardous waste as defined in 40 CFR § 261.3 and (c) meets the definition of tank in 40 CFR § 260.10. A

waterborne ink systems

Ink and related coating mixtures whose volatile portion consists of a mixture of VOC solvent and more than five weight percent water, as applied to the gravure cylinder. A

waterborne or water reducible

A coating which contains more than five weight percent water in its volatile fraction. A

water-cooled baffle

A baffle composed essentially of closely spaced boiler tubes.

water-cooled wall

A furnace wall composed of boiler tubes.

water pollution

The addition of harmful or objectionable material causing an alteration of water quality. N

water quality assessment and segment classifications

(1) An assessment of existing and potential water quality problems within the approved planning area or designated areawide planning area, including an identification of the types and degree of problems and the sources of pollutants (both point and nonpoint sources) contributing to the problems. The results of this assessment should be reflected in the state's report required under section 305(b) of the [Federal Water Pollution Control] Act. (2) The classification of each segment as either water quality or effluent limitation as defined in 130.2(O) of this chapter. (i) Segments shall include the surrounding land areas that contribute or may contribute to alterations in the physical, chemical, or biological characteristics of the surface waters. (ii) Water quality problems generally shall be described in terms of existing or potential violations of water quality standards. (iii) Each water quality segment classification shall include the specific water quality parameters requiring consideration in the total maximum daily load allocation process. (iv) In the segment classification process, upstream sources that contribute or may contribute to such alterations should be considered when identifying boundaries of each segment. (v) The classification of segments shall be based on measurements of instream water quality, where available. A

water quality criteria

Specific levels of water quality which, if reached, are expected to render a body of water suitable for its designated use. The criteria are based on specific levels of pollutants that would make the water harmful if used for drinking, swimming, farming, fish production, or industrial processes. N

water quality limited stream segment

A stretch of navigable waters where effluent limitations in NPDES permits for direct discharges are determined by water quality standards rather than technology-based effluent standards.

water quality management

The plan for managing the water quality, including consideration of the relationship of water quality to land and water resources and uses, on an area wide basis, for each EPA/state approved planning area and for those areas designated pursuant to section 208a(2), (3), or (4) of the [Federal Water Pollution Control] Act within a state. A

water quality standard

A management plan that considers (1) what water will be used for, (2) setting water quality criteria levels to protect those uses, (3) implementing and enforcing the water treatment plans, and (4) protecting existing high quality waters, and establish regulations designating standards for all stream and river segments. N Also, applicable water quality standards which have been approved, left in effect, or promulgated under section 303 of the Clean Water Act. A

water-reactive

A chemical that reacts with water to release a gas that is either flammable or presents a health hazard. N

watershed

The land area that drains into a stream. N

waters of the United States or waters of the U.S.

(1) All waters which are currently used, were used in the past, or may be susceptible to use in interstate or foreign commerce, including all waters which are subject to the ebb and flow of the tide; (2) All interstate waters, including interstate "wetlands;" (3) All other waters such as intrastate lakes, rivers, streams (including intermittent streams), mudflats, sandflats, "wetlands," sloughs, prairie potholes, wet meadows, playa lakes, or natural ponds the use, degradation, or destruction of which would affect or could affect interstate or foreign commerce including any such waters: (a) Which are or could be used by interstate or foreign travelers for recreational or other purposes; (b) From which fish or shellfish are or could be taken and sold in interstate or foreign commerce; or (c) Which are used or could be used for industrial purposes by industries in interstate commerce. A

water solubility

The maximum concentration of a chemical compound which can result when it is dissolved in water. If a substance is water soluble, it can very readily disperse through the environment. N

water supplier

A person who owns or operates a public water system. N

water supply system

The collection, treatment, storage and distribution of potable water from source to consumer. N

water table

The level of ground water. N

watertight
So constructed that moisture will not enter the enclosure. O

water used in agricultural or wildlife propagation
Produced water of good enough quality to be used for wildlife or livestock watering or other agricultural uses and actually put to such use during periods of discharge. A

waterwall furnace
A furnace constructed with walls of welded steel tubes through which water is circulated to absorb the heat of combustion. It can be used as an incinerator, and the stream or hot water generated may be recycled.

waterwall incinerator
An incinerator whose furnace walls consist of vertically arranged metal tubes through which water passes and absorbs the radiant energy from burning solid waste. Additional boiler packages in the flue control the conversion of water to stream of a specified temperature and pressure.

weak nitric acid
Acid which is 30 to 70 percent in strength. A

weatherproof
So constructed or protected that exposure to the weather will not interfere with successful operation. Rainproof, raintight, or watertight equipment can fulfill the requirements for weatherproof where varying weather conditions other than wetness, such as snow, ice, dust, or temperature extremes, are not a factor. O

weed
Any plant which grows where not wanted. C

welder and welding operator
Any operator of electric or gas welding and cutting equipment. O

well
(1) Any shaft or pit dug or bored into the earth, generally of a cylindrical form, and often walled with bricks or tubing to prevent the earth from caving in. A (2) A well is a permanent complete enclosure a-round a fixed ladder, which is attached to the walls of the well. Proper clearances for a well will give the person who must climb the ladder the same protection as a cage. O

well (UIC)
A bored, drilled or driven shaft, or a dug hole, whose depth is greater than the largest surface dimension. A

well injection (UIC)
The subsurface emplacement of "fluids" through a bored, drilled, or driven "well" or through a dug well, where the depth of the dug well is greater than the largest surface dimension. A

well log
A log obtained from a well, showing

such information as resistivity, radioactivity, spontaneous potential, and acoustic velocity as a function of depth. A

well monitoring
The measurement, by on-site instruments or laboratory methods, of the quality of water in a well. A

well plug
A watertight and gastight seal installed in a borehole or well to prevent movement of fluids. A

well record
A concise statement of the available data regarding a well, such as a scout ticket, etc. A

well stimulation
Several processes used to clean the well bore, enlarge channels, and increase pore space in the interval to be injected thus making it possible for wastewater to move more readily into the formation, and includes (1) surging, (2) jetting, (3) blasting, (4) acidizing, (5) hydraulic fracturing. A

wet
Those steelmaking air cleaning systems that primarily use water for furnace gas cleaning. A

wet barking operations
Includes hydraulic barking operations and wet drum barking operations which are those drum barking operations that use substantial quantities of water in either water sprays in the barking drums or in a partial submersion of the drums in a "tub" of water. A

wet desulfurization system
Those systems which remove sulfur compounds from coke oven gases and produce a contaminated process wastewater. A

wet location
Installations underground or in concrete slabs or masonry in direct contact with the earth, and locations subject to saturation with water or other liquids, such as vehicle-washing areas, and locations exposed to weather and unprotected. O

wet scrubber system
Any emission control device that mixes an aqueous stream or slurry with the exhaust gases from a steam generating unit to control emissions of particulate matter or sulfur dioxide. A

wet scrubbers
Air pollution control devices used to remove particulates and fumes from air by entraining the pollutants in a water spray. A

wetland hydrology
In general terms, permanent or periodic inundation or prolonged soil saturation sufficient to create anaerobic conditions in the soil. N

wetlands
Those areas that are inundated or saturated by surface or ground water at a frequency and duration sufficient to support, and that under normal circumstances do support, a prevalence of vegetation typically adapted for life in saturated soil conditions. Wetlands generally include swamps, marshes, bogs, and similar areas. A

wetting agent
A chemical that reduces the surface tension of water and enables it to soak into porous material more readily.

WF
Weighting Factor.

WHO
World Health Organization.

whole body dose
The radiation dose to the entire body.

whole body
All human organs or tissue exclusive of the integumentary system (skin) and the cornea. A

wholesale purchaser-consumer
Any organization that is an ultimate consumer of gasoline and which purchases or obtains gasoline from a supplier for use in motor vehicles and receives delivery of that product into a storage tank of at least 550-gallon capacity substantially under the control of that organization. A

wildlife refuge
An area designated for the protection of wild animals, within which hunting and fishing are either prohibited or strictly controlled. N

wind
The natural, horizontal movement of air.

windbox
A chamber below a furnace grate or surrounding a burner, through which air is supplied under pressure to burn the fuel.

window jack scaffold
A scaffold, the platform of which is supported by a bracket or jack which projects through a window opening. O

windrow composting
An open-air method in which compostable material is sorted, shredded, placed in long rows or piles, and turned for aeration. Modified windrowing involves blowing controlled amounts of air through the material in ventilated bins, which is a quicker and more efficient method. The process may be aerobic or anaerobic.

wireways
Sheet metal troughs with hinged or removable covers for housing and protecting electric wires and cable and in which conductors are laid in place after the wireway has been installed as a complete system. O

withdraw specification
To remove from designation any area already specified as a disposal site by the U.S. Army Corps of Engineers or by a state which has assumed the section 404 program, or any portion of such area. A

within the impoundment
When used for purposes of calculating the volume of process wastewater which may be discharged, shall mean the surface area within the

impoundment at the maximum capacity plus the area of the inside and outside slopes of the impoundment dam and the surface area between the outside edge of the impoundment dam and seepage ditches upon which rain falls and is returned to the impoundment. For the purpose of such calculations, the surface area allowance for external appurtenances to the impoundment shall not be more than 30 percent of the water surface area within the impoundment dam at maximum capacity. A

with modified-processes
Using any technique designed to minimize emissions without the use of add-on pollution controls. A

WL
Working Level.

WLM
Working Level Month.

women's business enterprise
A business which is certified as such by a state or federal agency, or which meets the following definition: An independent business concern which is at least 51 percent owned by a woman or women who also control and operate it. Determination of whether a business is at least 51 percent owned by a woman or women shall be made without regard to community property laws. For example, an otherwise qualified WBE which is 51 percent owned by a married woman in a community property state will not be disqualified because her husband has a 50 percent interest in her share.

Similarly, a business which is 51 percent owned by a married man and 49 percent owned by an unmarried woman will not become a qualified WBE by virtue of his wife's 50 percent interest in his share of the business. A

wood characteristics
Distinguishing features which by their extent and number determine the quality of a piece of wood. O

wood fiber furnish subdivision mills
Those mills where cotton fibers are not used in the production of fine papers. A

wood irregularities
Natural characteristics in or on wood that may lower its durability, strength, or utility. O

wood pulp
The mixture of pulverized wood fibers and water that is used to make cellulose derivatives (e.g., paper, rayon).

wood pulp waste
Fiber residue generated by a manufacturing process.

wood residue
Bark, sawdust, slabs, chips, shavings, mill trim, and other wood products derived from wood processing and forest management operations. A

wool
The dry raw wool as it is received by the wool scouring mill. A

wool fiberglass
Fibrous glass of random texture, including fiberglass insulation, and other products listed in SIC 3296. N

wool fiberglass insulation
A thermal insulation material composed of glass fibers and made from glass produced or melted at the same facility where the manufacturing line is located. A

working day
All days except Saturdays, Sundays, or federal holidays. O

Working Level Month
WLM. A unit of measure used to determine cumulative exposure to radon. N

Working Level
(1) WL. Any combination of short-lived radon decay products in one liter of air that will result in the ultimate emission of alpha particles with a total energy of 130 billion electron volts. A
(2) A unit of measure for documenting exposure to radon decay products.

One working level is equal to approximately 200 picocuries per liter. N

working load
Load imposed by men, materials, and equipment. O

working pressure
The maximum pressure to which a pressure containment device may be exposed under standard operating conditions. O

WOT
Wide Open Throttle. A

WQA
Water Quality Act of 1987.

wt.
Weight.

WWEMA
Waste and Wastewater Equipment Manufacturers' Association. N

WWTP
Wastewater Treatment Plant. N

XYZ

xenobiotic
Term for non-naturally occurring man-made substances found in the environment (i.e., synthetic material solvents, plastics). N

YTD
Year to Date. N

ZBB
Zero Base Budgeting. N

Zero-Based Budgeting
ZBB. A process that emphasizes management's responsibility for planning, budgeting and evaluation. ZBB provides for analysis of alternative methods of operation and various levels of effort. It places new programs on an equal footing with existing programs by requiring ranking of program priorities and thereby provides a systematic basis for allocating resources.

zero device-miles
The period of time between retrofit installation and the accumulation of 100 miles of automobile operation after installation. A

zero drift
The change in measurement system output over a stated period of time of normal continuous operation when the pollutant concentration at the time for the measurement is zero. A

zero gas
A gas containing less than 1 ppm sulfur dioxide. A

zero grade air
Artificial "air" consisting of a blend of nitrogen and oxygen with oxygen concentrations between 18 and 21 mole percent. A

zero-order reaction
A reaction in which the rate of disappearance of a chemical is independent of the concentration of the chemical or the concentration of any other chemical present in the reaction mixture. A

zero tolerance
No amount of pesticide chemical may remain on the raw agricultural commodity when it is offered for shipment. A zero tolerance for a

pesticide chemical in or on a raw agricultural commodity may be established because, among other reasons: (a) A safe level of the pesticide chemical in the diet of two different species of warm-blooded animals has not been reliably determined. (b) The chemical is carcinogenic to or has other alarming physiological effects upon one or more of the species of the test animals used, when fed in the diet of such animals. (c) The pesticide chemical is toxic, but is normally used at times when, or in such manner that, fruit, vegetables, or other raw agricultural commodities will not bear or contain it. (d) All residue of the pesticide chemical is normally removed through good agricultural practice such as washing or brushing through weathering or other changes in the chemical itself, prior to introduction of the raw agricultural commodity into interstate commerce. A

ZHE
Zero Headspace Extractor. N

ZOI
Zone of Incorporation. N

zone of aeration
The zone between the land surface and the water table. A

zone of influence
The area contiguous to a ditch, channel, or other drainage structure that is directly affected by it. N

Zone of Initial Dilution
ZID. The region of initial mixing surrounding or adjacent to the end of the outfall pipe or diffuser ports, provided that the ZID may not be larger than allowed by mixing zone restrictions in applicable water quality standards. A

zone of saturation
That part of the earth's crust in which all voids are filled with water.

zooplankton
Tiny aquatic animals that fish feed on. N

ZRL
Zero Risk Level. N

About Government Institutes

Government Institutes, Inc., was founded in 1973 to provide continuing education and practical information for your professional development. Specializing in environmental and energy concerns, we recognize
that you face unique challenges presented by the ever-increasing number of new laws and regulations and
the rapid evolution of new technologies, methods, and markets.

Our information and continuing education efforts include over 50 educational programs held nationwide throughout the year, and over 100 publications, making us the world's largest book publisher in these
areas.

Government Institutes, Inc.
966 Hungerford Drive, #24
Rockville, MD (Washington, D.C.) 20850-1714
(301) 251-9250

Other related books published by Government Institutes:

Environmental Law Handbook, 10th Edition - The recognized
authority in the field, provides practical and current information
on all major environmental areas by eleven nationally-recognized
legal experts. Hardcover/664 pages/Code 766

Directory of Environmental Information Sources, 2nd Edition -
Details hard-to-find Federal Government Resources; State
Government Resources; Professional, Scientific, and Trade
Organizations; Newsletters, Magazines, and Periodicals; and
Databases. Softcover/288 pages/Code 743

Environmental Statutes, 1990 - All the major environmental laws
incorporated into one convenient source. Hardcover/1,170
pages/Code 797; Softcover/1,170 pages/Code 796

1990-1991 Environmental Telephone Directory - Enables the user to
quickly call or write a congressman, subcommittee, and federal or
state agency to obtain the latest information on environmental
laws, regulations, policies, and court decisions. Softcover/256
pages/Code 781

Environmental Engineering Dictionary - Defines over 6,000
engineering terms used in pollution control technologies,
monitoring, risk assessment, sampling and analysis, quality
control and environmental engineering science. Softcover/630
pages/Code 786

Environmental Audits, 6th Edition - Details how to begin and
manage a successful audit program for your facility. Use these
checklists and sample procedures to identify your problem areas
now and avoid costly compliance expenses later. Softcover/630
pages/Code 776

Call or write us at the address above for our current book catalog and continuing education schedule!